English Delftware
in the Bristol Collection

English Delftware

IN THE BRISTOL COLLECTION

Frank Britton

Foreword by Arnold Wilson
DIRECTOR, CITY OF BRISTOL ART GALLERY

Preface by Michael Archer
DEPUTY KEEPER OF CERAMICS, VICTORIA AND ALBERT MUSEUM

Sotheby Publications

Acknowledgements for illustrations

Grateful acknowledgement is made to the following museums, who kindly supplied prints and gave permission to reproduce them:
   The British Museum (Department of Prints and Drawings) for figs 1, 4, 11, 12, 17, 18.
   The Merseyside County Museums for the colour plate on p. 38.
   The Trustees of the National Maritime Museum for fig. 16
   Somerset County Museum, Taunton for fig. 9.
   Fig 19 is reproduced by courtesy of Mrs Alwyn Harper.
The following illustrations are reproduced by permission of the British Library: figs 2, 3, 5, 6, 7, 8, 13, 15.
Fig. 14 is reproduced by courtesy of Earle D. Vandekar.

First published in 1982 for
Sotheby Publications by
Philip Wilson Publishers Ltd
Russell Chambers, Covent Garden
London WC2E 8AA
and
Sotheby Publications
Biblio Distribution Centre
81 Adams Drive, Totowa
New Jersey 07512

ISBN 0 85667 152 5

Designed by Gillian Greenwood

Printed in Great Britain
by BAS Printers Ltd, Over Wallop, Hampshire
and bound by The Garden City Press Ltd,
Letchworth, Hertfordshire

Contents

Foreword

The need had long been recognized for an adequate catalogue for the important group of English delftware in the City of Bristol Museum and Art Gallery. With the problem of production costs, it became increasingly unlikely that justice could be done to this collection. It was, therefore, a particular pleasure to welcome Group Captain A. F. Britton's offer to write the present catalogue, and to know that it could be splendidly produced by Sotheby Publications. Our thanks go to Frank Britton for tirelessly studying the collection, which had fortunately been entirely re-housed and adequately stored within the last few years. Mr Brian Morgan, with the assistance of Mr Peter Morey-Weale, spent many days photographing the collection and generously gave freely of their expertise and time. The fine colour photographs are the work of Mr Derek Balmer. Miss Cleo Witt, Curator of Applied Art, and Miss Karin Walton, Assistant Curator, gave valuable assistance over the whole project. Frank Britton has acknowledged the role of Mr Michael Archer, who has so kindly interested himself in Bristol's collection.

It was necessary to produce sufficient funds to make the project possible. Bristol & West Building Society and ECC International Ltd, St Austell, kindly agreed to buy a number of copies of the catalogue. This still left a large shortfall of committed sponsors. Mr A. M. McGreevy had already shown an agreeable interest in the Art Gallery and his Charitable Trust was able to provide the remainder of the funds for the initial realization of this catalogue. We are, therefore, most grateful to the A. M. McGreevy Charitable Trust for support. We also tender thanks to our anonymous American patron.

Frank Britton has traced the history of the past donors who helped to form Bristol's collection of delftware. In speaking of Theodore Charbonnier, our first benefactor, he quotes the words of the correspondent in the *Western Daily Press*:

> '*Bristol Museum and Art Gallery has always been fortunate in the co-operation of a number of experts who are willing, in an honorary capacity, to give freely of their knowledge and so increase the value of the collections.*'

It is gratifying that the wheel has come full circle so that Frank Britton, in his retirement, and as an amateur of delftware, follows Theodore Charbonnier in making a valuable contribution to Bristol's collection. For the final form which that contribution takes, we thank Sotheby Publications, the Publisher, Philip Wilson, and Anne Jackson.

Arnold Wilson
Director, City of Bristol Art Gallery

Preface

A knowledge of the superb collections of pottery and porcelain at the City of Bristol Art Gallery has long been essential to students of English ceramics. Although the city has a distinguished ceramic history reaching back to mediaeval times, it is probably best known for the porcelain produced in the eighteenth century and for the manufacture of delftware. The porcelain is of importance and charm but was only made for two short periods while, for the better part of a hundred and fifty years, the potters of Brislington and Bristol produced tin-glazed earthenware to a degree of technical excellence and artistic accomplishment unsurpassed anywhere in Britain. The three main centres for the manufacture of delftware were Bristol, London and Liverpool and all three are represented by masterpieces in the museum's collection.

Inevitably pride of place is taken by Bristol. This is hardly surprising because the nucleus of the collection consists of a number of major gifts from a handful of collectors with great local loyalty and pride. They formed a considerable proportion of their collections by buying in and around Bristol at a time when objects could still be found near their place of origin, before collectors were as numerous or antique dealers as well organized as they are today.

Prominent among these benefactors of the museum were Theodore Charbonnier, Sir Gilbert Mellor and Joseph Stone Hodges. To the present generation Charbonnier has been a shadowy figure with an unusual name but Frank Britton has discovered much about his long and interesting life. Although he was born in the Channel Islands, he lived in Bristol from his earliest childhood and from being a teacher of art and an antique dealer went on to become a great collector and authority on both pewter and delftware. Mellor, by contrast, had a more conventionally distinguished career. Like his father he was called to the bar and rose high in the legal branch of the War Office. His life was spent in or near London but he had a particular liking for Bristol delftware and left his collection to be divided between the Bristol and Victoria and Albert Museums. It was Stone Hodges who gave by far the largest collection to the museum, no fewer than 440 pieces. He was born in Bristol where he had a cabinet-making business and was collecting seriously at least as early as 1906.

Although the City Art Gallery's collection of delftware was not founded until after 1900, it is apparent from our knowledge of those who created it that many of the pieces had been purchased locally many years before. The early collectors were particularly fortunate in that the subject of their enthusiasm was admirably served by historical research. With the exception of Mayer's book on Liverpool pottery, which appeared in 1855, no other English delftware potteries had been investigated in depth, if at all; but in Bristol there had been Hugh Owen's *Two Centuries of Ceramic Art in Bristol* of 1873 and W. J. Pountney produced his *Old Bristol Potteries* in 1920. The latter contained much archival material as well as the results of the author's own excavations and both books gave collectors of Bristol delftware a valuable body of information. Unfortunately they also encouraged them to attribute far more to Bristol than was justified and a spate of articles followed which in general are now useful only for their illustrations.

Despite all this interest in Bristol delftware, no catalogue of the Art Gallery's collection was undertaken until Frank Britton started work in 1973. He was already a keen collector of delftware when his career as a pilot and engineer brought him to live near Filton; so he has known the collection for well over a quarter of a century. In his catalogue he is able to call on the information supplied by Owen and Pountney as well as the more up to date research by Anthony Ray on the collection of Robert Hall Warren, another distinguished citizen of Bristol. He has also been fortunate in having access to the results of the recent excavation of the Temple Back pottery site before their publication by Dr Roger Price. Apart from satisfying the normal requirements of a catalogue, Frank Britton has supplied some interesting new information relating to the manufacture of delftware and his book includes two other important innovations.

Collectors and historians of delftware have always been aware of the decorative motifs which appear on the backs of dishes and plates but hitherto no systematic study of them has been made. Frank Britton has arranged them in categories and by relating them to body, glaze and the decoration on the front has found a sufficient degree of consistency to suggest that, provided they are treated with caution, they can assist in attribution. The mobility of potters and the availability of certain prototypes, such as Chinese porcelain, to all potteries make it dangerous to carry the argument too far. Certain styles of decoration on the front of plates may well have been imitated widely if they were found to be commercially successful. However potters are unlikely to have copied patterns on the reverse which were generally too simple and rudimentary to have any effect on saleability. It is therefore plausible to postulate that different pottery centres and even the individual pot-houses within them may have evolved certain habits in the decoration of the underside. Such 'handwriting', taken with all other relevant considerations is clearly of value.

The other respect in which Frank Britton breaks new ground is in the use he makes of his genealogical research. Many pieces of delftware were made to commemorate betrothals, marriages, and other significant family occasions. Often the initials of the husband and wife are inscribed, normally in a triangular form. In the past many such initials have been allocated to individual potters, particularly in Bristol, with scant regard for evidence or plausibility. The author has avoided this pit-fall by concentrating on those initials which can be associated with a specific place or profession. In some cases the results have been spectacular. A plate (cat. no. 16.33) inscribed 'RICH WOOD Port Isaac 1764' enables us to identify its owner as a non-conformist shopkeeper and trader living in a small fishing village on the rocky north Cornish coast. He and his associate William Billings appear to have traded with Bristol, importing delftware and sending back minerals needed for its manufacture in the coaster the *Three Sisters*. In the case of the famous bowl (cat. no. 10.30) painted with a hen and chickens we can follow an extraordinary trail which takes us to Surrey, Hampshire, Oxfordshire, Bristol and even out to China and back.

Frank Britton is able to make use of his discoveries to propose attributions to particular delftware centres. Moreover he succeeds in bringing before us most vividly the very people for whom the pieces were made, thus placing the objects in a social and historical context far beyond the confines of the museum showcase.

Michael Archer
Deputy Keeper of Ceramics, Victoria and Albert Museum

Author's preface

The Bristol collection of English delftware, in the City of Bristol Museum and Art Gallery, must certainly be the largest public collection of its kind in the world, having developed from a few pieces at the beginning of this century to very nearly eight hundred pieces today. It has, however, never been catalogued, so that the wealth of its quality and quantity has perhaps not received the attention it deserves. Having lived and worked in the Bristol area for some years, on my retirement from business, I offered my services to the Director of the City Art Gallery, to compile a handlist of the collection, with a view to expanding it into a catalogue if this should subsequently prove possible. Through the helpful cooperation of many colleagues and friends, I am happy that this has now become a reality.

The work was started in the autumn of 1973, and the handlist completed by mid-1975, after which visits were paid to most public and some private collections in the United Kingdom to collate information on pieces in those collections with similar articles at Bristol. Research was also commenced in libraries, print collections, museums and record offices with a view to tracing design sources for the decoration of some pieces, and to interpreting the allusions contained in inscriptions, names, initials, coats of arms, dates, etc. A description of some of this work is included in the introductory chapters which follow, and plenty of examples of the interesting results it has yielded will be found in the catalogue entries.

Study of the collection also disclosed that a significant proportion of plates and dishes, and a few other pieces, had markings under their rims. Classification of all these, and comparison with the provenance already assigned to the pieces concerned, showed a remarkable correspondence between certain types of marking and cities of origin. The results of this work were first given in the form of a paper read before the English Ceramic Circle, but are now up-dated and included as a chapter at the end of this catalogue, where they can be related to the relevant catalogue entries, with greater benefit to the student.

In compiling this catalogue I have been conscious that there are two excellent books dealing at some length with English delftware generally, as well as other books dealing with the art and industry in its various centres of manufacture. For these reasons I have sought, while providing sufficient background information to enable the catalogue to stand on its own feet, both to minimize duplication of all the detailed information readily available elsewhere, and to complement those sources by concentrating my researches on aspects which have escaped the attentions of others.

The optimum arrangement of so large a catalogue poses particular problems.

First, we have tried to deal with matters chronologically in so far as that is possible. But, in the middle of the eighteenth century a very large quantity of delftware was being made, while at the same time it is seldom possible to date it at all accurately, so that it then becomes impossible to sort matters out on a purely chronological basis.

Second, there are many shapes of delftware articles, other than plates and dishes, about which there is something to be said. The shape of a particular article may, in the first place, have been derived from contemporary metalware, and may then change with time, or the shape may vary between one place of manufacture and another; while it is also desirable to explain the social uses of articles which are probably no longer familiar today.

Third, there are several distinctive styles of decoration which arose, either from foreign influences, which we can try to trace, or from native talent, whose development we can follow. In many cases a distinctive style was attributed to a particular artist, often on the basis of rather slender evidence. All this needs to be set out and illustrated with examples.

Claims have been made in the past, for example by Owen and Pountney in their books on the Bristol potteries, that particular styles of decoration may be attributed to certain individuals. In such cases I have tried to state the facts and to present the evidence on which they are based, and if a clear conclusion cannot then be reached, I have preferred to leave matters there; in effect, to deliver a verdict of 'not proven', and to leave the reader free to make his own judgement.

Inevitably, of course, different shapes of articles and different styles of decoration overlap, so that we have had to exercise subjective judgement in deciding in which chapter to include which specimens in the collection. Cross references between chapters make up for this shortcoming as far as possible.

I am most indebted to Arnold Wilson, Director of the City Art Gallery, Bristol, for making the whole project of this catalogue possible, and for giving it his unswerving support. Also to Cleo Witt, Curator of Applied Art, and Karin Walton for their constant help during all these years. My most grateful thanks are due to Michael Archer of the Department of Ceramics and Glass, Victoria and Albert Museum, the acknowledged expert on delftware, for being ever-ready to share his knowledge, for reading through the typescript and giving so much helpful advice, for spending two days at Bristol to go through the whole collection, and also for his personal friendship.

Brian Morgan most generously volunteered to undertake all the black-and-white photography himself with his own equipment, in which he was assisted by Peter Morey-Weale. This has been of enormous help and is a most practical example of the true meaning of friendship, which I deeply appreciate. The quality of his work speaks for itself.

Among those upon whom I have had to call for help most are Lionel Burman, Keeper of Decorative Art, County Museum, Liverpool; Mary Williams, Chief Archivist, Bristol Record Office, and the staffs of the Manuscript Department, Guildhall Library, of the Department of Prints and Drawings, British Museum, and of the British Library. Another friend to whom I am greatly indebted for so much practical advice is Alan Caiger-Smith of the Aldermaston Pottery. For all their generous help I thank them.

Nor would the research have been possible without help from the staffs of a multitude of organizations which I have visited, or with whom I have corresponded. To them this may have been all in the day's work, but I should like them to know that their unfailing courtesy and willingness to help are much appreciated.

We are also extremely grateful to the British Academy for the grant of a subvention towards publication of the catalogue, which has enabled the problems facing publishers, in these times of economic difficulties, to be overcome.

To many personal friends I am also grateful for so much practical help and encouragement in one way or another. Above them all must come a family friend in the United States of America, who wishes to remain anonymous, who has sent a very substantial donation towards the cost of publication of the catalogue. Without this most thoughtful act of kindness the project would surely never have materialized.

Frank Britton, London 1981

Chronological table of Delftware factories

		60	80	**1600**	20	40	60	80	**1700**	20	40	60	80	**1800**
Greenwich	MALLING JUGS	———————————												
Norwich		–					—————————							
Aldgate		—————————												
Southwark	Montagu Close			——————————————————										
	Pickleherring			——————————————————										
	Rotherhithe			——————————										
	Bear Garden			——————										
	Gravel Lane			————										
	Clink Street			————————										
Wapping	Hermitage Dock			——————————————										
Lambeth	Glasshouse Square			————————————————————										
	Norfolk House			——————————										
	Vauxhall			———————————————————										
	Carlisle House			————										
	Fore Street			——————————————										
Mortlake				—————————										
Isleworth				———————										
Bristol	Brislington			———————————————————										
	Temple Backs			———————————————										
	Limekiln Lane			————————										
	Redcliff *Franks*			——————————										
	Redcliff *Taylor*			————										
	Avon Street			————										
Wincanton				———										
Liverpool	Lord Street			————————————										
	Shaw's Brow *Gilbody*			———										
	Dale Street *Shaw*			———————										
	Dale Street *Poole*			———————										
	Shaw's Brow *Roscoe*			——										
	Shaw's Brow *Chaffers*			———										
	Patrick's Hill			———										
	Old Haymarket			———————										
	Copperas Hill			————										
	Harrington Street			————										
	Duke Street			——										
	Dale Street *Hillary*			—————										
	Park Lane			—										
Glasgow				——										
Dublin	Chambers			——										
	Delamain			—										
Limerick				–										

An introduction to delftware

What is known colloquially today as delftware, was known for most of the time it was made in this country as galleyware or galley-pots, mainly in referring to apothecaries' wares, and as white earthenware, or other local variations of similar sense, mainly for domestic wares. There is some doubt as to the origins and precise meaning of the first two terms; they may have derived from the earlier import of blue and white wares in galleys, or they may come from the Dutch word *glei*, meaning porcelain clay. However, the term white earthenware is very apt, as delftware is earthenware with some tin oxide added to the lead glaze to give it an opaque white surface. It is technically known as tin-glazed earthenware. The word delftware was not in fact generally applied to tin-glazed earthenware made in England until at least the second quarter of the eighteenth century.

The secret of tin-glazing probably originated in the Middle East, whence it spread across the Mediterranean to Europe. The manufacture of maiolica reached a high degree of perfection in Faenza in the fourteenth and fifteenth centuries, and from the name of that city the term faience came to be used in France and Germany for such wares, as the technique came to be adopted there. Its manufacture spread throughout northern Europe, reaching Brabant in the early sixteenth century, while the first potters appeared in the registers of the Guild of St Luke in Delft at the beginning of the seventeenth century.

The very first tin-glazed wares made in England were the 'Malling' jugs, so named because an early example was found in the church of West Malling, Kent. They were made from just before 1550 onwards, for a limited time, probably ceasing before the end of the century. The potters who made them appeared to confine themselves to this one specific product, and they had no influence on the mainstream of delftware manufacture, which began independently soon afterwards. There is an example of a 'Malling' jug in the Bristol collection, and we discuss them more fully in dealing with it.

Apart from this, then, the first delftware potters to appear in England were Jasper Andries and Jacob Jansen, Huguenot refugees from Antwerp, Brabant, who arrived in Norwich in 1567, and, according to Stow's *Survey*[1] followed their trade there, making tiles and drug pots. This is confirmed in a petition they made to the Queen in 1570, in which they state that they had 'continued almost three years, exercising the making of galley paving tiles and vessels for potycaries and others very artificially, even as it may appear by the chest with their handiwork by them unto your Majesty presented'[2]. However the site of the Norwich pottery has never been established, nor have any of its wares been identified.

Before leaving Norwich, it should be noted that there is clear evidence[3] that in 1698 there was 'one white earthenware house' there, which then went out of business, and that there are records of five potters in the city between 1651 and that date, of whom two became Freemen, though there is no proof that they were all delftware potters. There are, moreover, records of seven more potters in the first quarter of the eighteenth century, of whom six were Freemen, which suggests that the pottery revived.

Jacob Jansen next appears in Aldgate in 1571, where he was associated with the first London delftware pottery in Duke's Place. Thereafter, throughout the seventeenth century and on into the eighteenth century, factories sprang up close to the south bank of the Thames. The first was at Montagu Close, in the shadow of

Southwark Cathedral, in 1613, and it was closely followed by one at Pickleherring Quay nearby, in 1615. Other London factories were established at sites mainly in Southwark and Lambeth, until delftware was produced in such quantities that it became the common household crockery of the common people of London. There is a tendency for all London delftware to be called 'Lambeth'; but as it is seldom possible to differentiate between that made in Southwark, Lambeth, or elsewhere in the city, for the purposes of this catalogue we shall call it 'London'.

The London factories were notable for the wide variety of their products and for their longevity. There was scarcely any article they did not produce, nor any style of decoration they did not practise; the sole exception is perhaps Fazackerly decoration. The first two south bank factories kept going for 150 years, and a later factory at Vauxhall was probably the last to cease delftware production in England, lasting well on into the nineteenth century.

The early London factories were soon to be followed by the establishment of a factory at Brislington, near Bristol, in about 1645, set up by a potter from Montagu Close. This being so, it is scarcely surprising that the early products of Brislington were very similar to contemporary London wares. Towards the end of the seventeenth century, some of the potters from Brislington moved into the city of Bristol, and in the early eighteenth century more factories were started there, so that it became a centre for delftware manufacture, to such an extent that the term Bristol delftware later became almost synonymous with English delftware. Bristol was fortunate in being close to the mineral resources of Cornwall, and in being a thriving seaport, with quays in the centre of the city. Thus supplies could readily be brought in, and delftware could readily be exported, not only in coastal vessels, but also in shipping to more distant lands.

In the course of the eighteenth century Bristol became very fertile in developing its own special decorative styles. The blue-red-green style exploited these three rich colours to the full; the monochrome blue figures in a landscape became very popular and were copied elsewhere, while the most famous Bristol speciality was surely their perfection of the *bianco-sopra-bianco* technique in the purest white against a clear sky-blue glaze. Each of these styles is treated in a separate catalogue chapter. An important development in the identification of some Bristol wares is the imminent publication of a monograph on the pottery kiln-waste from Temple Back.[4] An advance copy of the illustrations from this report has permitted positive attributions for certain pieces for the first time.

A factory was also established in Wincanton, Somerset, in the mid-eighteenth century, and the similarity of its wares, in many respects, to those of Bristol, bears testimony to the fact that it recruited workmen from there. It was noted for its 'mimosa' pattern, and for powdered grounds, and a few inscribed pieces help us to identify its products; but it was shortlived.

The third major delftware centre in these islands was Liverpool. Factories started there early in the eighteenth century, and it very quickly established a high reputation for the quality of its wares. It seems probable that the first two pot houses were started by workmen from London, although they soon developed a Liverpool individuality. There was a greater proliferation of manufacturers here than elsewhere, and around the middle of the century, as many as a dozen factories seem to have been in operation. Liverpool became notable for the number of ship bowls it produced; it developed a remarkably charming palette of colours which it used for a style of floral decoration known as 'Fazackerly'. Liverpool experimented with tin-glazing of stoneware, of which we have two examples, and it also developed transfer printing techniques, which are beyond the scope of this catalogue, as they were applied almost entirely to tiles.

In Ireland, some very fine wares were made in Dublin starting in 1735, the artistic merit of their landscape decoration being most notable, though some other articles are so like Liverpool wares that it is hard to distinguish between them. Among Dublin specialities were bowls with sides pierced to form an interlaced pattern, and a lotus leaf decoration copied directly from Chinese ceramics. A pottery also operated in Limerick for a short time, and there is some evidence to suggest one in Belfast.

Finally, there was a factory in Glasgow, started in the middle of the eighteenth century by workmen from London, and continuing at least to the end of the century. There were some problems in getting it running efficiently; however, when it did function, it produced large quantities of wares, much of which was exported to the American colonies.

We are not attempting to recite the histories of all these factories, and of the persons involved with them, in any detail, as this has been ably done by other authorities, whose works will be found in the bibliography. We produce, however, for easy reference, a table showing the periods during which most of the known factories were in operation; this will, moreover, give readers a graphic idea of the rise and fall of the manufacture of delftware in the British Isles. We do deal more extensively with specific types of articles, notable styles of decoration and some of the potters held to have been primarily responsible for them, in the introductions to the chapters of the catalogue section, and under the entries for individual specimens.

The relatively soft earthenware body of delftware does not provide a strong foundation for the glaze, thus allowing it to chip or crack. There were literally millions of pieces of delftware made in this country, and a vast amount was exported, this being easy from factories close to the ports; but comparatively little delftware has survived. Chipped and cracked articles were presumably thrown away, and only those more prized pieces, used for display on the dresser or cabinet, or put away in cupboards, seem to remain. It should be noted, moreover, that archaeological evidence from sherds at pottery sites shows that a large majority of the delftware made was plain white, for everyday domestic use; this was evidently regarded of so little value that when damaged it was discarded, so that it is very rarely that any of its survives.

The perfection of the manufacture of creamware, china and porcelain, from the middle of the eighteenth century, and its increased serviceability and volume of production, caused the decline of delftware manufacture in the latter part of the century, so that by the end of that century it can be said to have practically ceased. The industrial revolution hastened this process, with the introduction of mechanized mass production methods to which delftware manufacture was not susceptible.

The raw materials
The primary raw material of delftware is clay. Factories had to be sited within easy reach of suitable clay, bearing in mind that the available means of transport were ships, a horse and cart, and a wheelbarrow. Local clays, found in the vicinity of all the factories, if used alone produced an earthenware body that was too soft and frangible, and was prone to too much shrinkage in firing. A leaner clay had therefore to be found and added to it, in order to make the body more refractory and to reduce shrinkage. Such clay had to contain calcium, and also silica in a form fusible at the moderate temperature of the delftware kiln. This clay was only to be found in a few places, and had to be imported in coastal vessels.

Rhoda Edwards[5] records that in the seventeenth century East Anglian clay was imported by the London potters, and indeed also for a time by the Dutch. She points to evidence that some came from pits on land owned by Edmund Warner at Boyton, Suffolk. The author has obtained samples of clay from a pit at Boyton, which the Institute of Geological Sciences has kindly analysed. The report indicates that this could have been the clay that was used by London potters over a considerable period; a larger sample has since been passed to Mr Alan Caiger-Smith who is putting it to practical test in his Aldermaston Pottery.

All the west coast potteries – Bristol, Liverpool, Glasgow and also Dublin – used clay from Carrickfergus, on Belfast Lough, to mix with their local clays. The Bristol import is shown in port records[6] as follows:

27 April 1742   *In the Rotterdam Merchant Dan Holdrick @ Carrickfergus & Belfast. Thos Pennington & Co 60 tons Potters Clay val 6.6 p ton*

4 May 1742   *In the Rotterdam Merchant Dan Holdrick @ Carrickfergus Thos Pennington & Co 25 tons 11.1.0 (sic) Potters Clay val 6.6 p ton.*

17 July 1742   *In the Charming Molly Peter Wright @ Carrickfergus Thos & R Frank 20 tons clay for potters use @ 6.6 per ton.*

The Franks owned the Redcliff potteries in Bristol, while Pennington seems to have been a general merchant who bought the clay in bulk and re-sold it to the potteries as needed.

The extent of its importation into Liverpool is shown by the fact that the first Lloyd's *Register of Shipping*, published in 1764, lists a ship the *Hope*, Master W. Reed, of thirty tons, based in Liverpool and trading with Carrickfergus. She had been launched in 1752. It does not seem likely that anything much, other than clay, would have been exported from Carrickfergus, so one can conjecture as to the considerable extent of this trade. There is a ship bowl in the Liverpool Museum inscribed 'Success to the Hope 1761', which suggests that this ship was not unknown to the delftware potters.

Once obtained, these clays had to be properly mixed and matured before use, and this was done by sieving, wetting and kneading in troughs. When the clay was ready for use articles were shaped from it on the potter's wheel, or in some cases moulded, and then given a first firing in the kiln. The resultant product was known as the biscuit state. This was then dipped in the glaze, which was basically lead glaze, with the addition of tin oxide[7]. The glaze was absorbed by the porous biscuit ware and dried instantly. It was then ready for decoration.

Colours were obtained from metallic oxides; cobalt for blue, iron for brick red, antimony for yellow, copper for green – though a mixture of blue and yellow was later used – and manganese for a variety of colours from almost black to pale amethyst, according to the concentration. To obtain a real black it was necessary to use manganese with the addition of other minerals, usually copper and cobalt. A tin calx[8] was also used for white, in the technique known as *bianco-sopra-bianco* to which we devote chapter 16. All these colours were mixed into a slurry[9] with, in some cases, a powdered glaze to facilitate their absorption during firing in the kiln.

In the Entwistle papers (10/149) in Liverpool Public Library is a recipe for making 'Lawrence Harrison's Yellow':

    9 *Litharge*
    6 *Antimony*
    3 *Lead & Tin Ashes*

Burnt in a Biscuit Dish, at top of a Potters Kiln – when it comes out Pound it, and put it in again three times over.

It will be realized that this process would have taken several weeks to complete. And it is not clear whether in this case there was any glaze material in the mixture:

John Hill's *History of the Materia Medica* of 1751 says 'Litharge is properly lead vitrified', and goes on to explain that it is a byproduct of the refining furnaces; but it is not certain that 'vitrified' meant what it does today. Moreover litharge, chemically, is very similar to masticot; however Piccolpasso in his *Three Books of the Potter's Art*[10] in the sixteenth century gives a recipe for masticot which includes silica sand, a glaze material.

It should here be added that in a few cases, and notably in Liverpool, decoration was added in low temperature colours fired in a muffle kiln. There is unfortunately no English example of this in the Bristol collection.

Once the painter's brush touched the surface its mark was indelible and dried at once; thus no error could be corrected. When one examines some finely decorated wares, bearing this in mind, one marvels at the skill which these artists attained. After painting, the article was sometimes given another coat of lead glaze before the final firing – a highly vitrified surface is the clue to this – but in most cases it went straight into the kiln.

Articles were placed in protective fireclay vessels, called saggars, and after these had been stacked in the kiln firing commenced. This was an expert process, as the temperature had to be increased gradually up to the required heat of *c.* 1050°C, at which it had to remain for some hours. The temperature then had to be reduced equally gradually, the whole process taking up to three or four days. In firing, the colours were absorbed into the glaze. Some colours, notably red and yellow, showed a reluctance to absorption, and can be felt rough on the surface. If an article was misfired in the kiln, usually by being subjected to too high a temperature, various imperfections may become evident. The colours may be 'wrong', or the glaze may have run, distorting the decoration. If the kiln was heated or cooled too rapidly, then the glaze could become crazed, though this may also be due to the thermal characteristics of the clay not matching those of the glaze sufficiently closely.

Cylindrical saggars were used for firing plates, the articles being suspended in the saggar by a series of three tapered triangular pins inserted in triangular holes pierced through the walls of the saggar at each appropriate level. The marks made by these pins will be seen beneath the rim of the plate. Other shapes of saggar were used for other articles. Chargers were stacked one upon another separated by trivets, of which we illustrate an example in the relevant chapter. Bowls appear to have been fired, usually standing up, but sometimes resting on their rims on three little slips of clay. All wares had to be protected from direct contact with the flames, but so long as the bases were cleaned of glaze they could be safely stood on the base of their saggar.

It is perhaps interesting to note that, at the 'Porceleyne Fles' factory, which still survives in Delft, they today apply decoration directly onto the biscuit body, dipping it in the glaze only after this operation is completed. However, considerable refinements have taken place since the eighteenth century both in the clay and the glaze, making this now the preferred technique. The decorative pattern is applied to the wares by pouncing through a plastic template and painting over the resulting outlines by hand. Moreover they have done away with the protective saggars, which they called *casettes*, for the past thirty years, thanks no doubt to the better materials and also more precise control of temperature in the ovens, and avoidance of direct flame or smoke.

Research and sources of design

The student will be amazed at the wide variety of designs used in the decoration of delftware. A lot of the decoration is in blue alone, but there survives an almost equal amount of polychrome wares. In most cases the design was done freehand, no doubt from a master pattern; but in some cases a design was copied from a contemporary print. In such cases the print, or a tracing of it, was usually pricked through, placed on the surface to be decorated, and pounced onto the delftware article by tapping with a bag of powdered charcoal. The artist then followed the dotted lines with his brush, and the charcoal was of course burnt off in subsequent firing. Our research has enabled us to trace back a considerable number of such pieces to their design sources, and these are illustrated in their appropriate sections of this catalogue.

To find such prints, when it looks as though the scene depicted is one too sophisticated for the delftware decorator to have originated, it is a matter of discovering which artists portrayed such scenes, and of searching through collections of their works. The same procedure applies for portraits, but it is greatly assisted by the catalogue published by the British Museum's Department of Prints and Drawings[11] which is an invaluable aid. But researchers should realize that it was common practice in the seventeenth and eighteenth centuries for engravers to alter a copperplate by erasing the head or other parts of a portrait, by burnishing, and to re-engrave to depict a different person.[12] Thus the 'original' of a portrait may in fact be an engraving of another person. Of course the print may also be reversed in the process of transfer to the delftware, so that one must look equally for the mirror image of a portrait. A reversed portrait may sometimes be detected from the fact that the subject has his sword slung on the wrong side.

If altering engravings was common practice, it is clear that it was equally common for the decorators of delftware to use the same basic print with minor alterations to depict different people over a considerable number of years. We shall deal with several instances of this in the chapter on chargers.

Another aspect of research has been to elucidate the meaning of inscriptions, even though they may consist only of a trio of initials and a date. It will be noted that we have been able to suggest an identification of the person or persons concerned in many cases, and also sometimes to indicate the special event which the inscribed article was intended to commemorate.

A trio of initials, with the central one raised above the other two, usually indicates a marriage; and the central initial is usually that of the man's surname, while that on the left is usually his christian name, and that on the right the wife's christian name. This thesis is proved by articles which are inscribed, not only with the three initials, but also with the full names of the subjects, as for instance the cup in the Museum of London, dated 1658 and inscribed both 'G M F' and 'George & Frances Makine'. However, this rule does not apply without exception, for in this collection we have the 'Hotwell' plate, no. 10.46, inscribed 'I S F' and '1741/2', which undoubtedly refers to the marriage of the well-known Bristol delftware decorator Joseph Flower to Sarah Lamb in that year.

In researching marriage records to correspond with such initials and dates, the marriage indexes produced by Percival Boyd of the Society of Genealogists, and others, are invaluable. There is also a computer file index on microfiche, mainly of births but also with some marriages, produced by the Latter Day Saints of Salt Lake City, Utah, containing some twenty-five million entries. Some of these are available for the appropriate county in local public libraries. It helps to have a fair idea of where the article being researched was made, as one can then start the search in the right city or county. Having found possible solutions in these indexes, one can then turn to the relevant parish registers or marriage licence allegations for fuller information. Sometimes it will be found that the husband, or a witness, or a bondsman, was a potter, and the records of potteries may then be able to provide some supplementary information. Additional or confirmatory evidence may also be found in wills, usually either in the Public Record Office, or in County Records Offices.

Where the arms of a livery company are shown, or a trade represented by a livery company is illustrated, then a search for a solution to the trio of initials can be narrowed by reference to the excellent records of the London livery companies in the Guildhall Library, from which one can find the names of Freemen in the appropriate company, which one can attempt to match up with a name found in a marriage index. It should not be forgotten that there were livery companies in some provincial cities, and while not many of their records survive, their lists of Freeman or Burgesses are usually annotated with the trade which they practised.

Family coats of arms should assist the researcher, as books, such as Papworth's *Ordinary of British Armorials* should enable the family to be identified from the arms; and if these are associated with any inscription or date, then it should be possible to make an attribution with even greater certainty.

Ship bowls, of which there are four in this collection, present a special field for research. Here one usually has the name of a ship, and sometimes the name or initials of her master and a date. Lloyd's *Register of Shipping*, of which the first edition was produced in 1764, may list the ship, in which case it should indicate where it was built, where it was based, where it traded to, and usually the names of master and owner together with other data. However, the Public Record Office also contains customs records for most ports, which are a mine of information, though one which demands much patience to delve into. Moreover, in Bristol, the Society of Merchant Venturers was entitled to levy a charge for anchorage and wharfage on all visiting vessels, and their records are invaluable for any ship trading with that city. The great majority of ship bowls were made in Liverpool, as were three of the four in this collection; small wonder then that the Liverpool Museum itself contains thirty-two of these delftware ship bowls.

The determination of provenance

It is seldom easy to determine the date and provenance of a piece of English delftware. The date will usually be determined by comparison with pieces which are actually dated; but even this may often lead to inaccuracies. For example, the earliest dated piece of the Ann Gomm pattern is 1749, and the latest 1793, no. 10.39. It is true that the first is decorated in blue only, while the later ones are in polychrome, but even so it indicates that one basic pattern could survive for forty-four years, which does not help in dating.

As for place of manufacture, it is dangerous to try to propound hard and fast rules for its determination, and nothing can replace experience. One can say that 'Fazackerly' decoration was largely confined to Liverpool, and that *bianco-sopra-bianco* decoration on a pale blue glaze was made in Bristol. One can say that seventeenth-century pieces with a pure white glaze, with a minimum of blue decoration or often with no decoration at all, were of London origin, and these pieces often display the characteristic of a tinge of pink at the edges or where the glaze is thin. Typical of eighteenth-century London pieces is a glaze with a greenish-blue tinge, which does not seem to have been used elsewhere, while the most notable Liverpool glaze was a fine, clear pale bluish tint. But workers in delftware factories were inclined to move from one place to another, and thus one should not be surprised to find the same techniques and the same design patterns emerging from different places. There is also some suspicion that certain notable decorators worked as freelances for more than one factory in a city, and this is perhaps just one reason why one can so seldom ascribe an article to a particular factory.

The blue pigment used in decoration is often rather a dead colour in London factories, but has much more warmth to it in Bristol; while that used in Liverpool is often of a soft pastel shade, but in other cases where it is darker and has been applied thickly, it causes the surface of the glaze to sink. Furthermore the method of depicting foliage on trees, clouds in the sky, etc. varies from place to place[13]. No one of all these characteristics should be taken in isolation as the true indication of provenance, but rather a combination of as many as possible. Even so, the truth may sometimes prove to be in direct contradiction of the provenance which certain characteristics first seem to indicate.

Notes
1 John Stow, *A Survey of the Cities of London and Westminster and the Borough of Southwark* (1598), 6th edn, London 1755, vol. II, p. 327.
2 British Museum, Burghley Papers, Lansdowne MSS, vol. XII, nos. 58 and 59.
3 House of Commons *Journal*, vol. XII, p. 282.
4 R. H. Price, 'Pottery Kiln-Waste from Temple Back, Bristol'. *City of Bristol Museum and Art Gallery Research Monograph* no. IV (forthcoming publication).
5 Rhoda Edwards, 'London Potters circa 1570–1710', *Journal of Ceramic History*, no. 6, Stafford 1974, p. 19.
6 Public Record Office, Bristol Port Records, Overseas Inward, for dates quoted.
7 For details see Anthony Ray, *English Delftware Pottery in the Robert Hall Warren Collection, Ashmolean Museum, Oxford*, London 1968, p. 86.
8 Calx: the product of calcining or roasting in a kiln 'in reality it was usually the metal oxide, but in some cases the metal itself in a state of sublimation'. *Oxford English Dictionary*.
9 Slurry: 'A watery mixture or suspension of insoluble matter.' (*Encyclopaedia Britannica*). The glaze and colours were finely powdered, but were not soluble in water and had to be kept stirred.
10 R. Lightbown and A. Caiger-Smith, *The Three Books of the Potter's Art by Cipriano Piccolpasso*, London 1980.
11 F. O'Donoghue, *Catalogue of Engraved British Portraits preserved in the Department of Prints and Drawings in the British Museum*. London 1908 etc.
12 See G. S. Layard, *The Headless Horseman*, London 1922, and *Catalogue Raisonné of Engraved British Portraits from Altered Plates*, London 1927.
13 See *Fair as China Dishes. English Delftware from the Collection of Mrs Marion Morgan and Brian Morgan*, Washington D.C. 1977, p. 128.

The evolution of the collection

We have already remarked that the Bristol collection of English delftware must certainly be the largest public collection of its kind anywhere in the world. It is perhaps illuminating to trace its development from its foundation, with one or two pieces at the beginning of this century, to the present day. In this way we may appropriately acknowledge our debt to those who made significant contributions to the collection, and in exploring their backgrounds, may shed some light on how, why and where the pieces came to be collected.

Foremost among the contributors must come Theodore Charbonnier. He comes first from the point of view of time, he also comes first on account of the amount of his own time which he devoted to delftware in the City Art Gallery; and his collection was moreover remarkable both in quality and quantity.

The City Art Gallery possesses a manuscript catalogue of his collection, started by W. J. Pountney in March 1917. This lists 155 pieces, the first forty-one in Pountney's own handwriting. Some of these were loaned to the Art Gallery, and then presented to it in 1918; more were acquired by purchase in 1923, and finally the Art Gallery obtained most of the remainder, partly by gift and partly by purchase, in 1925. The final total, including some tiles, amounted to some 180 pieces.

Theodore Charbonnier died on 30 March 1932, and a few days later the following appeared in the *Western Daily Press*:

> '*Bristol Museum and Art Gallery has always been fortunate*' writes a correspondent, '*in the co-operation of a number of experts who are willing, in an honorary capacity, to give freely of their knowledge and so increase the value of the collections. Pre-eminent amongst these collaborators stands the name of Mr T. Charbonnier, who has passed away at the advanced age of 86.*
>
> *Mr Charbonnier was well known amongst archaeologists over the whole of the South West of England, and for many years he attended the summer meetings of the Gloucestershire, Somersetshire and Devonshire Societies. In the realm of pewter and delft, however, his reputation was national and even international. His own collection of pewter was housed at Taunton Museum, but was later dispersed.*
>
> *Since 1917, until recently, Mr Charbonnier worked every morning in the Bristol Museum and Art Gallery. He dealt chiefly with the pewter and delft, but was interested in all Bristoliana, and at one time worked laboriously over a collection of tokens. Many of the cases and labels on exhibition bear witness to his skill and care. Through the help of Mr Charbonnier the Museum and Art Gallery Committee was able to purchase rare and unique pieces of china.*'

From all this it would appear that Theodore Charbonnier arrived in Bristol out of the blue in 1917, at the age of seventy, and proceeded to give up most of the rest of his life to work for the City Art Gallery. But where did he come from, and why did he do it? We were able to trace his death certificate and his marriage certificate in Somerset House, but could find no trace of his birth. Eventually, through the kind help of the Devon County Librarian, we were able to find an obituary notice in the *Transactions* of the Devonshire Association[1] which proved to be a model of its kind:

Theodore Charbonnier was born at St Helier in the Island of Jersey on 16 August, 1845. His early years were passed in Bristol, where his widowed mother carried on business as a jeweller and he attended the School of Art. Showing an aptitude at the school he was led to adopt art teaching as a profession and was successively master of the Schools of Art in Ryde (Isle of Wight), Southampton and Barnstaple, at the last named from about 1882 to 1906. Always a collector and connoisseur of artistic curios, he found a business suited to his tastes in antique furniture and other articles at Lynmouth, and with his wife's assistance carried it on successfully until 1917. It was during this period that he built up a very fine collection of pewter, which was housed for several years at Taunton Museum. On retiring from business he returned to Bristol and for the remaining years worked in the Bristol Museum and Art Gallery, not only in arranging the collections of pewter and delft, for his knowledge of which he possessed an international reputation, but also in other directions.

His wife (Sarah Ann Morgan, daughter of a Bristol Merchant), who was for over fifty years his companion and helper, died in 1928 . . .

So when he arrived in Bristol in 1917, he was returning to the place where he had spent his childhood and been to school. It would seem from Pountney's catalogue that he had only some forty pieces of delftware in 1917, and hence that he acquired the remainder in and around Bristol thereafter.

In October, 1947, one hundred and twenty-three pieces of delftware arrived in the City Art Gallery from the estate of Sir Gilbert Mellor. His will shows that he left his collection of 'Old English Earthenware', which must have exceeded 250 pieces, to trustees to be bequeathed in whole or part to the President of the Board of Education for 'a collection in the Victoria and Albert Museum to ensue for the benefit of the nation, to be known as the Mellor Bequest'. Any pieces not selected were to revert to the estate.

Sir Gilbert had died in April, 1947, and after the curator from the Victoria and Albert Museum had visited Lady Mellor at Ulcombe Place, Maidstone, twenty-two pieces of English delftware were accepted by them. It was then, apparently, in pursuance of her husband's wish, that Lady Mellor offered some pieces to Bristol.

There is evidence that Sir Gilbert had been in touch with Bernard Rackham of the Victoria and Albert Museum in the early 1920s. Sir Gilbert was then living in Kensington, and in 1921 made a gift to the Victoria and Albert Museum of a bowl and a tile. Further small gifts followed, and in 1924 Sir Gilbert made his will leaving his whole collection, in effect, to the Museum. In subsequent years he contributed articles on delftware to *The Connoisseur* and to *English Ceramic Circle Transactions*.

In 1951, after a delay due to editorial difficulties, an obituary notice appeared in the latter journal[2], from which we quote:

Sir Gilbert Mellor KBE, CB, CMG, KC, Chevalier of the Legion of Honour, died at his home, Ulcombe Place, Maidstone, on 16 April, 1947, aged seventy five.

Member of a well-known Victorian legal family, he was the eldest son of Sir James Mellor, King's Remembrancer, and Senior Master of the Supreme Court, and a grandson of Mr Justice Mellor. Born in 1872, he was educated at Charterhouse and Trinity Hall, Cambridge, of which he was a scholar. The Inner Temple called him to the Bar in 1900, and he obtained silk when Deputy Judge Advocate-General twenty-four years later. He enlisted in the City Imperial Volunteer Mounted Infantry and served in the South African War in 1900. He returned to South Africa

*in 1902 as Secretary to the Royal Commission on the revision of
sentences passed under martial law. In 1907 he entered the Judge
Advocate-General's Office and on the outbreak of the war in 1914 he
was made Deputy J.A.G. and went to France.*

*After his retirement from the legal branch of the War Office in 1932,
he took an increasing interest in local affairs in Kent. He was a J.P. and
since 1944 had been Deputy Chairman of the West Kent Quarter
Sessions. In 1911 he married Isabel, daughter of the late Henry F.
Makins, who survives him.*

*To his friends in the E.C.C., of which he was one of the early
members, he will be remembered for his happy, attractive personality. A
man of much culture and taste, he was an enthusiastic collector of rare
judgement. On English and foreign delft he was an undoubted authority,
and when members of the Circle were entertained by him and Lady
Mellor at their house in London, and later at Ulcombe, they saw an
unusually fine collection of delftware, several pieces of which he has
bequeathed to the Victoria and Albert Museum. He took an active
interest in the affairs of the Circle and served on the committee for some
thirteen years until his death.*

It seems then that Sir Gilbert must have done most of his collecting in London
and south-east England over the last twenty-five years of his life. It may be
significant that Lady Mellor referred to his collection as of 'Bristol delft' in her first
letter to the Victoria and Albert Museum after his death, and that all Sir Gilbert's
articles dealt with different aspects of Bristol delftware.

The largest bequest of delftware ever received by Bristol Art Gallery came
from Joseph Stone Hodges, who died in 1951 at the age of sixty-nine. He left
some 440 pieces, of which the greater part were English.

Joseph Stone Hodges was born in Bristol in 1882, and served an apprenticeship
to the cabinet-makers Crofton Gane on College Green. He then started his own
furniture shop in Bishopston, where he employed a dozen or so craftsmen, but had
to close it down when he went to fight in the First World War. He resumed
business after his return, in different premises in the same neighbourhood, and
this survived with a slight change in its nature until very recently, still under his
name. He was married in 1906 to a wife who survives him still. Soon after their
marriage, she recounts, he said 'My dear, I think we should have a hobby'. To
which she dutifully replied 'Yes dear, what shall it be?' His answer was 'Well I
have always liked Bristol delftware', and so their hobby was established.

They did not have a car, and so took buses on their afternoons off to all the local
county towns, where they visited the antique shops and bought any nice pieces
they could find. They also visited local auction sales at country houses, or got Fred
Elson, a dealer with a shop half way up Christmas Steps in Bristol, to bid for them.
They also looked in the antique shops in seaside towns which they visited for their
summer holidays. Later in life Joseph Stone Hodges attended sales of notable
collections at the big London salerooms. Their objective was always to collect
Bristol delftware, but inevitably they also acquired pieces from other factories,
and some indeed from Continental sources. Mrs Stone Hodges also turned her
attention to collecting Bristol pottery.

There were several other notable contributors. Mrs Hall Warren gave fifteen
pieces in 1946. She was a resident of Bristol, whose collection was formed between
the wars, and she later gave what she had retained as the Robert Hall Warren
collection to the Ashmolean Museum, Oxford, in 1963.[3] Miss Nancy Nesbitt gave
twenty-five pieces in 1955 from the estate of her mother, Mrs Alice Nesbitt of
Clifton, Bristol. Mr Ernest Blatch gave forty pieces in 1964. The Blatch family

owned the brewery at Theale, near Reading, and the major part of their collection is in the Reading Museum.

Some twenty pieces were purchased from the Maddicks collection in 1936, and some forty pieces from the Hodgkin collection in 1947. The rest of the City Art Gallery collection is made up from individual gifts and purchases.

During the last war, the Bristol Art Gallery building was hit by two enemy bombs, one of which caused damage specifically to the delftware collection, when it appears that about seventy pieces were lost, or so damaged that only fragments remain.

Delftware tiles have been excluded from this catalogue, as Anthony Ray's recent book includes no fewer than 163 from the Bristol collection.[4]

Notes
1 Devonshire Association, *Transactions*, vol. 64, 1932.
2 *English Ceramic Circle Transactions*, vol. 3, part 1, 1951, p. 85.
3 Anthony Ray, *English Delftware Pottery*, preface by Nigel Warren.
4 Anthony Ray, *English Delftware Tiles*, London 1973.

1.1 'Malling' jug, perhaps Greenwich *c.* 1580

3.10 Royal Yacht charger,
probably London 1668

3.40 Charles II portrait charger,
Bristol (Brislington) 1682

4.18 Posset pot, probably London *c.* 1740

5.1 Pill slab, probably London *c.* 1700

6.32 Bottle with black 'enamel' decoration, probably Liverpool *c.* 1760

7.19 Dark blue wall pocket

7.17 Pale blue wall pocket; both,
probably Liverpool *c.* 1770

7.1 Baluster vase with trophies of war
decoration, probably Liverpool *c.* 1760

8.1 The 'Flower' bowl,
Bristol 1743

9.1 Ink stand, Bristol
(Brislington) 1685

10.27 Bowl and cover with the arms of the Worshipful Company of Carpenters, Bristol 1709

10.30 'Hen and chickens' bowl,
probably Bristol 1759

10.54 'The *Lively* of Emsworth'
bowl, probably Liverpool 1747

11.1 *Chinoiserie* dish, probably Bristol 1703

12.14 Dish with 'Niglett' decoration, Bristol 1733

13.8 Dish with blue-red-green decoration, Bristol, *c.* 1730

14.8 Rustic plate with peacock; both, probably Bristol c. 1720   14.1 Rustic plate with cock

15.2 and 15.3 Basin and bottle decorated with blue powder ground, probably Liverpool c. 1760

15.18 'Libertas Populi' plate, probably Bristol *c.* 1740

16.30 Bristol *bianco-sopra-bianco* bowl, *c.* 1765

16.31 *Bianco-sopra-bianco* puzzle jug, Bristol *c.* 1765

16.34 'Ann Scott' tea caddy, Bristol 1763

16.32 'De Moeder ende haar Dogter' dish, Bristol 1755

Fazackerly decoration on mugs: water colour paintings by
an unknown artist in the Liverpool Museum

Courtesy Merseyside County Museums

17.1 'Rowland' jug with Fazackerly decoration, Liverpool 1763

18.8 and 18.9 Basin and matching bottle with decoration of figures in a landscape, Bristol *c.* 1750

THE CATALOGUE

Notes on the Cataloguing

1 The system of numbering indicates first the number of the chapter, and hence the nature of the article or its style of decoration. The succeeding numbers then indicate the place of the article in its chapter.

2 Plates and dishes are regarded as basically the same and are differentiated by size. Under twenty-five centimetres is regarded as a plate, and over, as a dish.

3 The catalogue entries refer to shapes of all flat wares as A, B, C, etc. These are all shown in Appendix I, which also has a diagram indicating the nomenclature adopted in referring to parts of a plate or dish.

4 Dimensions, in centimetres, are given as accurately as possible. Where there is slight variation, as often occurs with delftware, an average measurement is given. Where the variation is regarded as significant, a maximum and a minimum figure are quoted, with an oblique stroke between the figures.

Diameters of hollow ware were determined by measuring the circumference and dividing by π.

5 Under-rim markings are noted in the catalogue entry, where they occur. For further details in each case, and for an understanding of their nature and significance, the reader should turn to p. 309.

6 References to other collections, and to books, and articles in magazines and journals, should be traceable by consulting the Bibliography, p. 331.

SHAPES

1 'Malling' jugs

These rare and beautiful articles, unique in form, are the earliest tin-glazed earthenware made in England – if indeed they were made here, for there is no proof of it. They acquired their name from the discovery of one such jug in the church at Malling, Kent. They are always of the same shape (see plate, p. 25) and in very many cases have a silver lid and base added, and sometimes a cane binding on the handle, suggesting that they were for use in drinking something hot. They are found in many colours, from brown, blue and turquoise to speckled effects including black, blue, manganese, yellow and tortoiseshell. The speckled examples suggest that they were trying to imitate Rhenish stoneware bottles.

Their silver mounts enable us often to date them accurately from the hall marks. The two earliest are in the Victoria and Albert Museum and the British Museum, both with silver-gilt mounts which give us the dates 1547–48 and 1549–50 respectively[1]. They probably ceased to be made before the end of the century. However, in the exhibition of English earthenware at the Burlington Fine Arts Club in 1914, catalogue number D.22 was a 'Malling' jug whose cover was engraved with the arms and crest of Miller (descended from Nicholas Miller of Wrotham, Kent), and whose mount on the neck bore a Latin inscription, which may be translated: 'This fragile vessel was bought by me in A.D. 1618 and soon given to my uncle Nicholas Miller, Armiger, who ending his last day in 1621 at the age of 85, left it to me among other things so worthy of note that I would be ungrateful if I did not record them. Nicholas Miller, Soldier, June 12, 1658, age 65.' This might suggest that 'Malling' jugs were still being made – in south-east England moreover – in 1618, although there is nothing to say that Nicholas Miller acquired it new.

The question of where 'Malling' jugs were made must remain unproven until some archaeological evidence is forthcoming. Ivor Noël Hume[2] discusses the suggestion that they were made in Sandwich, and discounts it, with which we agree. He leaves open the possibility that they were imported from the Continent. However, Rhoda Edwards[3] points out that some Dutch potters were working in Greenwich as early as 1542, and were joined by others in 1550. Nothing is known of the wares they made or of the sites at which they worked. She adds: 'It would be unwise to put forward any theories about Greenwich tin-glaze at this date, but an explanation is yet to be found for the Malling Jugs of 1550.' We, too, must leave it at that.

Notes
1 Victoria and Albert Museum no. M33–1929, and British Museum Franks Collection no. 26.
2 Ivor Noël Hume, *Early English Delftware from London and Virginia*, Colonial Williamsburg 1977, pp. 2–3.
3 Rhoda Edwards, 'London Potters circa 1570–1710', p. 6.

1.1 **'Malling' Jug** A spherical body with wide cylindrical neck, silver mounted base and neck, with silver lid, all stamped and engraved; hall marks illegible. Handle wrapped with cane binding, tail of handle curled. Coloured turquoise blue outside and inside, the base unglazed.
Height to rim 17.6cm, bowl diameter 12.1cm
No. N.7391, gift of Sir Harry and Lady Garner, 1965
Perhaps Greenwich *c.* 1580   COLOUR PLATE, p. 25

Sir Harry Garner was brother of Professor F. H. Garner, author of *English Delftware*. Sir Harry was himself a connoisseur of Chinese ceramics, and it is believed that this jug came to him from the estate of his brother, who died in 1964. It was broken and was repaired before it was presented to Bristol Art Gallery.

2   Early wine vessels

Wine bottles

These bottles, which it is thought were all made in London factories, competed with Rhenish stoneware bottles during the mid-seventeenth century, but were themselves superseded by glass bottles by the late 1670s. The earliest known delftware bottle is dated 1629 and the latest of the same type 1676. They were always the same traditional shape, with a white glaze often tinged with pink as was typical of London wares of the period.

A few are decorated in polychrome, notably with the arms of City of London livery companies. But the bottles were usually inscribed in blue only with either 'Sack', 'Claret' or 'Whit' and were often dated. It has been suggested that such bottles, with an indication of their contents and date, were given as New Year gifts; however, those such as ours, with a trio of initials and a date, would be more likely to commemorate a marriage. But for what sort of people, in what sort of circumstances? Perhaps for the first time we can attempt to answer this from the evidence provided by 2.1.

Fuddling-cups

Another early receptacle for wine or other liquor was the fuddling-cup. The *Oxford English Dictionary* defines 'fuddle' as 'to confuse with, or as with, drink'. The fuddling-cup is made up of three or four small vessels, individually thrown, whose handles are intertwined and whose bodies intercommunicate. One can only assume that by this means the drinks got mixed to befuddle the tippler. These vessels are sometimes called 'tygs', but this really means any drinking vessel designed for communal use with three or more handles.

2.1 **Wine bottle**   Globular shape, neck with raised bands, strap
handle with pinched off tail. Initialled and dated in blue
'W$^\text{P}$F/1644' (the date repeated) in shaped cartouche, marked out
with double-lined curves, and decorated with radial lines
terminating in small round heads. White glaze with pink tinge
showing through in places.
Height 19.7cm, maximum diameter 14.4cm
No. N.3765, purchased 1949
London 1644

Now the initials on this wine bottle do happen to tally with the
marriage of William Prestley, widower, to Frances Herris, widow,
which was authorised by a Bishop of London licence to be held
either in the Parish Church of Cheshunt, Hertfordshire, or St
Bride's, Fleet Street, London. It did, in fact, take place in Cheshunt
on 24 March 1644.

William Prestley lived at Wild Hill, Essenden, Hertfordshire. He
died in 1664, and his will in the Public Record Office shows that
he owned considerable property, not only in Hertfordshire and
Essex, but also as far afield as Lincolnshire and Bristol. He also
owned premises in 'Holborne & Castle Yard & White's Alley in the
parish of St Andrew', a house and shop in Breadstreet, a house in
Charterhouse Yard, a stable in 'Red Lyon Yard' and chambers in
Gray's Inn.

He left all this property to his wife, and the children of both his
marriages, failing which he made made extensive trusts for the
benefit of the poor in many parishes in the City of London. He was
admitted to Gray's Inn on 4 August 1612, as son and heir of
'William Priestley, Citizen & Merchant Taylor of London'. His
father was indeed made a Freeman of the Merchant Taylors in 1587
and served on the court of the Company in 1619.

We are reminded by Sir John Fortescue, the fifteenth-century
Lord Chief Justice, that 'Knights, barons and the greatest nobility
of the Kingdom often place their children in these Inns of Court,
not so much to make the laws their study, much less to live by
their profession, having large patrimonies of their own, but to form
their manners'.

Perhaps we may conclude that a dated and initialled wine bottle
was an appropriate gift in the seventeenth century for an eminent
and well-mannered gentleman.

2.2 **Fuddling-cup**   Vessel with three bowls interconnecting at
their points of contact, their twin handles intertwined. No
decoration or marking. Off-white glaze.
Height 8.6cm, each mouth diameter 3.0cm
No. N.5101, purchased 1951
Probably London *c.* 1680

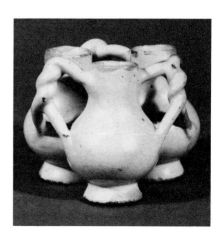

3   Chargers

Some of the earliest and most decorative pieces of English delftware are known as chargers. In fact the first known dated charger is one in the Fitzwilliam Museum, Cambridge, and is inscribed 'ANO DOON 1620'[1] on the back. They continued to be made for about a century, though the number being produced in the eighteenth century was probably falling off considerably.

Chargers are large saucer-shaped dishes[2], mostly with a continuous curvature from edge to edge, but sometimes with a discontinuity in the curvature foreshadowing the flat rim of later dishes. The edges are usually rounded and slightly everted, and often decorated with blue, diagonal brush strokes, leading to the use of the term 'blue dash charger'. This description comes from the title of a book on the subject published by Father E. A. Downman in 1919.[3] There is a theory that blue dashes which are long strokes of constant width at about $45°$ to the edge of the charger denote a London provenance, while dashes which taper, or are of the nature of a blob, denote a Bristol origin. While there does seem to be some substance in this, it should be treated with caution, as should all such generalisations. Some, mostly earlier, chargers have no such edge decoration at all; other, later, examples have blue sponge marks round the edge. Another edge decoration to be found is one or more lines encircling the circumference. The foliage of trees was usually sponged in later chargers, whereas it was depicted earlier by a scale pattern of foliage or by a few oversized leaves.

Chargers stand on a small diameter footrim which is often perforated to receive a cord for hanging on the wall. The hole is frequently in the wrong position for the charger to hang the right way up, and anyway the shape of the footrim is such that a cord could equally well be put round it for suspension. One suspects that many such cords broke and that a large number of chargers failed to survive on this account.

It is interesting that chargers were made in London and Bristol, but not in other, later, centres, and the clay from which they were made appears coarser and of lower specific gravity than in later wares, and was often of a brown or reddish tinge. A few chargers are in blue and white, but the preponderance are in polychrome. On earlier pieces the tin glaze was only applied to the front, and transparent or pigmented lead glaze was used on the backs; this was probably done to save money. Later chargers were tin-glazed all over. Chargers were fired in the kiln in stacks separated by trivets, of which there is an initialled and dated example in the collection, no. 3.1. Because of this one will notice three spots in the glaze on the face of the charger, where the trivet was removed.

Chargers were more decorative than utilitarian, and we may identify a number of distinct decorative styles on them:

1 GEOMETRIC   The first two chargers, nos. 3.2 and 3.3, are pure examples of this style, but it is also to be found recurring in the decoration of the outer circumference of other styles.

2 OAK LEAF AND FRUIT   Again, there is one pure example of this style, no. 3.5, and it is also to be found used as a border design, enhancing the merit of other pieces. The earliest known dated charger, referred to above, has this style of decoration.

3 FLUTED   There is one, pure white, undecorated example of this style. It derives

from the shape of contemporary silverware, and several other examples are to be found among the properties of City of London Livery Companies, decorated in the centre with their arms.

4 CHINOISERIE   There is one example of this style of decoration on a conventional shaped charger. Many fluted *chinoiserie* chargers were made in Frankfurt, and were very similar in appearance to English ones, leading to the liability of confusion in attributing provenance. There are, in fact, two such chargers in the Bristol collection. Two other chargers in this section, decorated with flowers, birds and insects also show the Chinese influence, which is indeed such a dominant influence in English delftware that we devote two later chapters to it entirely.

5 ROYAL YACHT   The collection contains one rare example of a charger depicting a Royal Yacht, with a more familiar scene of fanciful buildings on shore. This piece also has a fine specimen of oak leaf and fruit border.

6 TULIP   There are no fewer than fifteen examples of this style of decoration in the collection. Some early pieces are very rudimentary, displaying little botanical knowledge of their subject; but on the other hand there are three very elaborate ones with oak leaf and fruit borders, and two of a type with a central flower face, of which there are examples elsewhere where the central point is used instead to display seventeenth-century dates. At the height of their perfection, tulip chargers display a fan-shaped array of leaves, among which are tulip, and often also gillyflower, flowers, buds and seedheads. These sometimes spring from the ground, or, more elegantly in some earlier versions, from a vase. In later tulip chargers the decoration becomes less fluent and more stylized, with broad flat leaves filling all available space.

7 ADAM AND EVE   This is a very popular style of decoration, of which we have eleven examples of five different types. Two of these types we have been able to relate to contemporary prints as the design source. It will be noted that the drawing of Adam and Eve was not very faithfully copied, and does not do justice to the prints from which it was taken. The other three types, all later, do not appear to have an engraved design source, and despite their evident popularity, display very much cruder draughtsmanship.

8 PORTRAITS   As many as one third of the chargers in this collection come under this category, and most of them are of kings and queens. They include:

Charles II	2	Anne	4
James II	2	George I	3
William III	5	Duke of Ormonde	1
Mary II	1	Anonymous	3

The most interesting thing to observe is the extent to which one print source was used to depict different people, with often little or no attempt to change anything, and with periods of several years intervening. Thus we have the following:

   One print source for one William III and probably one Charles II and two
      James II chargers.
   One print source for one Mary II and one Anne charger.
   One print source for one William III and one George I charger.
   One print source for one Duke of Ormonde and one anonymous charger.

In some cases the portrait is reversed – left to right – between the two chargers, and in the case of the third print source a sword in the right hand gets changed to an orb. Clothes are also varied.

Fig 1   Adam and Eve by Crispin de Passe (1564–1637) from a painting by John Overbeck. British Museum, Department of Prints and Drawings no. 1873.8.9.702.C.62.

Fig 2   Adam and Eve by Pierre Lombart, Undini, an illustration inserted in Bible L9.e.6 in the British Library. This Bible was published by J. Field, Cambridge, in 1659. It contains a frontispiece by Pierre Lombart, and other prints by W. Hollar are inserted, which are dated 1656, 1657, 1659 and 1660. The illustration reproduced here is a detail.

9 RARITIES   Finally there is one charger of a unicorn, and one of two countrymen meeting in a rural landscape. These are unusual, though one does find quite a variety of unique decoration such as this.

Design sources

The prints illustrated above have been traced as the design sources of some of these chargers. The figure of the monarch on the first four equestrian chargers in this chapter (nos. 3.36 to 3.39) is taken from the engraving of Charles I illustrated in fig. 3. The fourth, which is reversed, is identified by initials as William III, but the other three are not identified. Several versions of chargers from this design exist. One from the Harland collection, sold as lot 116 in a Sotheby sale on 11 February 1931, is marked 'C.R.' – presumably for Charles I. This charger is in blue only, it does not have the inner border of interlocking crescents, and it has an unusual foreground of rows of hummocks with clumps of grass; it is thus unlike any in this collection. A number of other chargers are known with the initials 'W.R.', the majority of which – but not all – show the king riding from right to left. In any case the same print was used from the time of Charles I to that of William III.

The border pattern of interlocking crescents, which appears on two of the unmarked chargers, is not found generally until about the turn of the century, and this has led to suggestions that all these chargers should be attributed to William III. However a plate, sold in London as lot 38 in the first Louis Lipski sale at

Fig 3   Charles I entering Edinburgh, an event which took place in 1641. This print by Cornelius van Dalen is to be found in the Department of Prints and Drawings in the British Museum, and it also appears inserted as frontispiece in one of five copies of J. Nalson's *Journal of the Tryal of King Charles I*, published 1684, in the British Library.

Fig 4   William III by T. van Merlen (born 1661), a print in the British Museum, Department of Prints and Drawings, no. 1848.9.11.353.

Sotheby's on 10 March 1981, has this border pattern and is dated 1686. This is within the span of only four years which separated Charles II from William III, so that dating from the border pattern really only serves to exclude Charles I.

It may be argued that the King in two of the unmarked chargers does not have a moustache, and should therefore be identified as William III; but James II was clean shaven, and in any case the portrait identified by initials as Charles II in no. 3.40 has no moustache, while the King in no. 3.36 does appear to have a pencil line moustache, which would be correct for Charles II. In the light of these considerations, and after studying contemporary prints, we have decided to attribute one of the unmarked chargers to Charles II and two to James II.

The print illustrated in fig. 4, with altered head, appears to be the design source of the last two equestrian chargers in this chapter. There are no initials on either of these chargers to identify their subject, nor do initials appear on other such chargers elsewhere. The plumed headgear sported by the riders may be the delftware artist's concept of a Scottish bonnet. The appearance of the chargers suggests an early eighteenth-century date, and the engraving is presumed to be temp. William III. It therefore seems most likely that these chargers are intended as the Old Pretender.

Notes

1 Glaisher collection no. 1394 (see Bernard Rackham's *Catalogue of the Glaisher Collection of Pottery and Porcelain at the Fitzwilliam Museum. Cambridge,* Cambridge 1934).

2 Appendix I, shape A.

3 E. A. Downman, *Blue Dash Chargers*, London 1919.

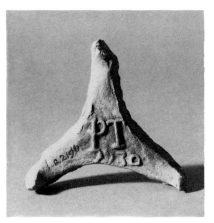

3.1 **Trivet** For supporting a charger during firing, cut from a slab of clay with points bent up. Unglazed biscuit ware. Marked 'PT' and '1730' in raised lettering. Average distance between points 10.0cm, thickness 1.2cm
No. G.2190, purchased 1925
Found at site of Temple Back pottery, Bristol

It seems probable that 'PT' stands for Paul Townsend who was apprenticed to Edward Ward at the Temple pottery in 1716 and obtained his freedom as a Burgess Gally pot maker in 1731. This is a good average size for a trivet; they were never made accurately, but the scar marks on chargers are usually between 9.5 and 10.5cm apart. 1730 is of course a late date for a charger trivet.

3.2 **Charger** Geometric swirl pattern, with a central helix and concentric semicircular arcs around it. Border of interlocking crescents and double circular lines. The whole decoration in shades of blue on a pale bluish glaze; the back with a thin tin glaze.
Diameter 34.5cm, height 5.8cm, footrim diameter 12.4cm
No. G.1164, gift of T. Charbonnier, 1918
Probably London c. 1700

3.3 **Charger** Geometric swirl pattern, with a floral petal design in the centre, surrounded by nine feathery leaves with step pyramids between. Everted rim with blue dashes. The decoration in blue and orange, on a pinky-white glaze, and with lead glaze on the back.
Diameter 33.4cm, height 6.5cm, footrim diameter 10.5cm
No. N.6777, J. Stone Hodges bequest, 1961
Probably London c. 1660

3.4 **Charger** Geometric with buildings. A group of buildings with a domed church in centre, surrounded by seven sets of four concentric arcs interspersed with triple dots. Decorated in blue on a dirty white glaze, the back a rough surface covered with brownish lead glaze.
Diameter 31.8cm, height 6.5cm, footrim diameter 12.2cm
No. N.6685, J. Stone Hodges bequest, 1961
Possibly London c. 1680

3.5 Charger Oak leaf and fruit pattern. One central oak leaf with eight oak apples, surrounded by six oak leaves, half blue-green, half yellow, with manganese veins, and stylized fruit between the leaves. Everted rim with blue dashes. Decorated in blue, blue-green, yellow and manganese on a white glaze; the back with a brownish lead glaze.
Diameter 34.8cm, height 6.3cm, footrim diameter 11.9cm
No. N.3782, found in store and accessioned 1949, ex Charbonnier collection
Probably Bristol c. 1700

3.6 Small Charger Fluted, with twenty-four flutes each starting convex at the edge, turning to concave and running down to a raised centre. White glazed and undecorated, traces of pinky tinge on back.
Diameter 24.9cm, height 5.0cm
No. G.195, purchased 1917
Perhaps London c. 1680, or Continental

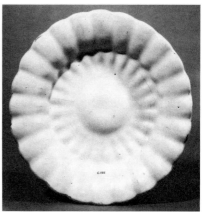

3.7 Charger *Chinoiserie:* a Chinaman among mossy rocks surrounded by a border with similar Chinamen at top and bottom and rocks extending down the sides. Circular lines and outlines in manganese, with blue, pale blue wash and orange colours on a pale bluish glaze. The back with a brownish lead glaze and some pitting of the surface.
Diameter 34.7cm, height 6.5cm, footrim diameter 11.4cm
No. G.1181, gift of T. Charbonnier, 1918
Probably Bristol (Brislington) c. 1680

3.8 Charger *Chinoiserie:* a goose and two butterflies among several leafy sprays and insects, scattered over the surface. The decoration outlined in manganese and coloured in blue and orange, against a pastel blue glaze. The back with a brown lead glaze.
Diameter 34.5cm, height 5.3cm, footrim diameter 12.0cm
No. N.3145, Sir Gilbert Mellor bequest, 1947
Probably Bristol (Brislington) c. 1670

Compare Victoria and Albert Museum no. Cl-1969, and Sotheby London sale 17 April 1973, lot 178

3.9 **Charger** *Chinoiserie* floral: one central bunch of many flowers, and four others sprouting from rocks on edges; a butterfly and several insects. Decorated in shades of blue within manganese outlines against a blue-green glaze. The back with a brownish lead glaze, pock marked.
Diameter 47.2cm, height 8.5cm, footrim diameter 15.8cm
No. N.5586, Mrs E. L. Manton bequest, 1955
Probably Bristol (Brislington) *c.* 1680

3.10 **Charger** Royal Yacht. Central scene of fanciful buildings with domed church, and yacht in water to the left, flying the St George's Cross, the Lord High Admiral's pennant, and other unidentified flags at mast heads. The scene surrounded with an oak leaf and fruit border, and blue dashes. Decorated in blue, green, dark red, yellow and brown on an off-white glaze. The back lead-glazed, the footrim pierced for suspension.
Diameter 41.7cm, height 8.8cm, footrim diameter 12.6cm
No. N.8774, purchased 1975
Probably London 1668   COLOUR PLATE, p. 26

This must be compared with charger no. 89 in the Burnap collection whose centre is entirely occupied by a similar yacht, and whose border is of very similar oak leaf and fruit design. It is suggested that that represents the Royal Yacht *Mary* given to Charles II on his restoration by the City of Amsterdam, and that the King is on board. Unfortunately, however, the King did not keep the *Mary* beyond 1661, and any one of the Royal Yachts built on the Thames by 1663 bears a closer resemblance to the yacht on the charger. Also, Charles II established the custom of flying the Royal Standard, with the Lord High Admiral's pennant and the Union Flag, to indicate his presence on board. Furthermore Willoughby Hannam, whose initials are said to be those on the charger, commanded a man of war named the *Mary* in 1668, and not the Royal Yacht, while his wife's name in the Rotherhithe parish registers is Frances and not Anne.

But the Burnap charger is dated 1668, and from the similarity to that in the Bristol collection, this same date can certainly be attributed to it. The Royal Yachts, first built on the Thames in the 1660s, to prove that we could build them better than the Dutch, set a new and popular fashion, which no doubt explains why this subject was chosen to decorate these chargers, and one can justifiably claim that the Bristol charger represents one of them. The Lord High Admiral's pennant could be flown by royalty, by the Lord High Admiral (in this case the Duke of York, brother of Charles II, and later to become James II), by any member of the Board of Admiralty, and by certain Admirals commanding fleets, so that one cannot specify who was on board. The author is indebted to the Royal Thames Yacht Club for access to their copy of C. M. Gavin's *Royal Yachts*, London 1932, which is a mine of information on the subject.

3.11 **Charger** Tulip: a flower and two buds among foliage, surrounded by geometric floral motifs in eight panels. Decorated in blue, the slightly everted edge with a solid blue band, all on an off-white glaze. The back with a lead glaze of greenish tinge.
Diameter 33.2cm, height 6.0cm, footrim diameter 10.9cm
No. N.6776, J. Stone Hodges bequest, 1961
Probably London *c.* 1670

3.12 Charger A tulip with four leaves either side, springing from a small mound, filling the whole surface of the dish, surrounded only by two blue lines. The decoration in blue, pale green and manganese on a dirty white glaze. The back with a brownish lead glaze.
Diameter 33.5cm, height 6.7cm, footrim diameter 10.1cm
No. N. 6703, J. Stone Hodges bequest, 1961, ex Revelstoke collection
Probably Bristol *c.* 1680

3.13 Charger Tulip: a single flower with eight leaves alternating from a single stem, which rises from a small mound. The whole surrounded by four circular lines, one wavy line and blue dashes on the edge. Decorated in blue, green, manganese and yellow, on an off-white glaze. The back lead-glazed.
Diameter 33.3cm, height 7.5cm, footrim diameter 9.7cm
No. G.1443, purchased from T. Charbonnier collection 1919, ex Downman collection
Probably London *c.* 1710

3.14 Charger Three tulips and two carnations, with buds, seed heads and foliage springing from a globular narrow necked vase, surrounded by four panels of oak leaf and fruit decoration alternating with panels of trellis diaper. Blue dashes on a narrow edge. The decoration in blue, green, yellow and brown against a white glaze. The back with lead glaze.
Diameter 41.5cm, height 9.0cm, footrim diameter 10.7cm
No. G.2021, purchased from T. Charbonnier collection, 1923
Probably London *c.* 1675

Illustrated in the catalogue of *English Delftware* exhibited in the Rijksmuseum, Amsterdam, 1974, no. 40, and in the booklet *Delftware* issued by Bristol Art Gallery, 1975. W. J. Pountney describes and discusses this charger at length in *Old Bristol Potteries* (Bristol and London 1920) on p. 44, and illustrates it in pl. V. The vase from which the flowers spring may be compared with those on two chargers: one in the Glaisher collection (no. 1484) dated 1668, and one dated 1676 shown on pl. VI of *English Pottery* by Bernard Rackham and H. Read (London 1924). Though the arrangement of the flowers is also generally similar, the central flower face or medallion of these two pieces does not appear on the Bristol charger.

3.15 Charger Tulip: one flower and two buds, with pale green leaves outlined in blue, surrounded by a wide border of stylized oak leaves and fruit, and a narrow flat rim with blue dashes over which are blue and yellow circumferential lines. Decorated in two shades of blue, yellow, pale green and orange, on a white glaze. The back with lead glaze.
Diameter 33.9cm, height 6.3cm, footrim diameter 12.2cm
No. G.1182, gift of T. Charbonnier, 1918
Probably London *c.* 1700

3.16 **Charger** Central tulip flower flanked by two buds growing among vertical grey-green leaves, surrounded by a border of oak leaves and stylized fruit, outside which are blue dashes, on a slightly everted rim. The decoration in blue, yellow, red shading, and grey-green on a white glaze. The back tin-glazed.
Diameter 33.8cm, height 7.5cm, footrim diameter 13.1cm
No. N.3132, Sir Gilbert Mellor bequest, 1947
Probably Bristol *c.* 1700

Compare Victoria and Albert Museum no. C.191–1927, and Glaisher collection nos. 1607 and 1608.

3.17 **Charger** Single central tulip flower and two buds, growing vertically from level ground between alternate green and yellow leaves, surrounded by a debased oak leaf and fruit border. The flat rim sponged. Decorated in blue, green, yellow and red on a pale bluish glaze. The back tin-glazed.
Diameter 33.2cm, height 7.2cm, footrim diameter 10.7cm
No. N.6700, J. Stone Hodges bequest, 1961
Probably Bristol *c.* 1720

3.18 **Charger** Three large tulips in brown outline with manganese shaded petals, and a daisy flower face appearing in the centre. Leaves in manganese outline and blue wash, all growing on a vine from a small hummock. Solid blue banded edge. The decoration in brown, blue, manganese and yellow against a dirty white glaze; the back lead-glazed.
Diameter 32.6cm, height 5.3cm, footrim diameter 10.7cm
No. G.1643, purchased from T. Charbonnier, 1920
Probably London *c.* 1675

This charger, and the next, must be compared with one sold at Sotheby's sale in London on 15 May 1979, dated 1663, and also with two in which a very similar arrangement of flowers spring from a vase: Glaisher collection no. 1484, dated 1668, and Rackham and Read, *English Pottery*, pl. VI, dated 1676. In two of these cases the date is in a medallion placed in the centre of the dish in lieu of the central daisy flower face.

3.19 **Charger** Three tulip flowers and three multi-petalled flower faces with foliage on several stems from a hillock, surrounded by a yellow band within the blue dash edge. Decorated in blue, green wash, yellow and red on an off-white glaze; the back lead-glazed.
Diameter 33.5cm, height 7.1cm, footrim diameter 11.7cm
No. N.6699, J. Stone Hodges bequest, 1961, ex Maddicks collection
Probably London *c.* 1675

See comments on previous entry.

3.20 Charger Three tulip flowers, two buds and six seed heads among alternate blue and green leaves from a small mound. Blue dashes circumferentially on the outer edge. The decoration in blue, green, yellow and red on a white glaze; the back tin-glazed.
Diameter 34.2cm, height 6.4cm, footrim diameter 12.0cm
No. N.6673, J. Stone Hodges bequest, 1961
Probably Bristol *c.* 1700

Compare Glaisher collection nos. 1499 and 1502, there attributed to Lambeth

3.21 Charger Three tulip flowers and two seed heads, with alternate dark and pale blue leaves in a globular vase. Cabbage-like leaves falling from vase. Decorated in two shades of blue, red and yellow on a white glaze. The back tin-glazed. Many blobs of blue dash round edge.
Diameter 29.0cm, height 6.0cm, footrim diameter 10.8cm
No. N.6734, J. Stone Hodges bequest, 1961, ex Beaumont and Maddicks collections
Probably London *c.* 1680

3.22 Charger A central tulip flanked by three leaves on either side, with flower buds and smaller leaves beyond, all from a small mound. Four circumferential lines round the rim. The decoration in blue, including the outlines, with green and orange colour on a dirty white glaze. Thin lead glaze on the back.
Diameter 25.9cm, height 4.8cm, footrim diameter 10.3cm
No. G.2520, purchased 1930
Probably London *c.* 1680

3.23 Charger Three tulips with other flowers and leaves of pale green in blue outlines, all rising from a small mound. Everted rim with blue dashes. Decorated in blue, pale green and orange on an off-white glaze. Thin tin glaze on the back.
Diameter 34.8cm, height 6.4cm footrim diameter 10.2cm
No. G.1197, purchased from T. Charbonnier, 1919, ex Downman collection
Probably London *c.* 1680

Mentioned by Pountney on pp. 44–45, and illustrated in pl. V. Compare with illustration in Downman p. 101, and with Glaisher collection no. 1493.

3.24 Charger Three tulip flowers, two buds and two seed heads in blue-green foliage. The edge with blue dashes and a yellow band inside them. Decorated in blue, blue-green, and yellow with black outlines, on a white glaze; the back partially lead-glazed.
Diameter 35.6cm, height 5.6cm, footrim diameter 13.1cm
No. N.6702, J. Stone Hodges bequest, 1961, ex Revelstoke collection.
Probably Bristol *c.* 1710

3.25 Charger Three tulip flowers, two buds and two seed heads among broad olive green vertical leaves from level ground. The decoration in olive green, blue, red and yellow on a white glaze. The back tin-glazed with some pitting. Blue dashes on edge.
Diameter 29.4cm, height 5.7cm, footrim diameter 15.2cm
No. N.6687, J. Stone Hodges bequest, 1961
Probably London *c.* 1680

3.26 Charger Adam and Eve. She stands with hair round the waist and tosses an apple to Adam, who walks towards her. Snake twined round trunk of tree and branches dislodging another apple. Trees with sponged foliage, foreground painted in with three little bushes. Circumferential blue dashes on edge. The decoration in blue, green and red on a white glaze; sparse tin glaze on back.
Diameter 34.8cm, height 7.0cm, footrim diameter 12.4cm
No. N.6725, J. Stone Hodges bequest, 1961, ex Downman collection
Probably Bristol *c.* 1710

This charger, and the next, show Adam and Eve in the same pose as in no. C26-1931 in the Victoria and Albert Museum, and no. 1401 in the Glaisher collection, which are dated 1635 and 1640 respectively. They all derive from the print by Crispin de Passe illustrated at the beginning of this chapter, but the two examples in the Bristol collection are debased copies and clearly of much later date than the two dated pieces just mentioned.

3.27 Charger Adam and Eve. She stands handing an apple across the tree with her right hand to Adam, who walks towards her. A big serpent is wound round the tree with another apple in its mouth taken by Eve in her left hand. She has long manganese hair coiled round her loins. Blue dashed edge. Finely sponged trees and foreground. Decorated in pale blue, blue outlines, green and blue sponged foliage, green tree trunk and yellow apples with red marks, on a white glaze. The back with pinkish tin glaze.
Diameter 34.1cm, height 6.5cm, footrim diameter 11.8cm
No. G.1186, gift of T. Charbonnier, 1918
Probably London *c.* 1700 (note the differences from the previous example)

3.28 Charger Adam and Eve; standing either side of the tree, she offers him a red apple, which he accepts. The serpent is in the branches of the tree. Foreground treated as in no. 3.26, sponged foliage to trees, circumferential blue dashes on edge. Decorated in blue, green, red and yellow on a white glaze; the back with a thin tin glaze.
Diameter 29.6cm, height 7.0cm, footrim diameter 11.5cm
No. N.6662, J. Stone Hodges bequest, 1961, ex Downman collection
Probably Bristol *c.* 1700

The pose of Adam and Eve derives from the print by Pierre Lombart illustrated at the beginning of the chapter, with the exception of the serpent's head, whose position is changed.

3.29 Charger Adam and Eve, identical with the previous entry. Some pitting may be noted on the tin glazed back.
Diameter 29.9cm, height 7.5cm, footrim diameter 11.0cm
No. G.1185, gift of T. Charbonnier, 1918
Probably Bristol *c.* 1700

3.30 Charger Adam and Eve, both walking to their left holding leaves in their right hands. Five large yellow apples with brown shading among separately drawn leaves of tree, the trunk and leaves washed over in green. Striped serpent with wolf's head and arrow tail coiled round tree trunk. The decoration in blue, pale blue wash, green wash, yellow and brown, against a pale blue glaze; the back lead-glazed.
Diameter 33.4cm, height 7.0cm, footrim diameter 10.0cm
No. G.1184, gift of T. Charbonnier, 1918
Probably Bristol *c.* 1700

3.31 Charger Adam and Eve, similar to previous entry, except that the leaves and tree trunk are washed in pale green, the serpent does not have an arrow tail, and there is a white glaze on the face, with thin tin-glazing on the back.
Diameter 34.5cm, height 7.8cm, footrim diameter 11.5cm
No. N.6728, J. Stone Hodges bequest, 1961, ex Downman collection
Probably Bristol *c.* 1710

3.32 Charger Adam and Eve, similar to the two previous examples, except that it is more clearly outlined in manganese, and the leaves are individually washed in green within their outlines, the tree trunk is painted in manganese, and Adam and Eve each carries an apple in the right hand. The glaze is of pale blue tinge, with a lead-glazed back.
Diameter 34.4cm, height 5.2cm, footrim diameter 11.6cm
No. N.6729, J. Stone Hodges bequest, 1961
Probably Bristol *c.* 1700

3.33 Charger Adam and Eve. She hands an apple to him, both walking towards the central tree. Each holds a large rhubarb leaf. Serpent coiled round trunk of tree with another apple in its mouth. Nine apples among branches of tree, which has sponged foliage. The decoration in blue and pale green, with yellow apples marked with red, on a white glazed surface. The back with a light beige lead glaze. Blue dashes on edge.
Diameter 31.7cm, height 6.3/7.2cm, footrim diameter 11.3cm
No. N.6660, J. Stone Hodges bequest, 1961, ex Pountney collection
Probably Bristol *c.* 1700

3.34 Charger Adam and Eve. The scene very similar to the last example, though differing in many details; but the crudity of the drawing of the two faces in profile is even more marked. The snake's tail is more like a water lily leaf than the arrow head of nos. 3.30 and 3.32. Border pattern of crescent and dot, interspersed with tufts, on a flattened rim. Decorated in blue, green sponging, yellow and red on a pale bluish glaze; the same glaze on the back.
Diameter 33.5cm, height 7.5cm, footrim diameter 10.9cm
No. G.2054, purchased from T. Charbonnier, 1923.
Probably Bristol *c.* 1740

Compare Victoria and Albert Museum no. C.375-1926, which is dated 1741. An example of this type in the Burnap collection, no. 124, has sponging on the rim.

3.35 Charger Adam and Eve facing one another either side of the slender tree, a yellow snake with red stripes hands apple to Eve, yellow fruit banded in red. Sponged foliage to tree and on either side; the rim also sponged. Decorated in blue, green, yellow and red on a pale blue glaze. The back tin-glazed with some pitting.
Diameter 32.6cm, height 6.3cm, footrim diameter 12.6cm
No. G.2053, purchased from T. Charbonnier, 1923
Probably Bristol *c.* 1720

Compare Victoria and Albert Museum no. C.55-1967, and Burnap collection no. 125. Burnap collection no. 126 shows the same scene on an ordinary dish which they date *c.* 1750.

3.36 Charger Monarch on horseback, galloping, crowned, in ermine robes, baton in his right hand and reins in his left. Trees with chain link foliage, green and brown banded foreground. Decorated in blue, green, yellow, brown and manganese on a white glaze. The back with a blue glaze. Blue dash edge.
Diameter 33.9cm, height 7.8cm, footrim diameter 10.5cm
No. N.6701, J. Stone Hodges bequest, 1961, ex Gautier and Hall Warren collections
Probably London *c.* 1680, perhaps Charles II

This, and the next three chargers, all derive their design from the Cornelius van Dalen print illustrated at the beginning of this chapter.

3.37 Charger Monarch on horseback, as described in the previous entry, but with a border design of interlocking crescents inside the blue dash edge. The back lead-glazed.
Diameter 42.6cm, height 9.4cm, footrim diameter 13.4cm
No. G.190, purchased from W. J. Pountney, 1915
Probably London *c.* 1685, perhaps James II

Mentioned by Pountney on p. 33; in *English Delftware* by F. H. Garner and Michael Archer (London 1972) on p. 10 and illustrated in pl. 23; illustrated in catalogue of the Rijksmuseum exhibition, no. 64.

3.38 Charger Monarch on horseback, as described in the previous entry, differing in only very minor points of detail.
Diameter 42.8cm, height 9.3cm, footrim diameter 13.7cm
No. N.6691, J. Stone Hodges bequest, 1961
Probably London *c.* 1685, perhaps James II

3.39 Charger King William on rearing horse, marked 'W R', with reins in right hand and baton (or sword?) in left. Sponged trees on either side, blue circumferential lines within undecorated edge. This evidently derives from the same source as the last three chargers, but has been reversed, and the ermine-lined cloak has been converted to all ermine. Decorated in blue, green and yellow on a pale bluish glaze; the back with a brownish lead glaze.
Diameter 34.9cm, height 7.4cm, footrim diameter 12.1cm
No. N.6669, J. Stone Hodges bequest, 1961, ex Pountney collection
Probably London *c.* 1700

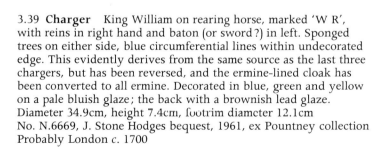

3.40 **Charger** Crowned head and shoulders of monarch marked 'C R²' and '1682' surrounded by a wide border of twelve stylized acorns with leaves, alternately erect and on their sides. Four fine pale blue lines within the border and two outside it. The decoration in blue and yellow on a white glaze; the back lead-glazed
Diameter 43.2cm, height 6.2cm, footrim diameter 14.6cm
No. G.2237, gift of Alderman J. F. Eberle, 1926
Probably Bristol (Brislington) 1682   COLOUR PLATE, p. 26

Mentioned by Pountney on p. 33 and illustrated at pl. V. Compare with Glaisher no. 1642, which is a similar portrait of Catherine of Braganza, marked 'K R' and '1682'; there are only four repeats of the border motifs on that, compared with six on the Bristol charger. See also Michael Archer, 'Delftware from Brislington', *The Connoisseur* (vol. 172, no. 692), July 1969, pp. 152–161.

3.41 **Charger** King William III, head and shoulders portrait, marked 'K W', surrounded by a wide border of iris-like flowers and insects, repeated three times. Decorated in manganese, yellow and pale blue against a pale blue glaze; the back lead-glazed.
Diameter 34.5cm, height 6.5cm, footrim diameter 11.4cm
No. N.3366, purchased ex Maddicks collection, 1936
Probably Bristol (Brislington) *c.* 1690

Compare Victoria and Albert Museum no. 3872-1901, which is a very similar charger marked 'Q M', showing a head and shoulders portrait of the Queen, with a rim decoration of thistle-like flowers and insects. These two pieces are discussed and illustrated by Michael Archer in 'Delftware from Brislington', *The Connoisseur*, July 1969, pp. 152–161.

3.42 **Small Charger** 'Q M' either side of a head and shoulders portrait of Queen Mary in décolleté dress with gold necklace, earrings and brooch. Decorated in blue and yellow with manganese outlines on a pale blue-green glaze.
Diameter 22.5cm, height 3.4cm
No. N.8461, found in store and accessioned 1974
Probably Bristol (Brislington) *c.* 1690

See the comments on the previous charger of King William. The portrait of Queen Mary on this one is remarkably similar to that on Victoria and Albert Museum charger no. 3872-1901. This, too, must have been made at the Brislington factory.

3.43 **Small Charger** Marked 'D M' either side of a head and shoulders portrait of the Duchess of Marlborough in décolleté dress with a veil from the back of her hair. Decorated in blue and yellow with manganese outlines on a pale blue glaze with a tinge of green.
Diameter 22.6/23.1cm, height 4.7/5.1cm
No. G.2213, gift of T. Charbonnier, 1925
Bristol (Brislington) *c.* 1690

The Duchess of Marlborough, née Sarah Jennings, married the Duke in 1678, and later became Mistress of the Robes and Keeper of the Privy Purse to Queen Anne. This charger has many similarities to the previous one, and must also have been made at Brislington.

3.44 Charger Horseman on a prancing horse, wearing feathered hat among sponged foliage trees. Blue dash edge. Decorated in blue, yellow and green on a white glaze; the back tin-glazed with some pitting. There are no trivet marks on the face of this charger.
Diameter 28.7cm, height 4.6cm, footrim diameter 9.1cm
No. N.6665, J. Stone Hodges bequest, 1961, ex Freeth collection
Probably London *c.* 1710

This charger is copied from the print by T. van Merlen of William III, discussed and illustrated at the beginning of the chapter, where we argue that it is probably intended here to portray the Old Pretender, James Francis Edward Stuart, known also to Jacobites as 'James III', and the only son of James II. The absence of trivet marks indicates that it must have been fired face down, resting on three pegs under the rim, or face upwards, standing on its footrim. There are several other points of difference between this charger and the next, which derives from the same print source. This, and the fact that the engraver was Dutch, leads one to consider the possibility of a Dutch origin; but on balance a London provenance is thought most likely.

3.45 Charger Horseman on a prancing horse, baton in hand, with feathered hat and sash flying from the waist. Sponged foliage trees. A yellow band within the blue dash edge. Decorated in blue, pale green wash, manganese and yellow on a white glaze; the back with a pinkish lead glaze.
Diameter 34.9cm, height 7.7cm, footrim diameter 12.2cm
No. G.2044, purchased from T. Charbonnier, 1923
Probably Bristol *c.* 1710

See remarks on the previous entry. This charger is discussed by Pountney on p. 43 and illustrated in pl. IX, where it is suggested that it represents George I.

3.46 Charger King William III, standing, marked 'WR', crowned, in ermine cloak with sceptre in the left hand and orb in the right, among trees with runny washed foliage. Two manganese lines encircle the edge. The decoration in blue, green and manganese on a white glaze; the back greenish with porridgy surface.
Diameter 33.4cm, height 7.0cm, footrim diameter 11.4cm
No. N.6772, J. Stone Hodges bequest, 1961, ex Pountney collection
Probably London *c.* 1690

The back of this charger was evidently covered with a clay slip.

3.47 Charger King William III standing, marked 'WR', crowned, with ermine robes, sceptre in his right hand and orb in his left. He stands on a tiled floor, with a small fence behind and trees with foliage washed with green within outlines. Blue dash edge. The decoration in blue, yellow and pale green on a white glaze tinged with pink; the back lead-glazed.
Diameter 34.5cm, height 6.6cm, footrim diameter 12.0cm
No. N.6727, J. Stone Hodges bequest, 1961
Probably Bristol *c.* 1690

3.48 Charger King William III standing, marked 'WR', crowned, flourishing a sword in his right hand, his left hand on the hip, wearing armour. Trees with green washed foliage, perhaps sponged. Two manganese circumferential lines within the rim. Decorated in blue, green, brown and manganese on a pale beige glaze; the back with a greenish lead glaze.
Diameter 34.3cm, height 6.6cm, footrim diameter 11.3cm
No. N.6682, J. Stone Hodges bequest, 1961, ex Pountney collection
Probably London *c.* 1690

The similarity of the pose to that of no. 3.55 is discussed in the chapter introduction.

3.49 Charger Queen Mary, seated, marked 'M.R', crowned, with the orb in her outstretched right hand and sceptre in her left. She is flanked by trees with blue stems and green-washed foliage. Blue dashes overlap a blue band round the edge. Decorated in blue, red and green on a white glaze; the back with mottled brownish lead glaze.
Diameter 35.2cm, height 7.2cm, footrim diameter 13.0cm
No. N.6680, J. Stone Hodges bequest, 1961
Probably Bristol *c.* 1690

The similarity of the pose to the following portrait of Queen Anne is discussed in the chapter introduction.

3.50 Charger Queen Anne seated, marked 'A R', crowned, with orb in her outstretched right hand and sceptre in her left. Heavily sponged foliage on trees and green-washed foreground. Blue and yellow lines within the blue dashes on the edge. The decoration in blue, yellow and green on a pinky-white glaze; the back lead-glazed with some brown and green coloration.
Diameter 30.5cm, height 5.6cm, footrim diameter 10.5cm
No. G.2919, gift of R. Hall Warren, 1931, ex Dawnay and Beaumont collections
Probably Bristol *c.* 1705

3.51 Charger 'AR' either side of a head and shoulders portrait of Queen Anne, uncrowned and fashionably dressed. Surrounded by a border of interlocking crescents and arcs, the flat rim with circumferential blue dashes. Decorated in blue on a white glaze; the back thinly glazed.
Diameter 34.3cm, height 6.7cm, footrim diameter 12.7cm
No. G.2920, gift of R. Hall Warren, 1931, ex Beaumont collection
Probably Bristol *c.* 1705

3.52 **Charger** Queen Anne standing, marked 'AR', crowned and wearing an ermine cloak on her right shoulder, with the orb in her outstretched left hand and sceptre in her right. Trees with many thin red stems and blue sponged foliage, the foreground sponged in green. Blue dashes on the rim outside a blue line. The decoration in blue, red, green, yellow and brown on a white glaze; the back with a smooth lead glaze.
Diameter 33.8cm, height 7.0cm, footrim diameter 12.9cm
Loaned 1929
Probably Bristol *c.* 1710

Discussed by Pountney on p. 42, and illustrated in pl. X. He compares it to a sherd found at Brislington pottery site. Note also the very similar charger illustrated by Garner and Archer at pl. 24.

3.53 **Charger** Queen Anne standing, marked 'AR', crowned, with the sceptre erect in her outstretched right hand and the orb held to her waist in her left. Trees with sponged foliage, the foreground washed in green and painted with tufts. Decorated in blue, green and yellow on an off-white glaze; the back with a brownish lead glaze. Blue dashes on edge.
Diameter 35.3cm, height 6.3cm, footrim diameter 12.4cm
No. N.6678, J. Stone Hodges bequest, 1961, ex Freeth collection
Probably Bristol *c.* 1710

3.54 **Charger** Queen Anne standing, marked 'A R', crowned, with orb in extended left hand and sceptre in the right, wearing flowing robes. Trees with sponged manganese foliage. Blue and yellow bands within the blue dashes on edge. Decorated in blue, yellow, pale manganese and green on a white glaze; the back tin-glazed a warm pink.
Diameter 29.8cm, height 5.6/6.4cm, footrim diameter 11.2cm
No. N.6664, J. Stone Hodges bequest, 1961, ex Freeth collection
Probably Bristol *c.* 1705

3.55 **Charger** George I standing, marked 'GR', crowned, in uniform and ermine cloak, with the orb in his right hand outstretched, and his left hand on hip. Spindly trees with sponged foliage. Blue dash edge. The decoration in blue, red, green and yellow on a white glaze; the back lead-glazed with a yellowish tinge.
Diameter 34.6cm, height 7.1cm, footrim diameter 12.6cm
No. G.1440, purchased 1919
Probably Bristol *c.* 1720

Discussed by Pountney on p. 43 and illustrated in pl. IX. Note that the pose is the same as in no. 3.48, which there represents King William, though several changes have been made in the dress, etc.

3.56 Charger King George I standing, marked 'G R', crowned, in an ermine cloak, with the sceptre in his right hand and the orb balanced in his left. Trees, shrubs and foreground sponged. A yellow band through blue dashes on the rim. Decorated in blue, red, green and yellow on a white glaze; the back lead-glazed.
Diameter 34.8cm, height 6.5cm, footrim diameter 12.2cm
No. N.6719, J. Stone Hodges bequest, 1961, ex Clarke collection
Probably London c. 1715

3.57 Charger King George I standing, marked 'G R', crowned, with ermine cloak, holding orb balanced on his right hand and the sceptre in his left, among trees and bushes of sponged decoration. Two narrow lines within the blue dash edge. Decorated in blue, red, green and yellow on an off-white glaze; the back tin-glazed.
Diameter 35.7cm, height 9.1cm, footrim diameter 12.6cm
No. G.1192, gift of T. Charbonnier, 1917
Probably Bristol c. 1715.

In the Glaisher collection no. 1638 the same figure is marked 'G R II'; compare also Hall Warren collection no. 6.

3.58 Charger The Duke of Ormonde standing, marked 'D O', in knee-length jacket, his sword hung from a sash over his right shoulder, holding a baton in his left hand while his gauntleted right hand rests on his hip. Among sponged-foliage trees, the foreground painted. Two narrow lines within the blue dashed border. Decorated in blue on a white glaze; the back tin-glazed.
Diameter 34.2cm, height 7.7cm, footrim diameter 12.3cm
No. N.2241, gift of Mrs Hall Warren, 1946, ex Harland collection
Probably Bristol c. 1710

This probably represents James Butler, the second Duke, who succeeded Marlborough as captain-general 1711 to 1714.

3.59 Charger A uniformed soldier stands, hatless, holding a baton in his outstretched right hand and wearing a sword on a sling from his left shoulder, his gauntleted left hand resting on his hip. Among trees with sponged foliage on a painted foreground. The decoration in blue on an off-white glaze; the back tin-glazed with some pitting. Two lines within the blue dash edge.
Diameter 32.4cm, height 7.3cm, footrim diameter 10.5cm
No. N.6733, J. Stone Hodges bequest, 1961
Probably Bristol c. 1710

Note the similarity to the previous charger of the Duke of Ormonde, except that this is reversed, either by accident, or because the anonymous subject is left-handed.

3.60 **Charger** A unicorn with spotted coat and yellow mane and tail, walking in a sparse landscape between trees with washed foliage. Blue dashes on the edge. The decoration in blue, green and orange-yellow on an off-white glaze; the back tin-glazed.
Diameter 35.0cm, height 9.1cm, footrim diameter 13.0cm
No. N.3365, purchased ex Maddicks collection, 1936
Probably Bristol *c.* 1720

3.61 **Charger** Two peasants meeting in a landscape, with sponged-foliage trees and houses in the distance; the trees bearing red fruit. A single line round the edge with no blue dashes. The decoration in blue, green and red on a white glaze; the back tin-glazed.
Diameter 30.6cm, height 5.5cm, footrim diameter 12.0cm
No. N.6718, J. Stone Hodges bequest, 1961, ex Pountney collection
London or Bristol *c.* 1720

3.62 **Charger** Christ on the cross, a halo round his head, and the inscription 'INRI', against a background of trees and buildings. The wide flat rim decorated with twelve floral motifs. The decoration in shades of blue on a white glaze; the back lead-glazed.
Diameter 25.5cm, height 4.0/5.1cm, footrim diameter 9.9cm
No. G.2228, purchased from T. Charbonnier, 1925, ex Gautier collection
Perhaps London *c.* 1660, or Continental

4 Posset pots

Posset was a 'drink composed of hot milk curdled with ale, wine, or other liquors, often with sugar, spices, or other ingredients; formerly much used as a delicacy, and as a remedy for colds or other affections'[1]. It is known as far back as the fifteenth century. Posset pots were made of pewter in Elizabethan times, an inventory of 1560 including 'A possett Boule of Pewter'[2].

Posset pots are vessels, usually spouted, with two handles and a lid. The spout starts from the lower part of the vessel, clings to its side, and then turns outward so that the contents could be sucked from it, or if necessary, poured from it. Early London specimens in delftware, going back to 1631[3], were generally straight-sided; but although we have a considerable number in the collection, we attribute nearly all to Bristol. The earliest of these is a straight-sided one which we date as c. 1680.

The next ten which follow are all of squat bulbous shape, without pedestals and with a collar which is either parallel or slightly everted. Where the lids survive they are of flattened dome shape, with a simple mushroom knob and no elaboration. The handles are nearly all of strap type, with blue banding on the outside, though some are of rounded section flattened on the outside. One would expect that such posset pots as these were used for remedial purposes, rather than for celebrations.

The twelfth pot is a miniature, without spout, and standing on tripod feet.

We then start to get elaboration of the design; with sea serpents surmounting the handles on the pot, as well as the handles now appearing on the lid; with a little bird perched on a pedestal between the handles on the lid; with handles terminating in elaborate corkscrew curls where they are attached to the pot, top and bottom, and with, in one case, handles reminiscent of wrought iron work. No. 4.17 has merely loops attached to the pot with corkscrew curls; it is evident that in this case a twisted or plaited cord was threaded through these loops to form the handles.

Finally, coming up to the middle of the eighteenth century, we find ornamental straps surmounting the lid, which is adorned with applied 'jewels', with Maltese crosses and with fleurs-de-lis, standing erect. Most of these elaborated designs stand on a foot, while one stands on curled feet, and they were obviously worthy of being kept for celebratory use on very special occasions.

Two of our posset pot lids have small cups mounted in place of the knobs. These are said to have been used for sampling; if so, one can only assume that some of the posset was poured from the spout into the cup for this purpose. However, one would have thought that a separate cup would have been much handier.

An authority on Dutch delft states that posset pots were a form peculiar to England[4], but the Rijksmuseum, Amsterdam, states that two posset pots are known in Holland, which are now recognized as of Dutch origin, the typical shape being with straight sides and a pronounced shoulder, tapering to a small-diameter lid[5]. There are others who agree with this[6]. We have two posset pots of this shape in the Bristol collection, which we have not included in this catalogue, as we do not believe them to be English.

Notes

1 *Oxford English Dictionary.*
2 Hubert Hall, *Society in the Elizabethan Age*, London 1886, p. 152, Inventory of Sir Henry
    Parkers.
3 Glaisher collection no. 1294.
4 E. Neurdenburg, *Old Dutch Pottery and Tiles*, translated by Bernard Rackham, London 1923,
    p. 139.
5 The author is indebted to Miss van Berge, Assistant Keeper of Ceramics at the Rijksmuseum, for
    this information.
6 J. K. Crellin, *Medical Ceramics. A Catalogue of the English and Dutch collections in the Museum of
    the Wellcome Institute of the History of Medicine*, London 1969, p. 224 and pls. 383–387;
    and Anthony Ray, *English Delftware Pottery*, p. 206 and pl. 74.

4.1 **Posset Pot** Cylindrical shape, with round-section handles
curled in at the top and out at the tail, decorated with blue dashes.
The sides with a seated Chinaman in a fenced garden, with rocks;
blue lines encircle top and bottom. The lid with a similar scene,
plus houses, and a border of stylized stiff leaf pattern. The knob of
simple mushroom shape. No spout. The decoration in manganese
trek with wash in shades of blue, on an off-white glaze. The inside
with a pale greenish tinge.
Height 12.9cm without lid, diameter 13.6cm
No. N.6631, J. Stone Hodges bequest, 1961
Probably Bristol *c.* 1680

4.2 **Posset Pot** Round body on a flattened base, and short conical neck widening to rim. The strap handles curled in at the top and out at the tail, and blue-dashed. The spout also blue-dashed. No lid. The body decorated with four panels of a bird on a floral spray embellished with *chinoiserie* scrolls, and the neck with a band of lines and loops. The decoration in blue, red, green and yellow on an off-white glaze.
Height 14.8cm, maximum diameter 16.7cm
No. N.6629, J. Stone Hodges bequest, 1961
Probably Bristol *c.* 1690

4.3 **Posset Pot** Round body on a flattened base, the neck widening slightly to the rim, broad strap handles curled out at the tail and blue-dashed, the domed lid with a mushroom knob. Decorated in blue on a pale bluish glaze, with four scenes of a bird on a rock under sponged trees. A similar bird on the lid. The neck border of pendent arcs.
Height to knob 22.0cm, maximum diameter 18.5cm
No. N.2248, gift of Mrs Hall Warren, 1946
Probably London *c.* 1700

Compare Hall Warren collection no. 65.

4.4 **Posset Pot** Round body on a flattened base, the body curving into a wide, slightly everted neck. Strap handles curled in at the tail and blue-dashed. Decorated in blue on an off-white glaze, with three areas of twining stems with flowers and leaves, the neck border of debased *ruyi* scroll. The clinging spout daubed with blue dashes and spots.
Height 8.5cm, maximum diameter 9.3cm
No. N.5325, purchased 1952
Probably London *c.* 1720

4.5 **Posset Pot** Round body on flattened base with rudimentary footrim, and short wide parallel neck. Simple strap handles with tight curls at tail. A clinging spout with blue bands. The body decorated in blue, red and green with four areas of floral sprays with *chinoiserie* embellishments, the neck with blue scrolls and red stars. No lid. The glaze pale bluish.
Height 14.8cm, maximum diameter 18.5cm
No. N.5952, found in store and accessioned 1959
Probably Bristol *c.* 1700

4.6 **Posset Pot** Body with slightly curved sides and flattened base and short, wide parallel neck. Wide strap handles with tight curls at tail and blue-dashed. Clinging spout with curl pattern decoration. Flat domed lid with small knob. The decoration in blue on an off-white glaze with five repeats of a floral spray with snippets of foliage scattered around. The lid with similar form of decoration; the neck with *chinoiserie* scroll pattern.
Height to rim 14.5cm, maximum diameter 17.0cm
No. G.2055, purchased from T. Charbonnier, 1923
Probably Bristol *c.* 1710

4.7 **Posset Pot** Squat bulbous body on flattened base, the neck widening to the rim. Strap handles, blue-dashed terminating in tight curls at the tail. The round domed lid with a mushroom knob. The clinging spout with blue dashes. The decoration in blue, red and green on a pink tinged glaze, with many sprigs of mimosa foliage, red 'spiders' and quadruple blue dots. A *chinoiserie* scroll band containing green lozenges round the neck.
Height 15.2cm to rim, diameter 18.5cm
No. G.1647, purchased from T. Charbonnier, 1923.
Probably Bristol *c.* 1710

Illustrated in Rackham and Read, *English Pottery*, fig. 121.

4.8 **Posset Pot** Round body on flattened base curving into a gently everting rim; strap handles, blue-dashed, curling out at the tail; domed lid with mushroom knob, and a clinging spout. The decoration in blue on a pale bluish glaze, of flowers sprouting from a stylized hollow rock, round the sides and on the lid. A twining floral border round the neck.
Height 15.4cm to rim, maximum diameter 17.6cm
No. N.3777, Miss M. Perry bequest, 1943
Probably Bristol *c.* 1720

4.9 **Posset Pot** Round body curving in to a smaller diameter base than is usual, and curving gently into a slightly everted neck. The clinging spout with scroll pattern decoration. Strap handles with blue dashes, curling out at the tail. Moderately domed lid with simple knob. The decoration in blue, green and yellow on a pale blue glaze, with polychrome floral arabesques all round the sides and on the lid, a lower border of formal blue scroll pattern, and an upper border of green scrolls embellished with red and blue.
Height 15.3cm to rim, maximum diameter 18.6cm
No. G.2026, purchased from T. Charbonnier, 1923
Probably Bristol *c.* 1720

4.10 Posset Pot Bulbous body on a small flattened base, with a gently everting rim, strap handles and clinging spout, both with blue dashes, and a domed lid with small mushroom knob. The decoration in blue on a white glaze, with three areas of floral sprays round the sides, and similar flowers on the lid, while the neck has a border of running vine with flower faces and *chinoiserie* scrolls. The whole nicely proportioned and decorated.
Height 15.2cm to rim, maximum diameter 17.6cm
No. G.2233, purchased from T. Charbonnier, 1926.
Probably Bristol *c.* 1730

4.11 Posset Pot Rather squat bulbous body on small diameter base, round section handles curling in at the top and out at the bottom, and clinging spout, all blue-dashed. High-domed lid with simple knob. The decoration in blue, red and green on a white glaze, red and blue trellis diaper round the sides, with four shaped reserves containing a flower and leaves, similar decoration on the lid, and a neck border of concentric arcs. The inside glaze pinky.
Height 13.7cm to rim, maximum diameter 15.8cm
No. G.174, purchased 1914
Probably Bristol *c.* 1730

4.12 Miniature Posset Pot Bulbous cup shaped with slight waist below the rim; two small vertical handles with blue dashes, and standing on three conical feet. No lid and no spout. The decoration in blue on a white glaze, with an all-over pattern of quatrefoil fern leaves, quadruple dots, six-point stars, etc.
Height 6.5cm, diameter 6.5cm
No. G.2058, purchased from T. Charbonnier, 1923
Probably Bristol *c.* 1700

This is an unusual article. It is possible that it was intended for a child, and it is also possible that it is of Continental origin.

4.13 Posset Pot Bulbous body on a flattened base, and curving gently up to the rim without forming a distinct neck. Tightly curled round-section handles on body and lid, with blue dashes on the sides and surmounted by sea serpents. The spout with *chinoiserie* scroll pattern. The slightly domed lid with a small bird on a perch between the handles. The sides and lid decorated in blue, red, green and yellow on a pale bluish glaze, with birds among flowers with *chinoiserie* scroll embellishments, and insects.
Height to rim 14.5cm, maximum diameter 17.0cm
No. N.6628, J. Stone Hodges bequest, 1961
Probably Bristol *c.* 1700

4.14 Posset Pot Very similar to no. 4.13, except that it is decorated in blue instead of polychrome, that the bird is missing from its perch on the lid, and that there is a band of decorative scroll work round the neck.
Height to rim 14.0cm, maximum diameter 16.6cm
No. G.2230, purchased from T. Charbonnier, 1925
Probably Bristol *c.* 1700

4.15 Posset Pot A spherical body on a domed foot, with a short conical neck widening to the rim. Handles on the body and lid of twin round section surmounted by serpents. The lid with a tall knob. The body and lid decorated in blue on an off-white glaze, with panels of cupids gathering and arranging flowers, the panels framed in acanthus leaves against a dark blue ground. The neck band with a continuous pattern of cherry blossoms.
Height to rim 19.6cm, maximum diameter 18.7cm
No. G.2217, gift of T. Charbonnier, 1925
Probably Bristol *c.* 1690

Compare plate no. 374 in the Wellcome Institute collection, with similar panels of cupids.

4.16 Posset Pot A cup-shaped body standing on a hollow domed foot, with short cuffed neck. Heavy strap handles surmounted by twin snakes twisted together, the handles joined to the body with corkscrew curls on either side, top and bottom. The spout, unusually, with a device to stop drips running back. No lid. The decoration in blue, red, green and yellow on a white glaze, with four panels of decoration containing a yellow bird among polychrome floral ground, borders of *ruyi* heads, alternating triangular leaves and *chinoiserie* scroll pattern. The base with red leaves and flowers among scrolls. The inside with a pinky tinge.
Height 22.3cm, maximum diameter 20.2cm
No. G.2030, purchased from T. Charbonnier, 1923
Probably Bristol *c.* 1700

4.17 Posset Pot Bulbous body on a flat base supported on four curled feet, the neck everting gently. Loops attached on either side, top and bottom, with corkscrew curls. A plaited cord is presumed to have been threaded through these loops to form the handles. The clinging spout with *chinoiserie* scroll pattern. No lid. Decorated in blue on a white glaze, with sprays of chrysanthemums and other flowers. The base marked 'A + S 1699'.
Height 17.9cm, maximum diameter 18.1cm
No. G.1554, purchased 1920
Probably Bristol 1699

4.18 **Posset Pot** Tall cup-shaped body extending straight up to the rim, but with a raised bead below the decorative band at the rim; standing on a short domed foot. The handles on body and lid reminiscent of wrought iron work. The nearly hemispherical lid surmounted by a sampling cup in place of a knob. No spout. The decoration in blue on a white glaze, with scenes of figures in landscapes with ruins and stipple-foliage trees between borders of formal leaf scrolls and flower panels.
Height to rim 17.3cm, diameter 13.8cm
No. N.6632, J. Stone Hodges bequest, 1961
Probably London *c.* 1740   COLOUR PLATE, p. 27

4.19 **Posset Pot** A bulbous body curving gently in to form the wide neck, and then everting to the rim. Standing on a tiered foot. The spout marked 'T ^{E} M' and decorated with applied lozenges and *chinoiserie* scroll pattern, and with simulated rivets attaching the spout to the body. Handles of twin round section attached to the body with corkscrew curls, and surmounted by serpents. The lid with four straps supporting a central ball and cross, and with fleurs-de-lis and Maltese crosses standing erect round the circumference. The decoration in blue on a white glaze, with scenes on the body of figures in a landscape with stippled-foliage trees, above bands of stiff-leaf borders round the base, and on the lid four winged angels' faces.
Height to rim 20.5cm, maximum diameter 19.7cm
No. G.2138, purchased from T. Charbonnier, 1924
Probably London *c.* 1700

Mentioned in Garner and Archer p. 15 and illustrated in pl. 45. Illustrated in the Rijksmuseum exhibition catalogue no. 74, and in the Bristol Art Gallery *Delftware* booklet no. 5.

4.20 **Posset Pot** The body acorn-shaped on a short collared stem with flanged foot, the lower part with ten leaves in relief with flower stems between, the upper part with scenes of a *chinoiserie* fenced garden. The handles moulded; no spout. The lid surmounted by four straps decorated with applied 'jewels', and with fleurs-de-lis, Maltese crosses and triangles standing erect round the circumference. The decoration in blue on a white glaze.
Height to rim 22.0cm, maximum diameter 23.6cm
No. N.5567, purchased 1955
Probably Bristol *c.* 1750

4.21 **Posset Pot Lid** Only slightly domed, with central pedestal on which there was probably a bird, and two strap handles with blue dashes, surmounted by serpents. The decoration in blue, red, green and yellow on a pale bluish glaze, with three Chinamen seated in a landscape.
Height 7.5cm, diameter 15.7cm
No. N.8452, found in store and accessioned 1974
Probably Bristol *c.* 1730

The decoration should be compared to that on dish no. 12.14, bearing initials thought to be those of John Niglett.

4.22 **Posset Pot Lid and Crown** The lid shaped with compound curvature up to a central peak on which sits a sampling cup; fitted with two handles of twin round section attached by corkscrew curls and surmounted by serpents. The decoration in blue, red and green on an off-white glaze, with peacocks on hollow rocks, and other birds and insects among flowers. The rim border of connected arcs with *chinoiserie* embellishment.
Height 27.8cm, diameter 31.0cm

The crown had four straps from the sides up to the central spherical knob, which probably had a bird surmounting it. The crown fits snugly over the sampling cup and rests on the flange at its base. Decorated on two sides with a bird perched on a bunch of flowers, and on the other two by a pendent bunch of flowers on which a bird hangs. Under each panel of decoration is a red embossed fleur-de-lis.
Height to knob 11.0cm, base diameter 8.5cm
No. G.1692, purchased 1921
Probably London *c.* 1700

This is an extremely rare arrangement; the author is aware of only one other recorded example, which is not identical.

4.23 **Posset Pot** With a globular body standing on a footrim, and a short conical neck widening to the rim. The handles of double round section, S-shaped, surmounted by snakes. Decorated with spreading floral vines with perched and flying birds. The neck border with blue painted panels with Chinese motifs. The footrim and clinging spout with a running Chinese classic scroll. The domed lid with a hollow cup in the centre. The decoration in blue on a white glaze, pinky inside.
Height 16.0cm, rim diameter 14.0cm (broken)
No. G.2017, purchased from T. Charbonnier, 1923
Probably Bristol *c.* 1680

This piece is now broken and cannot be illustrated; it is, however, illustrated in Pountney, pl. VIII, with comment on p. 36. It is very unusual to find a posset pot with a recessed cup in the domed cover. This cover had eight decorative devices standing up round it, all of which are broken off. This arrangement makes the purpose of so-called sampling cups even more difficult to understand.

5   Apothecaries' and other wares

It is convenient to deal in this chapter not only with apothecaries' wares, but also with other articles which may have been used for medical purposes or in the sickroom.

Pill slabs

These are sometimes called pharmaceutical tiles, but are in any case very decorative and much sought after. They were probably used for rounding pills and for mixing ointments; but some say that their primary use was as a sign to hang in the window of the shop, and it is true that they are always pierced with two holes for suspension. .

Pill slabs nearly always bear the arms of the Apothecaries' Company, which were granted in 1617, thus:

> *In a Shield Azure. Apollo, the inventor of phisique proper; with his heade Radiant, holding in his left hand, abowe and in his Right hande an Arrow, dor, Suplanting a Serpent, Argent, aboue the Shield an Helme, thereupon a mantle gules doubled Argent, and for their Creast vppon a Wreath of their Colours, a Rhynoceros, proper, Supported by too Unicorns, or, armed and ungulated argent, upon a Compartiment to make the Atchievement compleat, this motto, 'OPIFERQUE PER ORBEM DICOR'.*

The motto is from Ovid's story of Apollo and Daphne. Apollo, speaking to the nymph, tells her who he is: *'Inventum medicina meum est, opiferque per orbem dicor, et herbarum subiecta potentia nobis.'* ('The art of medicine is my discovery, and I am called help-bringer throughout the world, and all the potency of herbs is given unto me'.)[1]

An article in the *English Ceramic Circle Transactions*[2] reviews 104 known pill slabs, and categorizes them by shapes thus:

octagonal	67
shield	20
heart	16
oval	1

Of these only seven are in polychrome. Thirty-two have the arms of the City of London below the motto. Only four dated examples are known, one, with the arms of Charles II, dated 1664, was sold at Sotheby's,[3] an earlier one inscribed 'Edward W ..?' on a ribbon is dated 1663. Others are dated 1670 and 1703 respectively, and both of these bear the apothecaries' arms. Most pill slabs have their edges painted, and this is known in blue-black, dark blue, blue and maroon.

Drug jars

These are of two basic types, one with a spout, and standing on a short pedestal, for wet drugs, and one which is usually oviform for containing dry drugs, for powders, pills, ointments and confections. There are remarkably few of either type in the Bristol collection, and they are not easy to date, as they changed little in the course of time; in fact the main aid to dating is the style of the decorative cartouche which contains the name of the intended contents.

The prescriptions which drug jars contained are listed in the Pharmacopoeia, which were issued by the Royal Society of Physicians up to 1863, after which they became the responsibility of the Medical Council. Reference to the original Pharmacopoeia in the library of the Royal Society of Physicians, or to James' *Medicinal Dictionary*[4] will elucidate their meaning and composition; tracing the earliest recorded date of a prescription may be of some help in dating a drug jar.

Ointment pots

These vary in size and shape enormously.[5] The largest in this collection is 21.6cm high and 16.5cm in diameter, but they may be found even larger than this. The smallest may be under 5cm in height or diameter, containing literally a thimbleful. The ointment might be dispensed from a dry drug jar, or, if it had to be compounded, might be mixed on a pill slab with the aid of a spatula. Some ointment pots, of which there are two examples in the collection, bear the names of chemists written on them, the chemists having evidently ordered them in quantity from the delftware factory.

These are even more difficult to date than drug jars, as their many shapes and sizes did not change with time, and most are undecorated. All ointment pots have an indentation below the rim to allow a parchment to be tied over it with a string, which was probably then sealed with red sealing wax. Quite a lot of them are unglazed, which suggests that they were intended to be thrown away after they had served their purpose.

Bleeding bowls

The convention seems to be that single-handled bowls are called bleeding bowls, and that similar bowls with two handles are called porringers. The shape and size of the bowls is similar in either case, and we cannot be dogmatic about how they were used. Suffice it to say that there must have been quite a demand for bleeding bowls as it seems to have been the practice to regard bleeding as a panacea for all complaints and to indulge in it at the slightest provocation.

London handles were usually flat with a five or seven-lobed outline and with one or more perforations, often heart-shaped; Bristol handles usually had moulded surfaces with radial corrugations, and were pierced with one or more round holes. The attributions we have given to the four examples in this collection do tally with this formula.[6]

Barbers' bowls

There is little doubt that these were in fact used for shaving, as the instruments portrayed in one of the two examples in this collection show. But it is suggested[7] that barbers' bowls were also used for bleeding on occasions as there is evidence from bowls containing illustrations of lancets and of the appearance of such bowls in a contemporary print of a blood-letting scene. It should be remembered that the City of London Livery Company of Barbers started in 1461 as Barber-Surgeons, who practised surgery and dentistry as well as shaving and haircutting. Their practice of surgery was, however, officially ended in Henry VIII's reign, and that of dentistry only in 1745; nevertheless one of the parties to a lease of the Temple Pottery, Bristol, in 1749, was Samuel Tipton 'Barber-Surgeon'.

The other barbers' bowl in the collection bears the inscription: 'Sir Your Quarter's Up'. The probable relevance of this to a barbers' bowl is discussed in the catalogue entry.

Pap warmer

Pap, or caudle, was an infant or invalid food consisting of bread or flour soaked in water or dilute milk. Pap warmers were made in delftware in London and Bristol from about the middle of the eighteenth century. They are called by some *veilleuses* in recognition of their secondary function of providing a dim illumination in the sick room or nursery at night.

Hot water plates

These were presumably used for keeping food hot for invalids or others being served in a bedroom. In large houses there was such a distance from kitchen to bedroom that the food might otherwise be cold on arrival.

Such articles are rare in English delftware. There are examples in pewter from the second half of the eighteenth century[8], and also in Chinese porcelain[9], the latter said to have been copied from silverware of the period. We have happily found one in silver, which can be dated to 1765 from its hallmark. This appears to be about as early as they were made.

It will be noted that, for filling with hot water, our delftware specimens have a slot in the rim, which has a stepped edge, and there was evidently a lid of some sort which fitted this slot. The metalware examples all have a hinged flap at this point, and the Chinese example has a rectangular filler built on to the side, which is pierced with a hole, evidently for the pivot of a hinged flap.

Notes

1 Agnes Lothian, 'English delftware in the Pharmaceutical Society's Collection', *English Ceramic Circle Transactions*, vol. 5, part 1, 1960, pp. 1–4.
2 L. G. Matthews, 'Apothecaries' Pill Tiles', *English Ceramic Circle Transactions*, vol. 7, part 2, 1970, pp. 200–209.
3 Sotheby sale, London, 18 January 1972, lot 242.
4 R. James, M.D., *A Medicinal Dictionary*, London 1743.
5 See J. K. Crellin, *Medical Ceramics*, pls. 175–204; and Ivor Noël Hume, *Early English Delftware from London and Virginia*, figs. III, IV and V.
6 See J. K. Crellin, op. cit., pp. 273–4 and pls. 454–456; and Ivor Noël Hume, op. cit., fig. XIV.
7 See J. K. Crellin, op. cit., pp. 273–4 and pl. 457.
8 Victoria and Albert Museum, Croft Lyons bequest no. 491–1926.
9 Victoria and Albert Museum, no. 2912–1902.

5.1 **Pill slab** Shaped as a regular octagon with two holes at the top for suspension, decorated with the arms of the Apothecaries' Company and the motto 'OPIFER QUE PER ORBEM DICOR' on a scroll. The shield shows a man with bow and arrow standing astride a dragon; it is surmounted by a helm and a crest of a rhinoceros among a mantling of acanthus leaves; the supporters two unicorns. Decorated in blue on a white glaze; the edges also in blue.
Height and width 27.0cm, thickness 1.6cm
No. G.2915, purchased 1931
Probably London *c.* 1700   COLOUR PLATE p. 28

5.2 **Wet Drug Jar** Flattened bowl shape on a splayed foot, with a short straight spout and strap handle. Marked 'S:SIMPL:' on a label; birds with leaves perched on the top corners, an angel's face below with pendent tassels and bowls of fruit. Decorated in blue on a pale blue glaze.
Height 13.8cm, diameter of bowl 12.9cm
No. N.3766, purchased 1949
Probably London *c.* 1740

The inscription is an abbreviation of *Syrupus de Absinthio Simplex*: simple syrup of wormwood. James' *Medicinal Dictionary* says: 'Take of the clarified Juice of common wormwood, and of clarified Sugar, of each four pounds; and boil them together to the consistency of a Syrup.' The drug was used as a vermifuge.

5.3 **Dry Drug Jar** Of ovoid shape, marked 'T:ALHANDAL' on a label, surmounted in the centre by a basket of fruit and on either corner by a bird with leaves. Below, an angel's head with spread wings, and swags with tassels. Decorated in blue on an off-white glaze.
Height 8.9cm, maximum diameter 8.6cm
No. N.5395, purchased 1953
Probably London mid-eighteenth century

A paper label stuck on the base reads 'HINE Chemist & Druggist, Beaminster', which is a small town in Dorset. The inscription on the bowl is an abbreviation of *Trochisci Alhandal*; Alhandal lozenges. James' *Medicinal Dictionary* says: 'Take of white Colocynth Pulp cleared from its seeds, and cut small, of Gum Arabac, Tragacanth, and Bdellium, each siz Drams. Let the Gums be macerated for 3 or 4 days in a sufficient Quantity of Rose-Water, so that they may be dissolved in it; and with the forementioned Pulp let all together be beat up into a Consistence for Troches.' These lozenges were prescribed as a purgative.

5.4 **Dry Drug Jar** Tall ovoid shape, marked 'C.AURANT' on a label surmounted in the centre by a shell, and at the corners by an angel with a flower spray. Below, an angel's face with folded wings, and tassels and swags. Decorated in blue on a pale blue glaze.
Height 19.1cm, maximum diameter 14.8cm
No. N.5931, found at the Red Lodge and accessioned 1959
Probably London mid-eighteenth century

The inscription on the label is the abbreviation of *Conserva Auriantium*: conserve of the Seville or bitter orange; it was made from fresh oranges with three times the quantity of white sugar, and was used as a tonic.

5.5 **Ointment Pot** Straight-sided with curved indent below the
rim. Decorated in blue on a pale blue glaze, with twelve rings, two
rows of dots and a broad central band with alternately erect and
inverted patterns of diminishing arcs.
Height 21.6cm, diameter 16.5cm
No. G.2214, gift of T. Charbonnier, 1925
Probably Bristol *c*. 1700

5.6 **Ointment Pot** Straight-sided with curved indents below the
everted rim and above the base; decorated in blue with nine bands
of continuous lines and two bands of dotted lines. The glaze off-
white. Reported found on a Lambeth excavation site.
Height 14.9cm, diameter 17.8/19.0cm
No. N.5727, purchased 1957
Probably London late seventeenth century

5.7 **Ointment Pot** Straight-sided with indentations above the
base and below the rim. Banded with six blue rings on an off-
white glaze.
Height 7.4cm, diameter 7.6cm
No. G.3162, gift of H. Blatch, 1934
Probably Bristol *c*. 1700

5.8 **Two Ointment Pots and a Waster** The larger standing on a
solid footrim, bowl-shaped with everted rim, pale blue glaze,
undecorated. A label on the base reads 'Temple Back'.
Height 4.6cm, diameter of rim 7.3cm
No. N.5328, found in store and accessioned 1952
Probably Bristol mid-eighteenth century

The smaller, bowl-shaped on a small diameter stem, inscribed in
blue on an off-white glaze 'Waller & Son Guilford'.
Height 3.7cm, diameter 5.6cm
No. N.6644, J. Stone Hodges bequest, 1961.
Probably London late eighteenth century

Jesse Waller and his son were practising as apothecaries in
Guildford at the end of the eighteenth century, according to an
article by Agnes Lothian, 'Vessels for Apothecaries', in *The
Connoisseur Year Book*, 1953.

5.9 Two Ointment Pots The smaller, bowl-shaped on a short, solid footrim, with an everted rim, and marked 'DELESCOT' in gold letters on a pale blue-grey glaze.
Height 3.9cm, diameter 5.5cm
No. N.7158, Ernest Blatch bequest, 1964
Probably London mid-eighteenth century

The larger, bowl-shaped on a smaller diameter stemmed base, and with everted rim, decorated in blue with stylized floral motif on a greyish white glaze.
Height 5.1cm, diameter 7.6cm
No. N.7159, Ernest Blatch bequest, 1964
Probably London mid-eighteenth century

Delescot was an apothecary at 19 Duke Street, Pall Mall, where he patented his conserve of Myrtle Opiate in 1749, as reported by Agnes Lothian-Short, 'Apothecaries in the Haymarket and their unguent pots', *English Ceramic Circle Transactions*, vol. 10, part 1, 1976, pp. 69–71.

5.10 Two Ointment Pots Straight-sided with V-shaped indents below the everted rims and above the bases, in unglazed terracotta-coloured biscuit state, said to have been found on the site of the Brislington pottery.
Heights 5.9cm and 4.3cm
No. N.5420, gift of R. F. Thomas, 1953
Probably Bristol late seventeenth century

5.11 Ointment Pot In the shape of a bowl on a stem with pedestal foot, the inside of the bowl shallow; undecorated in off-white glaze. Reported found on Lambeth site.
Height 5.2cm, diameter 8.0cm, depth inside 2.3cm
No. N.5996, gift of K. Barton, 1960
Probably London early eighteenth century

5.12 Five Ointment Pots Of various shapes, the largest of 9.5cm diameter and the smallest of 3.5cm diameter. No decoration, their glazes variously tinged with pink, green or blue.
No. G.103, all the gift of J. E. Pritchard in 1902, and believed to have been found in excavations in various parts of Bristol.
Probably Bristol first half of the eighteenth century.

5.13 **Four Ointment Pots** Of various shapes as illustrated. The largest 5.8cm diameter and the smallest 2.9cm diameter. All undecorated, with an off-white glaze.
Nos. NX.949–952, found in store and accessioned 1975.
Probably Bristol early eighteenth century.

5.14 **Bleeding Bowl** The inside with six petal-shaped segments with simple embellishments, and on the rim nine looped garlands. The single handle with six moulded lobes decorated with brush strokes, and pierced with one round hole. No external decoration. The decoration in red, blue and green on an off-white glaze.
Diameter 14.4cm, height 6.6cm
No. G.1555, purchased from T. Charbonnier, 1920, ex Lloyd collection
Probably Bristol *c.* 1720

5.15 **Bleeding Bowl** The outside decorated with a continuous frieze of a bud and a leaf repeated five times, the rim painted blue. Inside the bowl a small sprig of leaves. The applied handle moulded in leaf-shape with eight lobes marked with brush strokes, and pierced with a round hole. The decoration in blue on a pale blue glaze.
Diameter 13.3cm, height 6.7cm
No. N.6646, J. Stone Hodges bequest, 1961
Probably Bristol *c.* 1740

5.16 **Bleeding Bowl** Inside, a *chinoiserie* scene of fenced garden with typical Chinese symbols. The applied handle moulded with eight lobes painted all over in blue, and pierced with a round hole. The outside undecorated. The decoration in blue, red and green on a white glaze.
Diameter 13.1cm, height 5.4cm
No. N.6653, J. Stone Hodges bequest, 1961
Probably Bristol *c.* 1740

5.17 Bleeding Bowl Bulbous-sided bowl with one applied seven-lobed flat handle with heart-shaped perforation, decorated all over in dark blue with scattered white spots.
Diameter 13.5cm, height 6.2cm
No. N.3217, Sir Gilbert Mellor bequest, 1947
Probably London *c.* 1690

This style of decoration is known as *bleu persan* or *bleu de Nevers*, and also appears on the fluted bowl no. 8.51. An identical bleeding bowl may be found in the Morgan catalogue no. 23, where its relationship to contemporary silverware is discussed. The potters at Nevers in France were the first in Europe to use this style of decoration, which began in about the mid-seventeenth century and includes *chinoiserie* scenes in white on the same dark blue ground.

5.18 Barbers' Bowl This is shaped with a deep centre well and a wide rim, with a cut-out for the neck and a small depression for the soap; two holes are pierced in the rim for suspension. Decorated in blue on a white glaze, depicting an assortment of barbers' instruments in the centre of the bowl, and multi-lobed hillocks with stylized floral decoration on the rim.
Diameter 26.6cm, height 9.1cm
No. G.2309, gift of T. Charbonnier, 1928
Probably London *c.* 1700

Compare Glaisher collection no. 1516, Liverpool Museum no. 65.130.1 and Garner and Archer pl. 53A, dated 1706.

5.19 Barbers' Bowl The shape of this bowl is similar to the previous example, except that the bowl is not as deep. Decorated in blue on a pale blue glaze with bamboo, peony and another flower (perhaps a variation on the three friends of Chinese symbolism) springing from a hollow rock, and inscribed 'SIR YOUR QUARTER'S UP'.
Diameter 26.0cm, height 7.0cm
No. G.2141, purchased from T. Charbonnier, 1924
Probably Liverpool *c.* 1720

The expression 'The Quarter is up' is recognized in the *Oxford English Dictionary*, which refers us to Guy Miège's *Great French Dictionary* of 1688, containing the expression '*Le Quartier est échu*' meaning the quarterly bill is due. But such inscriptions in the early eighteenth century usually had a *double entendre*, and the other meaning in this case may be that the exemption from being put to death is over – from the other sense of the word 'quarter' – or, in other words 'Watch out that you don't get your throat cut'. This would explain the use of such a catch phrase on a barbers' bowl. Compare Victoria and Albert Museum no. 297–1869, which has the same inscription, but is decorated with barbers' instruments in the bowl. Another bowl, which was exhibited by Jonathan Horne, the London dealer, at the Grosvenor House Antique Dealers' Fair in 1976, bears the inscription 'Quarter Day Pray Gentlemen Pay – 1716', which makes it quite clear that it was the custom to pay one's barber's bill quarterly.

5.20 Pap Warmer   Consisting of three parts:
(1) The cylindrical base with two attached double scroll handles on the sides, male masks applied back and front to shield holes for escape of smoke, and a rectangular hole at the base in front with bracket-shaped top for insertion of a lamp. Blue lines encircle top and base with stylized floral embellishments. The figures '23' on the flat base.
(2) The cup-shaped pap holder with straight sides and a flange to rest on the top of the main body. Foliate applied handles are on either side (one broken), decorated in blue, and on the unglazed base the figures '23'.
(3) The lid with a small candle holder for knob, decorated with blue circles and stylized flowers. The figures '23' inside. The whole in a pale bluish glaze; the lamp missing.
Height overall 25.9cm, diameter of body 11.0cm
No. G.2142, purchased from T. Charbonnier, 1924
Probably London *c.* 1770

Harold Newman, in *Veilleuses 1750–1860* (London 1967) says that delftware examples are thought to date from about 1750, 'those from Bristol and Lambeth being almost indistinguishable, even by experts'. But Pountney on p. 141 and pl. XXXIV describes and illustrates a Bristol one, attributed to Joseph Flower, whose decoration is quite distinctive. Bristol examples are also found in Reading Museum no. 241.61.28 and Victoria and Albert Museum no. C.50–1939. Morgan collection no. 88 is almost identical with that in the Bristol collection, and is complete with lamp. Compare also Liverpool Museum no. 8.10.68., and J. K. Crellin, *Medical Ceramics*, pl. 345.

5.21 Hot Water Plate   Consisting of a plate with a shallow receptacle for hot water beneath, filled through a rectangular slot in the rim; two simple handles attached. The top decorated in blue on a bluish-greenish glaze, with the scene of a man standing in a fishing boat, an island beyond with houses and a ruin. The sides with four Chinese lozenge symbols tied with ribbons. In the footrim, the figures '44'.
Diameter 21.9cm, height 6.4cm
No. G.183, purchased 1914
Probably Liverpool *c.* 1760

5.22 Hot Water Plate   Constructed as described in the previous entry. The top finely decorated with a Chinaman fishing from an island with a triple-roofed pagoda, willow tree and rocks, and with acanthus leaves either side of the filling slot, and four Chinese scroll symbols tied with ribbons round the sides. Within the footrim, the figures '21'.
Diameter 22.6cm, height 6.6cm
No. N.3062, purchased ex Hodgkin collection, 1947
Probably Liverpool *c.* 1760

The same *chinoiserie* scene appears on wallpocket no. 7.13 (see detail below).

6 Mugs, jugs and bottles

There does not appear to be any one basic shape in delftware mugs. They may be straight-sided, slightly tapering towards the top, or curviform; they may be tall or squat; they may have a flat or a hollowed-out base, and the base may swell out or remain straight-sided to the bottom. As for their handles, these may be round or flat in section, but are nearly always cross-banded with blue stripes. Some round handles have a hole through the top, presumably for attaching a lid, but it is doubted whether a single English delftware mug survives with lid attached in this manner, and the perforation appears rather to be a fashion copied from Continental practice. A few English delftware mugs with lids do exist, with flanges standing up on the top of the handle, pierced with a pin on which the lid is hinged. Some of the simpler mug shapes clearly derive from earlier earthenware, and other more sophisticated shapes from pewter and silverware. In addition to the eleven mugs illustrated in this chapter, one more may be found at no. 15.1.

The great majority of jugs that have been handed down to us are puzzle jugs. One suspects that this is what Nicholas Blundell meant when he wrote of a visit to a Liverpool delftware factory in 1710: 'I bought a fancifull Ring of Mugg Mettle to drink out of and brock it ere I got it home'[1], for it is true that they are both fanciful and fragile.

The lip of the jug is a tube of round section hollowed out, and carries three spouts. The hollow lip is connected to the base through a hollow handle. The neck of the jug is liberally perforated in a pattern of hearts, flowers or intersecting circles, so that ordinary drinking from it is out of the question. It is said that a neck with intersecting circles was the Bristol style, and other neck patterns came from London or Liverpool. The jug is invariably inscribed with a rhyming challenge to the would-be drinker that he will not succeed in emptying it without spilling some. The secret is to suck through one spout, and at the same time to close with the fingers, not only the other two spouts, but also one or even two hidden holes beneath the handle.

The earliest known puzzle jug in delftware is in the Glaisher collection[2] and is dated 1653. They were clearly popular over a long period; they probably originate from pewter ware, and they continue into later ceramics.

We illustrate nine puzzle jugs in this chapter. Others are nos. 16.31 and 18.20.

As for bottles, there are two beetle-shaped[3] and one pear-shaped in the collection, and sixteen that are globular or spherical. But one finds a great variation in their necks; some have a neck with a simple bell-shaped mouth, others have a spherical bulge in the neck below the mouth, and others have mouths which are cup-shaped, topped by an everted rim. Most mouths are circular, but one is pinched in to form a spout. The beetle-shaped bottles defy all convention as regards necks, remaining straight-sided inside right up to the lip, and falling away on the outside to form a sharp-edged rim.

The decoration on bottles is not to be differentiated from that on other articles of similar provenance and date, as will be pointed out in the catalogue entries which follow. In one case, no. 6.35, the bottle matches a basin catalogued at no. 8.46; they were received by the City Art Gallery together, and had no doubt been sold in the first place as a matching pair, for a wash-hand stand. The same applies to nos. 15.2 and 15.3, while nos. 18.8 and 18.9 also appear to be a matching pair, but in this case they were acquired separately. Another bottle may be found at no. 18.27.

Notes

1 Frank Tyrer, *The Great Diurnal of Nicholas Blundell*, Record Society of Lancashire and Cheshire, 3 vols. 1968–72, entry for 31 August 1710.
2 Glaisher collection no. 1321
3 'Beetle-shaped' refers to the shape of the cylindrical-headed wooden mallet. The other beetle-shaped bottle is no. 18.8.

6.1 **Mug**

6.1 **Mug** Straight sided with slight bulge below the rim and at the base. Marked 'union' in small script lettering. The handle oval shaped with blue dashes and pointed, flattened tail. The decoration in blue, red, green and yellow on a white glaze, with an all-over rectangular lattice in blue, with green crosses at the intersections and red stars within the squares. The top border of *chinoiserie* scroll pattern, and yellow bands at top and bottom.
Height 12.0cm, diameter 8.4cm
No. N.5486, purchased 1954
Probably Bristol *c.* 1707

This mug must have been made to commemorate the Act of Union between England and Scotland in 1707; it is referred to by Ray in *English Delftware Pottery* on p. 123.

6.2 **Mug** Shape slightly tapering, with an oval handle flattened on the inside, perforated at the top, and the tail pointed and flattened. The decoration in blue, red and green on an off-white glaze, with flowers sprouting from a triangular rock and a perched bird, the top border of ovals enclosing lozenges, and the handle with a *chinoiserie* leaf motif tied with ribbon. The base glazed.
Height 18.0cm, base diameter 11.2cm
No. N.3240, Sir Gilbert Mellor bequest, 1947
Probably Bristol *c.* 1750

6.3 **Mug** Slightly tapering shape, with an oval handle flattened inside, blue-dashed with dots either side, perforated at the top, and with a tapering tail. The decoration in blue, red, manganese, green and yellow on an off-white glaze with tinges of blue. The body covered with a polychrome spray of flowers and leaves.
Height 17.4cm, base diameter 12.1cm
No. N.7892, purchased ex E. F. Eberle, 1969
Probably Bristol *c.* 1750

6.4 **Mug** Straight sided with an oval handle flattened inside and perforated at the top, with blue dashes and dots either side. Decorated in blue, red and green on an off-white glaze, with a scene of a Chinaman seated against a rock in a landscape with two sheep and sponged-foliage trees and bushes.
Height 17.5cm, diameter 11.0cm
No. N.3239, Sir Gilbert Mellor bequest, 1947
Probably Bristol *c.* 1760

6.5 Mug Straight sided, with strap handle, blue banded, its base pressed into the body from which the tail then re-emerges. Dated '1720'. Decorated in blue on an off-white glaze, with flowers growing from a rock, two herons in water beside the rock, two more perched birds and one flying. The bottom border of a continuous band of oak leaves in reserve on a blue band.
Height 19.1cm, diameter 13.4cm
No. N.6624, J. Stone Hodges bequest, 1961
Probably London 1720

6.6 Mug The shape tapering from a flanged base, the strap handle attached flush with the rim at the top, blue-banded with dots either side, its tail curled out. The decoration in blue on an off-white glaze, with two birds perched on a hollow rock among flowers, a top border of blue ovals containing flowers, interspersed with pendent bell flowers. All decoration in the *chinoiserie* taste. Marked on the side 'I - D'. The base partially glazed.
Height 13.8cm, base diameter 13.8cm
No. N.5542, gift of Miss Nesbitt, 1955
Probably London *c.* 1700

6.7 Mug The shape swelling out immediately above a flanged base, and then tapering in gently until it curves out to the rim. The handle of flat oval section with repeated bud decoration, the tail flattened and curled up. Decorated in blue on a pale bluish glaze, with chrysanthemums and other flowers growing from a hollow rock, with a bird perched on a branch. The top border of stylized foliage and trellis with pendent floral motifs. The glazed base inscribed 'Millison Henry 1752'.
Height 15.8cm, rim diameter 11.5cm
No. G.2027, purchased from T. Charbonnier, 1923
Probably London 1752

The Gentleman's Magazine, in October 1810, records the death 'In Cornhill (City of London), Mr H. Millson, formerly of Bristol'. It is possible that this is the same person to whom this mug was given in childhood.

6.8 Mug Tapering from base to rim, the handle of oval section flattened inside, blue-dashed with dots either side, and the top perforated. Decorated in blue on a white glaze with an all-over pattern of flowers, quadruple dots and brush dabs. The base part-glazed.
Height 18.5cm, base diameter 11.2cm
No. G.1149, purchased 1918
Perhaps Bristol *c.* 1720, or Dutch?

6.9 Mug Decorated with two equal horizontal bands of Chinamen seated among rocks and flowers, with blue lines encircling above and below. The heavy oval handle flattened inside and pierced at the top, the pointed tail clinging to the body, decorated with blue dashes. The decoration in blue, red, green and yellow on an off-white glaze. The base glazed.
Height 15.5cm, diameter 9.9cm
No. G.2112, gift of W. Pountney, 1923
Perhaps Bristol *c.* 1720, or Dutch?

This mug and the previous one raise questions of provenance. No. 6.9 is actually recorded 'Found on the Brislington site'; but that does not mean to say that it was made at the Brislington pottery, for there could be many other explanations as to how it got there. Both mugs are rather heavily potted, with robust handles of the same shape, and pierced at the top, presumably so that a lid might be fitted. There is nothing uniquely English about their decoration, and one therefore has to ask oneself whether they may not have been made on the Continent.

6.10 Mug Of tin-glazed stoneware, with slightly curving taper from base to rim, and flat, unadorned handle, the tail neatly curled. The decoration in blue on a pale blue glaze, with a *chinoiserie* scene of an island with house, rocks, trees and a moored sailing boat. The top border of a formal scroll band.
Height 12.4cm, rim diameter 8.8cm
No. G.1441, purchased 1919
Probably Liverpool *c.* 1760

This and the next piece are rare examples of tin-glazed stoneware of which a small amount was made in Liverpool in the second half of the eighteenth century. See also no. 9.12.

6.11 Mug Of tin-glazed stoneware, standing on a wide flanged base with straight sides flaring very slightly at the rim. The short strap handle with blue dashes. Marked 'I - A 1764' and decorated in blue on a pale blue glaze, with flowers from a Chinese trellis fence.
Height 13.4cm, rim diameter 9.2cm
No. G.2028, purchased from T. Charbonnier, 1923
Probably Liverpool 1764

See the article by Alan Smith, 'An Enamelled, Tin-glazed Mug at Temple Newsam House', in the *Leeds Art Calendar* no. 82, 1978, in which a number of stoneware pieces are discussed.

6.12 Puzzle Jug With spherical bowl and wide cylindrical neck pierced with flowers and heart-shaped petals. Inscribed in bold script:

> *Here gentlemen come try you skill*
> *I'll hold a Wager if you will*
> *That you dont Drink this Liquor all*
> *Without you spill or let some fall*

Decorated in blue on a pale bluish glaze, with a spray of flowers either side of the handle; the handle decorated with Chinese scrolls.
Height 18.0cm, bowl diameter 13.2cm
No. N.2245, gift of Mrs Hall Warren, 1946
Probably Liverpool *c.* 1740

6.13 **Puzzle Jug** Spherical bowl and cylindrical neck pierced with flowers and heart-shaped petals. The handle decorated with a series of diminishing blue dashes, and dots either side, and with two holes beneath it. Inscribed in cursive script:

> *Fill me with wine, ale, or water* . .
> *Any of the three it makes no matter* . .
> *Then drink me dry if you be willing* . .
> *And in so doing you'll win a shilling* . .

Decorated in blue on a pale bluish glaze, with a large peony flower either side of the handle.
Height 20.0cm, bowl diameter 14.6cm
No. G.125, purchased 1909
Probably Liverpool *c.* 1750

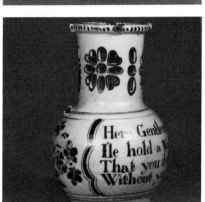

6.14 **Puzzle Jug** Spherical bowl with tall cylindrical neck pierced with flowers with heart-shaped petals. The tubular handle (missing) enters the body at the top of the bowl and runs down inside it. Inscribed in bold script:

> *Here Gentlemen Come try your skill*
> *I'le hold a Wager if you will*
> *That you dont Drink this Liquor all*
> *Without you spill or lett some fall*

The decoration in blue on a pale bluish glaze, with a floral spray beneath the handle, and blue dashes on the rim.
Height 22.0cm, bowl diameter 14.5cm
No. G.121, purchased 1907
Probably Liverpool *c.* 1740

6.15 **Puzzle Jug** Spherical bowl with a wide parallel neck liberally pierced with flowers and petals. The handle missing. Inscribed in delicate script:

> *Here Gentlemen Com Try your Skill*
> *I'le hold a Wager if you will*
> *That you Dont Drink this Liqur all*
> *With-out you Spill or Let Some Fall*

Decorated in blue on a pale blue glaze with two sprays of flowers.
Height 17.4cm, bowl diameter 14.1cm
No. G.158, purchased ex Hodgkin collection, 1914
Probably Liverpool *c.* 1740

6.16 **Puzzle Jug** With spherical bowl and wide neck pierced with flowers with heart-shaped petals, the handle with blue dashes and scrolls continued from the rim; one hole beneath it. Inscribed in script:

> *Here Gentlemen Come Try y^r Skill*
> *Ile hold a wager if you will*
> *That you dont drink this liq^r all*
> *Without you Spill or lett some fall*

Marked 'I ^{I} E/1736', and decorated in blue on a pale bluish glaze with a bird perched on a stem with veined leaves.
Height 17.8cm, bowl diameter 12.8cm
No. N.6612, J. Stone Hodges bequest, 1961
Probably Liverpool 1736

6.17 **Puzzle Jug** Spherical bowl with wide neck pierced with
flowers with heart-shaped petals, and handle with one hole
beneath it. Decorated in blue on a pale bluish glaze, with chevron
stripes round the rim, down the handle and among the flowers.
Inscribed in script:

> Here Gentlemen Come try y^r skill
> Ile hold a wager if you will
> that you Don't Drink this liq^r all
> without you spill or lett some Fall

Height 18.0cm, bowl diameter 12.2cm
No. N.6613, J. Stone Hodges bequest, 1961
Probably Liverpool *c.* 1740

6.18 **Puzzle Jug** Spherical bowl and wide neck pierced with
flowers with heart-shaped petals, with a large diameter tubular
handle. Inscribed in script:

> Here Gentlemen Come try your Skill
> I'le hold a wager if you will
> That you don't Drink this Liq^r all
> With out you Spill or lett Sume fall

The decoration, unusually, in polychrome: blue, red and green on
an off-white glaze, with a floral spray either side of the handle the
flower faces on the neck outlined in green, the rim and handle
with green leaves from a meandering blue vine.
Height 17.4cm, bowl diameter 12.0cm
No. N.6615, J. Stone Hodges bequest, 1961, ex Maddicks collection
Probably Liverpool *c.* 1740

6.19 **Puzzle Jug** Spherical bowl with a narrower neck than
usual, the neck pierced with intersecting circles. No inscription.
Decorated in blue on a pale bluish glaze with a fenced garden
containing peonies, chrysanthemum and other flowers in
profusion, the rim with a herringbone pattern, the handle with
leafy stems, and the neck perforations picked out in blue with fish-
roe in white.
Height 21.2cm, bowl diameter 14.2cm
No. N.6824, purchased 1962
Probably Bristol *c.* 1760

6.20 **Puzzle Jug** Spherical bowl with a wide neck pierced with
flower petals, the handle missing. Inscribed in copybook script:

> Gentlemen come try Youre skill
> I'll Hould A wager if you will
> That you don't drink this Liquor all
> Without you spill or lett some fall
>
> John Turner 1768

Decorated in blue on a pale blue glaze with a bunch of flowers
either side of the handle, and with a continuous Chinese scroll
pattern round the rim.
Height 18.2cm, bowl diameter 13.4cm
No. N.3356, purchased 1937
Probably Liverpool 1768

This may refer to Sir John Turner who succeeded his uncle as M.P.
for Kings Lynn in 1739. He studied law at Cambridge, and in due
course became a bencher of the Middle Temple. The peak of his
career was as Lord of the Treasury 1762–65. He was the third
Baronet, living at Warham, Norfolk. At the General Election of
1768 there was a contest at Kings Lynn in which he narrowly
escaped defeat. This inscribed jug may have been a token of his
success. For other election wares see nos. 10.23 to 10.25.

6.21 **Jug** Spherical body, narrow straight-sided neck and no spout. The handle of oval section with blue dashes and slender pointed tail. The decoration in blue and manganese on an off-white glaze with bold flowers and leaves, and a broad band round the neck.
Height 12.0cm, bowl diameter 9.6cm
No. G.2515, gift of T. Charbonnier, 1930
Probably London *c.* 1690

6.22 **Jug** Baluster shape with cylindrical neck with turning marks and a strap handle laid on the neck and returning to finish at the maximum diameter of the body. Decorated in blue on a pale blue-grey glaze with a bold floral pattern with fine twining stems and leaves. No spout.
Height 15.7cm, maximum diameter 9.4cm
No. N.8468, found in store and accessioned 1974
Perhaps London *c.* 1780

6.23 **Jug** Ovoid body standing on a footrim, with a short, narrow conical neck, the handle of oval section flattened inside. The decoration in blue, red and green on an off-white glaze, with rocks overhanging diminutive fences, long stemmed flowers and three aerobatic birds and four moths. Borders above and below of a meandering stem with leaves embellished with scroll pattern. Similar treatment on the neck and handle. The rim light brown.
Height 22.9cm, maximum diameter 13.5cm
No. N.3230, Sir Gilbert Mellor bequest, 1947
Probably Bristol *c.* 1720

The shape is not English, but could have been copied; from other characteristics there is no reason why it should not be English.

6.24 **Bottle** Pear-shaped tapering to the neck, a neck bulge below the everted rim. Decorated in blue on a pale bluish glaze with large chrysanthemums and other flowers among foliage, the knop with a trellis band and scrolls with pendants below.
Height 20.2cm, maximum diameter 13.0cm
No. N.6946, J. Stone Hodges bequest, 1961
Probably Liverpool *c.* 1750

6.25 Bottle Globular shape, heavily built, the neck cupping out and everting at the rim. The decoration in blue on a white glaze, with two large tied bunches of peony and cherry blossom, and two flying moths. The neck with a narrow band of lozenge trellis.
Height 26.1cm, maximum diameter 15.8cm
No. N.6641, J. Stone Hodges bequest, 1961
Probably London *c.* 1740

6.26 Bottle Beetle shape with the neck everted and then chamfered inwards. Decorated in blue with two chrysanthemums springing from leaves with graffito veins, and two bands of trellis on the neck. The glaze white.
Height 26.3cm, maximum diameter 12.6cm
No. N.5544, gift of Miss Nesbitt, 1955
Probably Liverpool *c.* 1770

6.27 Bottle Globular shape with neck cupping out and then everting. The decoration in yellow, brown, manganese and green, on a pale blue glaze, with two ostriches standing either side of a young chick, between trees with brown stems and green oak leaves, and a butterfly at the base of the neck; on the other side a single bird sitting with open beak.
Height 22.0cm, maximum diameter 14.0cm
No. N.4884, purchased ex Hodgkin collection, 1950
Probably Liverpool *c.* 1760

Similar decoration appears on a bowl, no. 50.60.72, in the Liverpool Museum, inscribed 'Success to the Plow 1762', illustrated in the catalogue of the Rijksmuseum exhibition, no. 154. Compare also dish no. 19.15 in this collection. The birds are fanciful, but very decorative.

6.28 Bottle Globular body curving gently into a somewhat broad neck, which is cupped and everted. The decoration in blue, red, green and yellow on a pale blue glaze, with flowers on the front and a lady carrying a basket of flowers on the other side. The neck band of trellis and floral motifs has slipped in the glaze.
Height 21.8cm, maximum diameter 13.0cm
No. N.3050, purchased ex Hodgkin collection, 1947
Probably Liverpool *c.* 1760

Illustrated in the catalogue of the Rijksmuseum exhibition no. 153. The palette is 'Fazackerly', but the flowers are different. Compare Glaisher collection no. 1724.

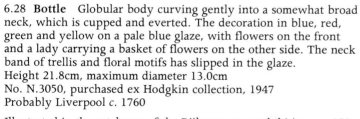

6.29 Bottle Globular body curving to very slender neck, and cupping and everting to the rim. Decorated in blue on a pale blue glaze, with two fenced gardens with large peonies, and two roughly drawn turkeys sitting between; on the base of the neck a band of ferns from rocks, and further floral decoration up the neck.
Height 27.0cm, maximum diameter 15.5cm
No. N.3048, purchased ex Hodgkin collection, 1947
Probably Liverpool *c.* 1750

6.30 Bottle A large globular bowl curving to a narrow neck with trumpet mouth. Decorated in blue on a pale blue glaze round the body with chrysanthemums, peonies and bamboo from rocks; the base of the neck with similar flowers on a smaller scale, and further decoration up to the rim.
Height 22.6cm, maximum diameter 15.4cm
No. N.6642, J. Stone Hodges bequest, 1961
Probably Liverpool *c.* 1750

6.31 Bottle Near spherical body with a narrow neck, and a neck bulge below the trumpet mouth. The decoration in shades of blue on a pale blue glaze, with very similar floral arrangements to the previous entry, the whole in the *chinoiserie* manner.
Height 27.8cm, maximum diameter 17.3cm
No. N.3049, purchased ex Hodgkin collection, 1947
Probably Liverpool *c.* 1750

6.32 Bottle Globular body curving to the neck, which contains a slight neck bulge, then everts to a flat rim. The decoration, unusually, in black not fully absorbed in the glaze and giving the appearance of enamel, of a *chinoiserie* garden with willow tree, peony and bamboo. The glaze pale blue.
Height 23.3cm, maximum diameter 15.6cm
No. G.3522, purchased 1932
Probably Liverpool *c.* 1760   COLOUR PLATE, p. 28

6.33 Bottle Globular body curving to slender neck, with everted rim pinched to form a spout. Decorated on both sides in blue on a pale blue glaze, with a figure in a halo laying hands on the head of a kneeling supplicant, while another figure stands by. Two borders above of pendent *chinoiserie* scroll pattern, and floral decoration at the spout.
Height 23.5cm, maximum diameter 15.0cm
No. G.3519, purchased ex Maddicks collection, 1936
Probably Liverpool *c.* 1750

6.34 Bottle Globular body with tapering neck, with spherical cupping below the flat everted rim. The decoration in blue on a pale bluish glaze, with, on one (damaged) side a *chinoiserie* arched bridge with panelled fencing, peonies, bamboo and cabbage leaf foliage with graffito veins; and on the reverse a single peony and foliage. Flying insects.
Height 23.9cm, maximum diameter 14.6cm
No. G.2018, purchased from T. Charbonnier, 1923
Probably Liverpool *c.* 1750

6.35 Bottle Ovoid body curving to neck and flared mouth. The decoration in blue on a pale blue glaze, with a profusion of flowers, rocks, trees from a fenced garden; cross-hatched bands inside and outside the rim, the latter with pendent flowers.
Height 29.5cm, maximum diameter 15.1cm
No. N.3045, purchased ex Hodgkin collection, 1947
Probably London *c.* 1770

This matches basin no. 8.46; note the differences in shape and decoration of this bottle from the Liverpool examples.

6.36 Bottle Ovoid body curving to the neck, which has a band of raised, moulded decoration round it below the trumpet mouth. Decorated in blue on a pale blue glaze, with Chinese houses and temples hidden among a profusion of trees; a floral border above. The neck decorated with a band of acute lozenges, and border of *ruyi* heads between trellis bands.
Height 26.0cm, maximum diameter 14.4cm
No. N.8769, found in store and accessioned 1974
Probably London *c.* 1770

7   Vases and flower holders

Four different shapes of delftware appear to have been used for holding flowers to decorate the home.

First are vases, of which we have one large and beautiful example of baluster shape; but the great majority are of urn shape, some with elaborate twined rope handles, others with scroll handles flattened against the side. We also have one most unusual branched vase, no. 7.9, which is one of the few examples of an English article which appears to be a direct copy of a Dutch shape, and known to them as a tulip vase. There is one other unusual shape of vase – spill shape – of which there is an example in the collection, no. 7.10.

Next are wall pockets, which is the term used for containers for flowers to be hung against the wall. Where these are not symmetrical, they come in pairs, left and right handed. There are three basic shapes: baluster, cornucopia and mask. We have only one example of the baluster shape, no. 7.11, which is attributed to London. All the rest we attribute to Liverpool, including five cornucopiae of representative shapes, mostly with twisted convex fluting, and quite elegant, and four mask wall pockets, presumably moulded, in light blue and dark blue glazes. Of the latter, two show signs of having been gilded, a characteristic representative of only a handful of English delftware articles of any sort. We know of no wall pockets that were made in Bristol.

Third are flower bowls, by which we mean bowls with a convex lid affixed to them, which is perforated, and whose purpose is assumed to be for holding flowers. Bowls with a concave lid were assumed to be for other purposes. One of the flower bowls in the collection has, unusually, an extension piece which fits into the centre of the lid, thus permitting a two-tier flower arrangement.

Fourth are bricks. These are brick-shaped hollow vessels with rows of perforations in their tops, about whose purpose we can only surmise. They are usually called flower bricks, particularly those perforated with small holes only. But because many of them have one or more large round, square or rectangular holes in their tops, interspersed between the small holes, these have been called inkwells. However there are four square bricks in the collection; these all have a mixture of large and small round holes in them, but nobody has suggested that they are inkwells.

On the other hand, one rectangular brick in the collection, in the form of a flat chest on bracket feet, has two cross partitions within it, splitting the interior into three compartments. This does suggest that the central one might have been used for ink; moreover the shallowness of its shape suggests that it would not have provided support for flowers with anything but the shortest of stems.

The usual rectangular bricks are often found in pairs; one would not be likely to buy inkwells in pairs, but one might well buy pairs of flower vases, for instance to set at either end of the mantelpiece.

The one or two bricks the author has found in Dutch delftware are at least twice the size of the English ones, and perforated entirely with small holes; thus they could not have been inkwells. Bricks are known in saltglaze and other ceramics in England, similar to those in delftware; but if one looks at contemporary Bow porcelain, one finds only circular inkpots, of which one example is dated 1750, with what is clearly a receptacle for ink in the centre and penholes round the outside.

7.27 **Brick**

One cannot help remarking that with all these articles there is a notable lack of any graphical evidence, from paintings or prints, as to how they were used in the houses of their time. But perhaps, after all, our concern about their practical use need not detract from our pleasure in their aesthetic beauty.

7.1 Vase Baluster shape with all-over blue scale pattern of whorls ceasing eight centimetres from the base with a wave pattern boundary. Decorated in blue on a white glaze, with four rococo shaped panels each with sailing ships, in which two frames are adorned with trophies of war. Between them, are interspersed four taller panels of floral vines from tubs.
Height 40.0cm, maximum diameter 26.7cm
No. G. 2056, purchased from T. Charbonnier, 1923
Probably Liverpool *c*. 1760   COLOUR PLATE, p. 29

7.2 Vase Urn shape, the rim with twenty two crimps, handles formed of two pieces of round section twisted together, and attached to the side with curls at top and bottom. Decorated in blue on a white glaze with fanciful *chinoiserie* floral panels between borders of stiff leaf, *ruyi* head and anthemion frieze.
Height 20.2cm, rim diameter 16.5cm
No. G.1195, gift of T. Charbonnier, 1917
Probably Bristol *c*. 1700

7.3 Vase Urn shape with heavy twisted handles, blue spotted. The decoration in blue outlined in black *trek* on a pale greenish glaze, with flowers from a hollow rock and a perched bird. The top and bottom borders of *chinoiserie* patterns.
Height 16.9cm, rim diameter 16.0cm
No. N.6597, J. Stone Hodges bequest, 1961, ex Mellor collection
Probably London *c*. 1700

7.4 Vase Urn shape with strap handles flat against the sides, blue striped and curled up top and bottom. Decorated in blue on a pale blue glaze, with scenes of flowers twining up from a hollow rock. A rounded flange below the rim with a Chinese scroll pattern, and the foot decorated with stiff leaves and scrolls.
Height 20.8cm, rim diameter 17.5cm
No. N.6596, J. Stone Hodges bequest, 1961, ex Mellor collection
Probably Liverpool *c*. 1750

7.5 **Vase** Urn shape with two strap handles flat against the sides, painted blue and curled top and bottom. The decoration in blue on a pale bluish glaze, with on one side the crucifixion with haloed figures standing either side, and on the reverse a saintly figure with staff standing in a country scene with a church beyond. The rim with a rounded flange with Chinese scroll pattern, and the foot with radial lines forming triangles. Bands with twining floral stems beside the handles.
Height 17.3cm, rim diameter 11.4cm
No. N.6656, J. Stone Hodges bequest, 1961
Probably London *c.* 1740

7.6 **Vase** Urn shape with two strap handles flat against the sides, curled top and bottom and buttoned in the centre, and blue striped. Decorated in blue on an off-white glaze with a flowing floral vine on each side. The top border of the 'three-brick' pattern, the lower border of diagonal stripes, and the foot with rhomboidal brush marks.
Height 14.6cm, rim diameter 10.3cm
No. N.6599, J. Stone Hodges bequest, 1961
Probably Bristol *c.* 1750

7.7 **Vase** A duplicate of the last.
Height 14.6cm, rim diameter 10.0cm
No. G.2009, purchased from T. Charbonnier, 1923
Probably Bristol *c.* 1750

7.8 **Vase** Very similar to the previous two, except for the rim, with fourteen crimps each decorated with a stiff leaf, with vertical shading between them.
Height 14.5cm, rim diameter 10.5cm
No. G.2010, purchased from T. Charbonnier, 1923
Probably Bristol *c.* 1750

7.9 Tulip Vase The fan-shaped body fitted with two rows of spouts to hold four stems in the front row, and five in the rear row; also blue painted birds' heads at each end with open beak to accept two further stems. The decoration in blue on a pale blue glaze, with a Chinese scene of a house among trees, and on the reverse with a vase of flowers. The spouts and the rectangular foot decorated with trellis, stiff leaf and scroll patterns.
Height 28.0cm, width 30.5cm
No. N.5396, purchased 1953
Probably London *c.* 1700, or Dutch

Compare H. Havard *La Céramique Hollandaise*, Amsterdam 1909, vol. II, fig. 19, and Henry-Pierre Fourest, *Les Faiences de Delft*, Paris 1957, pl. VII.

7.10 Vase Spill-vase with a trumpet mouth. Decorated in manganese on a pale blue glaze with two Chinamen in a garden, one below, the other standing on rocks among cactus-like plants and herringbone leaves.
Height 17.0cm, rim diameter 10.5cm
No. N.3376, purchased ex Maddicks collection, 1936
Possibly London *c.* 1700, or Continental

7.11 Wall Pocket Baluster shape of semi-circular section. The decoration in shades of blue on a pale blue glaze with a Chinaman in a fenced garden with plants and overhanging rocks. The waist with more flowers from rocks, and the lower parts painted in solid blue.
Height 18.0cm, width 13.2cm
No. N.8472, found in store, and accessioned 1974
Probably London *c.* 1750

The baluster shape is generally recognized as the London shape; compare Victoria and Albert Museum no. C.72–1967, and Reading Museum no. 241-61-26. However, Glaisher collection no. 1576 is attributed to Bristol, probably in error, and an evident Irish example is in the Castletown House exhibition catalogue, no. 38.

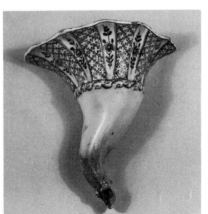

7.12 Wall Pocket Curved cornucopia shape, the mouth with five flutes decorated in blue on a clear blue glaze with a single flower each, with trellis pattern between. A scroll border at the base of the flutes, the bottom half of the horn smoothly curved with blue shading to the knop finial.
Height 17.1cm, width 15.2cm
No. N.3055, purchased ex Hodgkin collection, 1947
Probably Liverpool *c.* 1750

7.13 **Wall Pocket** Curved cornucopia shape, with eleven convex flutes in the tail. The top decorated in blue on a pale blue glaze, with a Chinese pagoda among willow and other trees.
Height 18.2cm, width 12.9cm
No. N.3054, purchased ex Hodgkin collection, 1947
Probably Liverpool *c.* 1750

The decoration matches that on hot water plate no. 5.22.

7.14 **Wall Pocket** Curved cornucopia shape with fluting. The decoration in blue on a thin bluish glaze, consisting of a border under the rim of hatched lines, and blue shading down the top of each flute.
Height 17.1cm, width 15.0cm
No. N.6605, J. Stone Hodges bequest, 1961, ex Maddicks collection
Probably Liverpool *c.* 1730

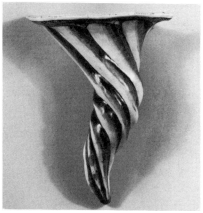

7.15 **Wall Pocket** Cornucopia shape, the smooth conical mouth decorated in blue on a clear pale blue glaze, with pendent peony and other flowers and buds, the body almost straight with multiple convex flutes with blue shading, the tail turned abruptly up and decorated with flowers and leaves.
Height 23.8cm, width 15.2cm
No. N.6606, J. Stone Hodges bequest, 1961, ex Maddicks collection
Probably Liverpool *c.* 1760

7.16 **Wall Pocket** Gently curved cornucopia shape with slight fluting. The rim decorated in blue on a clear pale blue glaze, with a border of chevrons with a central leaf, and the rounded knop painted as a bud.
Height 16.7cm, width 12.3cm
No. N.7154, Ernest Blatch bequest, 1964
Probably Liverpool *c.* 1760

7.17 **Wall Pocket** Symmetrical moulded shape with a female mask among foliage at the top, and a satyr's mask at the base. The whole in pale bluish glaze, with traces of gilding.
Height 20.0cm, width 16.6cm
No. N.3052, purchased ex Hodgkin collection, 1947
Probably Liverpool *c.* 1770

Compare Liverpool Museum no. 65.76.2.   COLOUR PLATE. p. 29

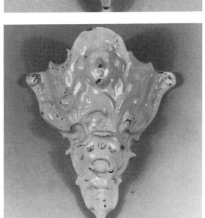

7.18 **Wall Pocket** A pair to the previous example.
Height 20.3cm, width 16.1cm
No. N.3053, purchased ex Hodgkin collection, 1947
Probably Liverpool *c.* 1770

7.19 **Wall Pocket** The shape very similar to the two previous, but the moulding sharper, the mask at the base more malicious, and the rim above the female mask at the top rising to a point. The decoration in deep blue all over, except for the female mask which is the pale blue of the glaze.
Height 21.8cm, width 16.6cm
No. N.3051, purchased ex Hodgkin collection, 1947
Probably Liverpool *c.* 1770   COLOUR PLATE, p. 29

7.20 **Wall Pocket** The shape generally similar to the previous three, but from a different, narrower mould. The mask at the base now appears to be a cupid. The whole in pale blue glaze with no added decoration.
Height 20.8cm, width 14.3cm
No. N.7157, Ernest Blatch bequest, 1964
Probably Liverpool *c.* 1770

7.21 Flower Bowl In two pieces; the base with a pronouncedly convex top with a large central hole and two rings of holes round the sides; the top fitting into the large central hole in the base, and forming a separate vase with large central hole and a ring of smaller holes round it. The whole decorated in blue on a pale bluish glaze, with sprays of flowers, stylized floral patterns and borders of interlocking circles and of trellis. Both parts marked with the figure '8'. It seems almost certain from comparison with a three-tier flower bowl, sold as lot 160 in the first Louis Lipski sale in London at Sotheby's on 10 March 1981, that this bowl also originally had a third tier which fitted into the central hole in the second tier.
Height overall 19.9cm, maximum diameter 19.9cm
No. N.3079, purchased ex Hodgkin collection, 1947
Probably London c. 1750

Compare Glaisher collection, no. 1539

7.22 Flower Bowl With a convex top, with large, flanged, centre hole and twelve small holes around it, fixed to a bowl standing on a footrim. The decoration in blue, red and green on an off-white glaze, with formalized flowers from rocks, and on the bowl itself, an angel in flight.
Height overall 10.6cm, diameter 13.6cm
No. N.3226, Sir Gilbert Mellor bequest, 1947
Probably Bristol c. 1715

7.23 Flower Bowl With a convex top, with large, flanged, centre hole and ten small holes around it, fixed to a wide spreading bowl standing on a small footrim. The decoration in blue, red and green on a pinky glaze, with a fort among sponged-foliage trees on the top, and a running animal below.
Height overall 9.0cm, diameter 14.6cm
No. N.6587, J. Stone Hodges bequest, 1961
Probably Bristol c. 1740

7.24 Flower Bowl Convex top, separate from the bowl, with large, flanged, centre hole and three rings, each of eight small holes around. The decoration in blue, red and green on an off-white glaze with, on the top, radial red lines like grasses, and Chinese scrolls, and on the base five half-flower faces, five smaller flowers and insects.
Height 12.1cm, diameter 18.5cm
No. N.3222, Sir Gilbert Mellor bequest, 1947
Probably Bristol c. 1740

7.25 **Square Brick** The top perforated with five large and sixteen small holes; hollow flat base. The decoration in blue on a pale blue glaze, with a willow tree springing from a tall striated rock on three sides and from a hollow rock on the fourth, with peonies and other flowers from a fence.
Height 10.4cm, top 12.5cm square
No. G.1868, purchased 1922
Probably London *c.* 1760

7.26 **Square Brick** The top perforated with three large and six small holes. Decorated in blue on a pale blue glaze, with a small Chinese house behind a fence with shrubs, and hills beyond, on all four sides.
Height 8.8cm, top 10.4cm square
No. N.6594, J. Stone Hodges bequest, 1961
Probably London *c.* 1750

7.27 **Brick** Shaped as a flat casket on four moulded pedestal feet. The top perforated with eight small holes on each side of a large central hole, and the inside, unusually, divided into three compartments by two internal partitions. Decorated in blue on a pale bluish-greyish glaze with, on each side, a different landscape with buildings, and on either end a man in a small boat.
Length 12.4cm, height 5.4cm
No. G.3509, purchased 1933
Probably Liverpool *c.* 1760

The few other known examples of this shape are similarly compartmented. Mr Brian Morgan has one decorated with Fazackerly flowers and inscribed on one side 'William, Done, Bricklayer Cheshire, 1761'. This almost certainly confirms the Liverpool origin.

7.28 **Brick** The base stands on the front and back flanges only; the top is perforated with twenty small holes surrounding one larger central hole. The decoration in blue on a pale bluish-greyish glaze with, on each side, a tall rock and house among trees, and each end an aerobatic bird. The top painted blue.
Length 10.1cm, height 6.0cm
No. N.3783, found in store and accessioned 1949
Probably Liverpool *c.* 1740

7.29 **A Pair of Bricks** The tops perforated with six rows of three small holes, with a large hole in the centre; the skirt cut away to bracket shape at the sides and to a curve at the ends. Decorated in blue on a pale bluish glaze, with a spray of peonies on each side, and a smaller sprig on the ends.
Length 12.5cm, height 6.7cm
No. N.6589, J. Stone Hodges bequest, 1961
Probably Liverpool *c.* 1750

7.30 **Brick** The top perforated with eleven small holes on each side of the larger central round hole. The skirt cut away at the sides to bracket shape, and to a curve at each end. Decorated in blue, red, green and yellow on a white glaze, with a delicate *chinoiserie* scene of a house amid rocks and trees on each side, and with a temple among trees each end.
Length 15.9cm, height 8.5cm
No. N.3359, purchased ex Maddicks collection, 1936
Probably Liverpool *c.* 1750

7.31 **Brick** The top perforated with eleven small holes on each side of the central hole. The skirt cut away to bracket shape at each side, and to a curve at the ends. Decorated in blue on an off-white glaze, with a tall rock with a weeping willow on top amid trees and hills on either side, and with a fern-like tree on either end.
Length 16.0cm, height 8.7cm
No. N.3074, purchased ex Hodgkin collection, 1947
Probably Liverpool *c.* 1750

7.32 **Brick** The top perforated with six small holes on either side of the large square central hole. The decoration in smudgy blue on a thin white glaze, with a Chinese lady with parasol on either side, backed by castle buildings with a round tower and gateway repeated twice on each side and once each end. A very similar lady with a parasol appears on nos. 12.50 and 12.51.
Length 15.3cm, height 9.0cm
No. N.3076, purchased ex Hodgkin collection, 1947
Probably Bristol *c.* 1750

7.33 **Brick** The top perforated with six small holes either side of the square central hole. Decorated in blue on a pale bluish glaze, with sprays of peony flowers and leaves.
Length 11.7cm, height 6.8cm
No. G.1986, purchased from T. Charbonnier, 1923
Probably Liverpool *c.* 1760

7.34 **Brick** The top perforated with six small holes either side of the square central hole. Decorated in blue on a pale blue glaze, with a basket of flowers upside down on each side, and with a delicate sprig of smaller flowers on each end.
Length 15.0cm, height 9.1cm
No. N.6593, J. Stone Hodges bequest, 1961
Probably London *c.* 1740

7.35 **Brick** The top perforated with six small holes either side of the square central hole. The base flat. Decorated in blue on a pale bluish-greyish glaze, with iris-like flowers in arcades of gothic arches framed with trellis diaper, both on the sides and ends.
Length 15.1cm, height 9.1cm
No. N.6592, J. Stone Hodges bequest, 1961
Probably London *c.* 1740

7.36 **Brick** The top perforated with three rows of three small holes, with two large square holes interposed. Flat hollow base. The decoration in blue on a pale blue glaze, with different versions of flowers and leaves roughly painted on the sides and ends.
Length 15.0cm, height 9.2cm
No. N.6591, J. Stone Hodges bequest, 1961
Probably London *c.* 1740

7.37 **Brick** The top perforated with three rows of three holes with two large square holes interposed. The decoration in blue on a pale blue glaze, with a spray of flowers and leaves from a panelled fence on each side, and a sprig at each end. Blue stripes outline the square holes.
Length 13.9cm, height 8.7cm
No. N.8471, found in store and accessioned 1974
Probably Liverpool *c.* 1760

7.38 **Brick** The top perforated by three rows of three holes each, with two large square holes between them. Decorate'd in blue on a pale bluish glaze with a spray of chrysanthemums and a tuft of rushes on each side, and a single flower and leaves at each end. The square holes bordered by a leaf pattern border.
Length 13.8cm, height 8.9cm
No. G.1985, purchased from T. Charbonnier, 1923
Probably Liverpool *c.* 1750

7.39 **Brick** The top perforated with three rows of three small holes, with two large square holes interposed. The skirt cut away to form L-shaped feet at the corners. The decoration in blue on a pale blue glaze, with a conical tree on an island with houses and trees, and two men in a small boat, and on the ends with two men back-to-back fishing. The rim picked out in brown.
Length 15.5cm, height 9.3cm
No. N.3075, purchased ex Hodgkin collection, 1947
Probably Bristol *c.* 1760

Note the similarity of the decoration to that of nos. 16.9 to 16.17.

7.40 **Brick** The top perforated with three rows of three small holes with two large square holes between them. Decorated in blue, red, green and yellow on a pale bluish glaze, with pendent floral motifs of red daisies and green leaves embellished with *chinoiserie* scrolls; three motifs on each side, and one each end.
Length 14.5cm, height 9.1cm
No. G.1693, purchased 1921
Probably Bristol *c.* 1750

7.41 **Brick** The top perforated with three rows of three small holes, with two large square holes between. The skirt cut away to form L-shaped feet at the corners. Decorated in blue, red and yellow on a pale bluish glaze, with gaudy flowers from a fenced garden on each side, and with a sprig at each end.
Length 15.5cm, height 9.3cm
No. N.3215, Sir Gilbert Mellor bequest, 1947
London or Bristol *c.* 1770

8   Bowls

Bowls were used for many purposes in the eighteenth century. They were used for purely decorative purposes, such as for holding flowers; they were used a great deal for celebratory purposes, to the extent that some people refer to them almost exclusively as punchbowls, regardless of shape or size; and they were used for more utilitarian purposes, such as holding fruit or pot pourri, etc., while the smallest were quite probably part of a tea service and intended as sugar or slop bowls.

The bowl which has pride of place in this chapter was undoubtedly a punch bowl, as suggested by the scene inside, and by one of the scenes outside. It is almost a pair to one in the Hall Warren collection, which has a pedigree, and is discussed fully in the catalogue entry. It is also notable because it stands on a foot, and because we are able to trace the prints which form the origins of most of its decoration.

But bowls were of different shapes, with some variation according to their date of origin and place of manufacture. It would be nice to be able to draw a series of diagrams of shapes and attribute them to a place and date of origin; unfortunately there were so many overlaps that this would be more confusing than helpful, and it will be observed that bowls in this chapter, which appear to be of the same shape, are not necessarily attributed to the same place of origin. Earlier bowls from London and Bristol were deep, with fairly steep tapering sides, as exemplified by no. 8.2. A group of several more such bowls is included in catalogue chapter 13 with other pieces of the same blue-red-green decorative style. By the middle of the eighteenth century bowls from all factories were less deep; some had straight tapering sides, curving in more sharply to the base, others had a more gradual curvature throughout. This latter shape tends to have been favoured by Liverpool potters, as is seen from the two Fazackerly bowls nos. 17.2 and 17.3. In the 1780s one finds London bowls becoming even shallower, as nos. 8.24 and 8.25, a shape that would not have been very practical for the serving of punch. One also finds articles which can either be called very shallow bowls or saucer dishes, of shape J, Appendix 1, and such as are exemplified by nos. 8.26 to 8.30.

A number of bowls carry inscriptions inside them, which would become visible as they became empty, and which are either patriotic slogans to which a toast might be drunk, such as 'Success to the British Arms' and 'Success to Trade', or exhortations to conviviality, such as 'One More Bowl and Then' and 'Drink Fair, Dont Swear'.

We have noted in catalogue chapter 7 a number of bowls with convex perforated tops, which are presumed to have been for holding flowers. We have now, with nos. 8.36 to 8.42, a group of bowls with concave perforated tops, like colanders. These, unlike those of chapter 7, all have a slot in the side through which they may be emptied. There is no certainty as to their intended use. Pountney[1] recalls having seen one used by placing cut-up fruit, sugar and spices upon it, and then pouring first boiling water, and then wine, over this to make punch. Ray[2] suggests more probably that they were used for serving watercress, and presumably there is no reason why they should not have been equally well used for serving hot vegetables which required the water to be drained off.

Nos. 8.43 to 8.45 are three bowls with crimped edges. All of this type appear to have decoration on the inside only, as is the case with no. 10.12 with a portrait of the Duke of Marlborough in it.

Basins for use in wash-hand stands are represented by no. 8.46, and also by nos. 15.2 and 18.8. In all these cases there are matching water bottles: nos. 6.35, 15.3 and 18.9 respectively. These basins, of course have a turned-over rim to rest on the circumference of the circle cut out in the flat top of the wash-hand stand.

No. 8.47 is a most unusual bowl with a spike standing up in its centre, said to be for serving pineapple; while no. 8.48 is a Monteith. This is copied from silverware of the period, and has cut-outs from the rim all the way round, to hold the stems of glasses intended for serving its contents.

Thereafter we have two Dublin bowls, also copied from silverware, with rims perforated to form interlocking circles and decorated with the typical perfection of the Dublin factory. These are not known to have been made elsewhere, although fragments of such a bowl have been found at a South London pottery site. Finally there is a *bleu de Nevers* bowl with fluted sides which may be compared with the bleeding bowl, no. 5.17.

Three ship bowls are catalogued at nos. 10.53 to 10.55 and another group of bowls all with *bianco-sopra-bianco* decoration will be found at nos. 16.2 to 16.8, while seven bowls with powdered grounds are at nos. 15.52 to 15.58.

Notes
1 W. J. Pountney, *Old Bristol Potteries*, pp. 141–2.
2 Anthony Ray, *English Delftware Pottery in the Robert Hall Warren Collection*, p. 166.

8.8 **Bowl**

8.1 The 'Flower' Bowl The outside decorated with four scenes divided by garlanded columns: 1. Five men round a table with a small punchbowl, glasses and pipes. 2. A lady and gentleman toasting each other in a country scene with a church and sailboat beyond. 3. A swordsman attacking a defender in a fort, and ships out to sea. 4. A lady in a bower on a hillock. The inside with a scene of a table laid with a punchbowl and glasses, and two empty chairs, the scene surrounded by five floral sprays. The foot decorated with flowers and leaves on a blue ground. All the decoration in blue on a pale bluish glaze.
Diameter 31.5/33.0cm, height 20.1/21.3cm
No. G.1690, purchased 1921
Bristol 1743   COLOUR PLATE, p. 30

This is known as the 'Flower' bowl after a closely identical one in the Hall Warren collection, inscribed on a ribbon inside 'Joseph Flower Sculp 1743'. Anthony Ray[1] illustrates both the Oxford and the Bristol bowls and discusses them at length. The bowl is also mentioned by Owen[2] and Pountney[3], and is included in the City Art Gallery's *Delftware* booklet.

The four outside scenes are taken from illustrations at the headings of songs in George Bickham's *Musical Entertainer* of 1737–38, as follows:

> Page 18, Cato's Advice or the Jovial Companions (fig. 5).
> Page 17, The Relief (fig. 6).
> Page 98, Britons Strike Home (fig. 7).
> Page 33, Beauties Decay (fig. 8).

The outside of both bowls is identical, except that, in the scene taken from The Relief, the right hand side is occupied in the Bristol bowl by a sailing boat and church(?), instead of by a man holding a wine glass, and two other figures, in a landscape.

The inside of the Oxford bowl has a repeat of the scene from Cato's Advice, as on the outside, whereas the Bristol bowl has a table set for two only, and unoccupied. As well as the inscription already noted, the Oxford bowl also has four out of six lines of a round by Thomas Otway set to music by Purcell, and first published in 1686[4]; the Bristol bowl has none of this, but floral decoration.

We certainly agree with Ray's hypothesis that these bowls were made by Joseph Flower to celebrate the conclusion of his apprenticeship to Thomas Frank, and his appointment as a Burgess in 1743.

Notes
1 Anthony Ray, *English Delftware Pottery*, pp. 161–3 and pls. 28–32.
2 Hugh Owen, *Two Centuries of Ceramic Art in Bristol*, Gloucester and London 1873, p. 334.
3 W. J. Pountney, *Old Bristol Potteries*, p. 139 and pl. XXXV.
4 J. Playford, *The Pleasant Musical Companion*, second book, 1686; but the copy in the British Library is autographed by the author 'Oct 1685'. In later editions this round acquired the title 'The Midnight Friendship'.

Fig 5 'Cato's Advice or the Jovial Companions': illustration from the *Musical Entertainer* by George Bickham, 1737–8, vol. II, p. 18. British Library. K10.613.

Fig 6 'The Relief': illustration from the *Musical Entertainer*, vol. II, p.17.

Fig 7 'Britons Strike Home': illustration from the *Musical Entertainer*, vol. II, p. 98.

Fig 8 'Beauties Decay': illustration from the *Musical Entertainer* vol. II, p. 33.

8.2 Bowl On the outside six panels containing floral motifs with rhomboidal leaves; inside, a spray of flowers surrounded by seven quadruple dots. The decoration in blue on an off-white glaze, pinky in places, including a line round the rim, and lines on the base of the bowl and footrim.
Diameter 25.8cm, height 14.7cm
No. N.3778, found in store and accessioned 1949
Probably Bristol *c.* 1740

8.3 Bowl Decorated on the outside with five repeats of a spray of flowers in red, hatched, and with ten swastikas. The rim border a band of diagonal hatching with triple scrolls interspersed. Two blue circles round the base. The decoration in blue and red on an off-white glaze, the edge painted brown. In the inside a small spray of flowers, surrounded by two blue circles, and two further circles round the bowl.
Diameter 22.8cm, height 11.7cm
No. N.3059, purchased ex Hodgkin collection, 1947
Probably Liverpool *c.* 1730

8.4 Bowl On the outside stemmed cups and knots embellished with *chinoiserie* scrolls and swastikas. The rim border a band of trellis diaper with floral motifs. Lines encircling the base. Inside, a spray of flowers in concentric circles. The decoration in blue on a pale bluish glaze.
Diameter 31.9cm, height 14.8cm
No. N.6792, J. Stone Hodges bequest, 1961
Probably Liverpool *c.* 1750

8.5 Bowl Outside, four repeats of a flower with twining stems and four ears of barley, all painted upside-down, and a lower border of lozenges laced with red ovals. The outside decoration in blue, red, green and yellow on a pale blue glaze; the inside decoration in blue only, consisting of a sprig of bare twigs and a border of trellis.
Diameter 25.7cm, height 12.1cm
No. N.6787, J. Stone Hodges bequest, 1961
Probably Bristol *c.* 1730

8.6 Bowl The outside with two twin bungalows with overhanging bamboo and willow trees, and a rim border of a red chain between blue lines. Inside, in blue only, a flying insect surrounded by four cornucopiae and four intersecting triple lines. The decoration in blue, red and yellow on a pale blue glaze.
Diameter 26.4cm, height 12.2cm
No. N.6788, J. Stone Hodges bequest, 1961
Probably London *c.* 1770

8.7 **Bowl** On the outside four bunches of red berries, yellow flowers and green leaves from interlocking rectangles. Inside, five red berries on blue stems, surrounded by four groups of four berries. All the decoration in blue, red, green and yellow on a pale blue glaze.
Diameter 25.7cm, height 12.4cm
No. N.3785, purchased 1949
Probably Bristol *c.* 1750

Compare dish no. 14.23.

8.8 **Bowl** On the outside an overall decoration of blue lattice, with three rows of pink florets at the intersections. In the inside eleven concentric circles in blue. The outside colours blue and pale manganese on a white glaze. The florets appear to have been applied by means of a stamp, perhaps made from carving the base of a cork from a bottle.
Diameter 29.2cm, height 14.7cm
No. N.6808, J. Stone Hodges bequest, 1961
Probably Bristol *c.* 1730

8.9 **Bowl** On the outside a lady sits by a fence and a gentleman doffs his hat to her; inside, a lady sits in a landscape and waves her hand. Decorated in green, manganese and yellow on a pale blue glaze, somewhat crudely.
Diameter 22.1cm, height 9.6cm
No. N.3208, Sir Gilbert Mellor bequest, 1947, ex Gautier collection
Probably London *c.* 1770

8.10 **Bowl** On the outside *chinoiserie* rocks, fence, trees and shrubs, and on the inside similar decoration featuring islands with rocks and trees and a Chinaman crossing a bridge between them, and with a fence and large peony flowers round the inside rim. The finely executed decoration in blue on a pale blue crazed glaze.
Diameter 35.0cm, height 14.5cm
No. N.5324, found in store and accessioned 1952
Probably Liverpool *c.* 1760

8.11 Bowl Outside, three repeats of plants growing from an oval bed, with a rim border of sketchy trellis pattern, and inside several concentric circles. Decorated in blue on a pale bluish glaze.
Diameter 22.3cm, height 10.0cm
No. N.6795, J. Stone Hodges bequest, 1961
Probably Bristol *c.* 1760

8.12 Bowl On the outside two pairs of Chinamen standing among rocks and another with a shepherd's crook, stylized trees, and a ship at sea. Inside, a floral symbol surrounded by a rim border of trellis diaper and panels of scroll patterns. The decoration in blue on a pale bluish glaze.
Diameter 29.2cm, height 14.1cm
No. N.6785, J. Stone Hodges bequest, 1961
Perhaps Bristol *c.* 1740

8.13 Bowl Outside, four floral motifs depending from a wide band of trellis diaper with Chinese fan symbols, and the date '1765'. Inside, a tulip with leaves, surrounded by three long shoots with leaves and three quatrefoils. Decorated in blue on a clear pale blue glaze.
Diameter 30.0cm, height 13.2cm
No. N.6793, J. Stone Hodges bequest, 1961
Probably Bristol 1765

8.14 Bowl On the outside fourteen panels with ogee-shaped arches each containing a single daisy flower on a leafed stem. Inside, a Chinese artemisia leaf symbol tied with ribbon, surrounded by five more. The decoration in red, green and yellow on a pale bluish glaze tinged with violet.
Diameter 22.2cm, height 10.3cm
No. N.6802, J. Stone Hodges bequest, 1961
Probably London *c.* 1730

8.15 Bowl On the outside four floral sprigs interspersed with flying insects, and a wide rim border with five smaller sprigs, divided by blue-painted panels with graffito scrolls. Inside, two concentric circles. The decoration in blue on an off-white glaze.
Diameter 25.2cm, height 12.7cm
No. N.6791, J. Stone Hodges bequest, 1961
Probably Bristol *c.* 1730

8.16 Bowl On the outside two large flower faces with meandering stems and leaves spreading round the bowl. Inside, a small sprig with six quadruple dots round the bowl. The decoration in blue on an off-white glaze.
Diameter 26.4cm, height 12.9cm
No. N.5951, found at the Red Lodge and accessioned 1954, ex Alderman J. F. Eberle collection
Probably Liverpool *c.* 1770

8.17 Bowl Outside, five pendants with connecting festoons, and five sprays of flowers with perched birds. Inside, Chinese symbols tied with ribbons, surrounded by three scrolling branches and three interlocking ovals. Decorated in blue, red, green and yellow on a pale bluish glaze.
Diameter 25.1cm, height 13.7cm
No. N.3244, Sir Gilbert Mellor bequest, 1947, ex Gautier collection
Probably Liverpool *c.* 1750

8.18 Small Bowl On the outside a hound chases a stag through trees with sponged foliage, and mossy rocks. Inside, a tree with sponged foliage from cultivated ground, surrounded by four stars and four circles with centre marks. The decoration in blue, red, green and yellow on a white glaze.
Diameter 21.7cm, height 11.5cm
No. N.3224, Sir Gilbert Mellor bequest, 1947
Probably Bristol *c.* 1740

8.19 Small Bowl Outside, six elongated panels with a flower in each, linked by panels of *chinoiserie* motifs. No inside decoration. Painted in blue, red and green on an off-white glaze with a trace of lilac tinge inside.
Diameter 18.9cm, height 11.2cm
No. N.6803, J. Stone Hodges bequest, 1961
Probably Bristol *c.* 1730

8.20 Small Bowl On the outside six motifs of flower and leaf, below a top border of 'three-brick' pattern in blue with red curls between, and with two broad and five narrow blue circles around the base. Inside, a single Chinese scroll. The decoration in blue, red and green on a white glaze.
Diameter 18.7cm, height 10.7cm
No. N.3219, Sir Gilbert Mellor bequest, 1947, ex Gautier collection
Probably Bristol *c.* 1760

8.21 **Small Bowl** Outside, a symmetrical garden with a central shrub, and plants with three flowering stems either side. Inside, a rim border of connected crescents. Decorated in blue, red, green and manganese on a pale bluish glaze.
Diameter 11.0cm, height 5.3cm
No. N.3209, Sir Gilbert Mellor bequest, 1947
Probably Bristol *c.* 1740

8.22 **Bowl** Inscribed inside 'One More And Then', with a border within the rim of a blue band and interconnecting arcs. Outside, a two-panelled fence with flowers and buds on long trailing stems, upside-down. The decoration in blue inside, and blue and manganese outside on a pale bluish glaze.
Diameter 19.3cm, height 8.1cm
No. G.1970, purchased from T. Charbonnier, 1923
Probably London *c.* 1770

8.23 **Bowl** Inscribed inside 'One Bowl/More & then' and 'T H M/1773', with a narrow band of trellis near the rim. Outside, a large peony and spreading foliage painted upside-down. Decorated in blue on a clear pale blue glaze, and with the rim painted red-brown.
Diameter 26.7cm, height 11.9cm
No. G.156, purchased ex Hodgkin collection, 1914
Probably Liverpool 1773

Illustrated in Pountney pl. XI.

8.24 **Shallow Bowl** On the outside a peony flower and spreading foliage, with a flying insect. Inside, in blue only, a rosette inside a circle, and a border band of petal diaper and scrolls. The decoration in blue, red, green, manganese and yellow on a pale bluish glaze.
Diameter 27.2cm, height 9.7cm
No. N.3245, Sir Gilbert Mellor bequest, 1947
London *c.* 1780

8.25 Shallow Bowl Outside, a Chinese island with 'haycock' bushes, a willow tree and houses. Inside, a 'haycock' bush and a rim border of alternating cloud scrolls and floral motifs in graffito on a blue band. Decorated in blue, red, green and yellow on a pale blue glaze.
Diameter 26.8cm, height 9.2cm
No. N.6805, J. Stone Hodges bequest, 1961
London *c.* 1780

8.26 Saucer Dish A Chinaman in a barren rocky landscape, surrounded by a band of geometrical motifs; no outside decoration. The decoration in blue and manganese on a pale blue glaze.
Diameter 22.0cm, height 4.5cm, shape J
No. N.5715, purchased 1957
Probably Liverpool *c.* 1750

Compare with dish no. 11.32 with the same scene.

8.27 Saucer Dish Decorated on the inside only in blue on an off-white glaze, with peonies sprouting from a hollow rock.
Diameter 22.7cm, height 4.6cm, shape J
No. N.6495, J. Stone Hodges bequest, 1961
Probably Liverpool *c.* 1760

8.28 Saucer Dish Decorated on the inside only with a house on an island, reeds growing from the water and a boy fishing from a boat, the whole surrounded by a band of scrolls. The rim with forty-seven flutes containing either floral stems or scale pattern. The decoration in blue, red and green on a white glaze, pinky on the back.
Diameter 34.0cm, height 5.3cm, shape J
No. N.6722, J. Stone Hodges bequest, 1961
Probably London *c.* 1720

Compare Garner and Archer pl. 55A.

8.29 Saucer Dish A central blue disc surrounded by a pattern of florets, quadruple dots and eight-pointed stars in an overall decoration. The rim with forty-five flutes marked alternately with a herringbone or a tongue. The decoration in blue on a pale blue glaze. Noughts and crosses under-rim marking and the figures '10' within the footrim.
Diameter 22.8cm, height 3.3cm, shape J
No. N.6526, J. Stone Hodges bequest, 1961
Probably Bristol *c.* 1730

8.30 Shallow Bowl On the inside a Chinaman fishing from a small boat with rocky hills beyond, surrounded by a band of the 'three-brick' pattern, and a scroll border within the rim. The flat everted rim marked with hatching in red and blue. Noughts and crosses under-rim marking, and undecipherable mark within the footrim. The decoration in blue, red and green on a white glaze.
Diameter 29.3cm, height 6.5cm
No. N.3221, Sir Gilbert Mellor bequest, 1947
Probably Bristol *c.* 1740

8.31 Bowl Inscribed inside 'Success to/Trade' surrounded by a circle with leaves, and with a rim border of curl pattern. On the outside three lobe-shaped areas of trellis diaper descending from the rim, with leaves and garlands depending from them. Decorated in blue on a pale bluish glaze.
Diameter 27.4cm, height 11.4cm
No. G.1988, purchased from T. Charbonnier, 1923
Probably Liverpool *c.* 1770

8.32 Bowl Inscribed inside

> *Our Noble Tars*
> *That fear no wars*
> *That seek no jars*
> *Nor faints with scars*

and a rim border of trellis and floral motifs washed in blue. Outside, a spreading spray of chrysanthemums and other flowers and leaves, large on one side, small on the other. The decoration in blue on a white glaze.
Diameter 26.7cm, height 10.5cm
No. N.6799, J. Stone Hodges bequest, 1961
Probably Liverpool *c.* 1760

8.33 **Bowl** Inscribed inside 'Success/To the British/Arms' within a decorative band, and with a rim border of floral motifs. The outside with a Chinese fenced garden with flowers growing from rocks. Decorated in blue on a pale blue glaze.
Diameter 19.6cm, height 8.5cm
No. N.6794, J. Stone Hodges bequest, 1961
Probably London *c.* 1760

8.34 **Bowl** Inscribed inside 'ONE BOWL MORE AND THEN,' round a spray of four iris flowers and leaves. On the outside two prancing ladies, one with a bulldog(?), and the other with a poodle(?) on long spindly legs with blobs on the ends, and a 'willow tree' tail. On the other side, a lady under a parasol. The decoration in blue on a pale blue glaze.
Diameter 26.0/26.5cm, height 9.6/10.1cm
No. N.3241, Sir Gilbert Mellor bequest, 1947
Probably Liverpool *c.* 1740

8.35 **Bowl** Decorated inside only with a tall building and two ships at sea, surrounded by circles and by a rim border of interlocking red arcs on blue bands. The decoration in blue, red and green on a pale bluish glaze. The rim everted.
Diameter 22.4cm, height 9.7cm
No. N.5366, gift of Mr F. Johns, 1953
Perhaps London *c.* 1700

8.36 **Colander Bowl** The top with a central hole and three rings of perforations, decorated in the centre with a sprig of chrysanthemums, and bordered with shaped trellis panels, blue reserves with graffito scrolls, and butterflies. The outside with rocks from which more flowers on twining stems emerge. The decoration in blue on a pale blue glaze. A slot in the side.
Diameter 19.8cm, height 8.0cm
No. N.3060, purchased ex Hodgkin collection, 1947
Probably London *c.* 1740

8.37 Colander Bowl The top with a large centre hole and thirty-five smaller holes, decorated with three large and several small sprigs of flowers and insects. On the outside a hollow rock with perched bird and two twining stems with flowers and leaves; the whole painted upside-down. The decoration in blue, red, green and yellow on a pale bluish glaze. A crescent-shaped slot in the side.
Diameter 22.6cm, height 8.7cm
No. G.162, purchased ex Hodgkin collection, 1914
Probably London *c.* 1760

Illustrated in Pountney pl. XI

8.38 Colander Bowl The centre hole embellished with a sunburst, and surrounded by four rings of holes interspersed with tufts of grass and floral motifs. The wide rim border of trellis diaper with reserves of delicate flowers. On the outside a triangle of trellis diaper with floral sprays on long vines each side. A slot in the side. The decoration in blue on a pale blue glaze.
Diameter 22.0cm, height 8.7cm
No. N.6786, J. Stone Hodges bequest, 1961, ex Revelstoke collection
Perhaps Liverpool *c.* 1750

8.39 Colander Bowl The central hole in the top decorated with a sunburst, surrounded by four rows of holes, some ringed with dots. The rim border a blue band with a pattern superimposed. Outside, two sprays of peony flowers and foliage, and a flying insect. A slot in the side. The decoration in shades of blue on a pale blue glaze.
Diameter 22.5cm, height 9.5cm
No. N.6804, J. Stone Hodges bequest, 1961
Probably Liverpool *c.* 1760

8.40 Colander Bowl The top with a central hole and four rings of perforations, embellished with green tufts and floral motifs, and with a border of trellis and blue reserves with graffito lines. On the outside a scene of houses, pagodas, rocks and trees. A slot in the side. The decoration in blue and green on a pale bluish glaze. The footrim splayed out.
Diameter 19.5cm, height 7.9cm
No. N.8467, found in store and accessioned 1974
Probably London *c.* 1780

8.41 **Colander Bowl** The top with a centre hole and three rings of holes interspersed with tufts of grass, and surrounded by a rim border of trellis and half-flowerheads. The outside with two Chinamen in a garden with fences, plants and rocks, and a man fishing from a small boat. A slot high up on the side. The decoration in blue on a pale bluish glaze.
Diameter 22.4cm, height 10.6cm
No. G.1429, purchased 1919
Perhaps Bristol *c.* 1750

8.42 **Bowl with Strainer** On the outside three spreading sprays of flowers and six flying insects. Inside, flowers from a rock and two insects surrounded by rim decoration of rocks, flowers and shrubs. Decorated in blue and blue wash, with manganese outlines on the outside, all on a pale bluish glaze.
Diameter 21.6cm, height 9.5cm
No. N.6789, J. Stone Hodges bequest, 1961
Probably London *c.* 1770

The strainer partitioning off a portion of the bowl is unusual. It is found in some tureens thought to be of Continental origin. The purpose of the strainer is not certain; it might have been to contain a bouquet of herbs which were not intended to be served with the contents of the bowl.

8.43 **Bowl** The everted rim with twenty-two crimps, each decorated with a stiff leaf with radial lines between. In the centre a spray of flowers, surrounded by an anthemion frieze border. Within the footrim the figure '6' in green. Decorated in blue, red and green on an off-white glaze.
Diameter 23.2cm, height 7.6cm
No. G.1974, purchased from T. Charbonnier, 1923
Probably Bristol *c.* 1730

Compare Victoria and Albert Museum no. C170–1912 and Reading Museum no. 241-61-21.

8.44 **Bowl** The everted rim crimped and marked with circles and double brush marks. In the centre a bowl of fruit with a bird perched on top, surrounded by a wide band with four repeats of a flower and foliage. Decorated sketchily in blue on a pale blue glaze. The base with a small diameter footrim.
Diameter 26.8cm, height 7.2cm
No. G.2482, purchased from T. Charbonnier 1929
Probably Bristol *c.* 1720

8.45 Bowl The everted rim with twenty-three crimps, marked with stiff leaves and radial lines. In the centre a stylized flower with rhomboidal leaves, surrounded by a border of anthemion frieze. The decoration in blue, red and green on an off-white glaze. The figure '2' within the footrim.
Diameter 17.4cm, height 6.2cm
No. N.6652, J. Stone Hodges bequest, 1961
Probably Bristol *c.* 1730

Note the resemblance to no. 8.43.

8.46 Basin The inside profusely decorated with flowers and trees springing from a rock in a fenced garden, surrounded by a trellis border interrupted by bunches of flowers. The everted rim decorated with interlocking circles. The footrim with floral decoration. All decoration in rather heavy blue on a pale blue glaze.
Diameter 24.6cm, height 9.8cm
No. N.3046, purchased ex Hodgkin collection, 1947
Probably London *c.* 1770

This matches bottle no. 6.35.

8.47 Bowl A triangular spike stands in the centre, and the rim is shaped to receive a lid. The outside decorated with five bunches of grapes on vines, with a border of Chinese scroll pattern. The decoration in blue with a black *trek*, on a pale bluish-greenish glaze.
Diameter 18.0cm, height 7.5cm
No. N.6654A, J. Stone Hodges bequest, 1961
Perhaps London *c.* 1700

The central spike is most unusual; the article is recorded in the City Art Gallery as a pineapple bowl, but if there was a lid it could scarcely have covered an object of that size. Sherds of several bowls of this nature have recently been found by the Southwark and Lambeth Archaeological Society at the site of the Vauxhall Pottery.

8.48 **Monteith**   Oval in shape, with ten cut-outs round the rim to
receive the stems of glasses, and two rolled knob handles. There
are ten lappet-shaped painted panels between the cut-outs, and the
outside of the bowl has four scenes of flowers from a rock, with
perched or flying birds, and insects. The rounded foot is decorated
with mille-fleurs, with a 'three-brick' pattern border below. All
decoration in blue on a pale blue glaze.
Maximum diameter 38.2cm, height 22.5cm
No. G.2231, purchased from T. Charbonnier, 1925
London or Bristol *c.* 1710

Anthony Wood, the Oxford antiquary and diarist, recorded in
December 1683, 'This yeare in the summer time came up a vessel
or bason notched at the brims to let drinking glasses hang there by
the foot so that the body or drinking place might hang in the water
to coole them. Such a bason was called a 'Monteigh', from a
fantastical Scot called 'Monsieur Monteigh,' who at that time or a
little before wore the bottome of his cloake or coate so notched.' It
seems probable that this refers to the Earl of Monteith or Menteith,
1661 to 1694, nineteenth and last holder of a title created *c.* 1160.
    Theodore Charbonnier recorded this Monteith as 'absolutely
unique in Bristol delft', but some of the decoration is more
reminiscent of London.

8.49 Bowl The rim perforated to form a pattern of interlocking circles. Decorated on the inside only with a scene of two deer with pine trees in a Chinese landscape, surrounded by a band of scroll pattern. The figure '4' within the footrim. The decoration in blue on a pale grey glaze.
Diameter 19.7cm, height 8.6cm
No. G.127, purchased 1909
Probably Dublin *c.* 1750

8.50 Bowl The rim formed of twenty-six interlocking circles each decorated with chain pattern. In the centre a delicate sprig of flower and leaves, surrounded by eight lotus flowers in petal-shaped segments on an all-over scroll pattern. The decoration in blue on a pale bluish glaze.
Diameter 18.7cm, height 5.2cm
No. N.1601, gift of Mr A. de Pass, 1936
Probably Dublin *c.* 1750

The pattern is directly derived from Chinese porcelain: see David Howard and John Ayers *China for the West* (London 1978) pls. 450 and 472, which they date *c.* 1745. Several Irish examples will be found in the catalogue of the Castletown House exhibition. Compare also the Morgan collection catalogue, no. 83.

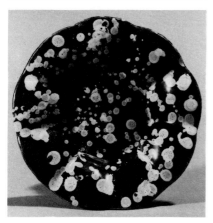

8.51 Fluted Bowl With nine-foliated rim springing from a flat centre, standing on a footrim. Decorated with scattered white blotches on a deep blue glaze.
Diameter 22.0cm, height 4.5cm
No. N.3061, purchased ex Hodgkin collection, 1947
Probably London *c.* 1700

Compare with the bleeding bowl no. 5.17 of similar *bleu persan* style, and where other examples of the style are cited.

9 Other shapes

There are no fewer than sixteen other shapes to be dealt with in this chapter, which are represented by forty-three specimens. In most cases, where there are only one or two specimens representing a particular article, it will be more appropriate to deal with that article fully in its catalogue entry, and only to make passing reference to it in this introduction.

In the case of both the first two items, the ink stand and the clock case, we know of the existence of only one other such article in any collection. We have been able to obtain photographs of them for comparison, and are able to publish that of the ink stand.[1] Both the ink stands were almost certainly made at Brislington, probably by the same master potter; both are initialled and dated, and we are able to make rational guesses as to the persons to whom the initials belong.

Bird feeders are not quite so rare; there are in fact two in this collection, and at least two more in other collections. The one candlestick in the collection is a comparatively dainty specimen evidently copied from metalware, whereas there are several earlier and more robust examples elsewhere which could receive a candle of twice the diameter, and provide light for the most lengthy of feasts. Of two little figurines in the collection one also serves as a taper-holder; these were probably sold as rather fanciful trinkets and are of no great artistic merit.

Delftware shoes must also surely come under the category of trinkets. There are several examples of them in other collections, and they are quite frequently initialled and dated, suggesting that they were mementoes of special occasions. One can conceive of them being used as vases for a bunch of small flowers, such as violets, or for containing a pot-pourri of rose petals and being placed on my lady's dressing table.

We come next to a group of articles of household use, derived from metalware in the case of sauce boats and salt cellars; but in the case of tea or coffee pots, cups and tea caddies, the articles were copied from Chinese ceramics, which were reaching England at the time in increasing numbers, and the copying extended not only to the shape of the articles but also to their decoration. All this is only natural, for tea and coffee drinking were of Eastern origin.

A few delftware fish strainers survive, of which there are two in the collection. Ray refers us to an article[2] showing that they were in great demand in Boston, Massachusetts, in the mid-eighteenth century. They are called 'mazarines' by some, but the *Oxford English Dictionary* does not seem to recognize this use of the word. Another fishy article is the char pot. As char came exclusively from Lake Windermere, it is not surprising that the Liverpool delftware factories were the only manufacturers; but the dating of them is an impossible task as char were being potted long before the Liverpool factories started up, and went on being potted after their demise, while the delftware char pots remained unaltered for as long as they were made.

Notes

1 The ink stand in the Somerset County Museum, Taunton, is reproduced in this catalogue with their kind permission. The watch case is being illustrated in the Waddesdon Catalogue of Pottery and other Earthenware, by John Mallet of the Victoria and Albert Museum, for which the National Trust naturally wish to reserve publication. There is also a watch case of completely different design in the Liverpool Museum.
2 Emily Manheim, 'A Toast to British Fisheries', *Antique Collector*, December 1961.

Delftware jars were mostly too decorative for purely utilitarian use, and so one suspects that they were probably used for pot-pourri or on the dining or tea table; while sweetmeat or pickle dishes were undoubtedly for use for serving various kinds of appetizers or accompaniments to the courses of the meal. These were sometimes single, and sometimes in three, four, five or six compartments; in most cases the compartments are all joined together as a tray, but in other cases they are separate, but nest together to form a set. Examples of all these variations will be found among the eleven pieces illustrated in this chapter.

9.1 **Ink Stand** Formed on a rectangular platform on flat bearers running diagonally from the front corners to meet at centre back. A candle holder at each corner, with twisted connecting rails and posts. Attached to the stand are an ink pot decorated in blue and manganese with stripes and floral motifs, and a bowl decorated inside with a bird and inscribed 'R C/1685/desem ye 3/day'. Loose, is a pounce pot in the shape of a flattened ball, with a perforated concave face, and inscribed '1685/R˙C'. The decoration in blue with fine manganese lines, and on the pounce pot bands of green wash, all on a pale bluish glaze.
The base 16.8cm × 10.4/10.8cm, height over candle holders 7.1/8.0cm
No. N.7956, purchased 1969
Bristol (Brislington) 1685   COLOUR PLATE, p. 30

The initials are likely to be those of Robert Collins, whom Pountney, on p. 28, refers to as the first name connected with the Brislington pottery that he has been able to discover. He also states that Collins was a party to a deed for the purchase of a field adjacent to the pottery in 1658. The Bristol Record Office have six deeds relating to Brislington properties between 1658 and 1673, three of which involve Robert Collins, but none of these tallies with Pountney's description. The significance of the date, 1685, could be that the inkstand was a retirement present to Robert Collins, who must by then have worked at the pottery for thirty-five or forty years.

The only other article of this nature, of which we are aware, is in the Somerset County Museum, Taunton, an ink stand in their Somersetshire Archaeological and Natural History Society's Collection. This is illustrated in fig. 9. It is inscribed 'I L/1674' and underneath one can make out the initials 'E W' and the date '1674' scratched into the earthenware body beneath the glaze. This strongly suggests that it was made by Edward Ward senior, who became a Burgess Potter in 1682, took on his three sons as apprentices, and became proprietor of Brislington and later of the Temple Pottery in Bristol. 'I L' could stand for John Lidyard, whom Pountney mentions on pp. 82–83 as a witness to Edward Ward senior's will, and as a trustee in the will of Edward Ward junior. As John Lidyard was made a Burgess on 4 November 1674, it seems probable that the inkstand was made to commemorate that event. He is listed in *The Inhabitants of Bristol in 1696* (Bristol Record Society vol. XXV, 1968) on the next page to the Wards in Temple Parish, which occupies thirty pages in all, so that it is probable they were near neighbours.

The general similarity of these two rare ink stands does suggest that they were made by the same master potter as special gifts for his close friends, and tends to reinforce the suggested interpretations of the initials on them.

Fig 9 Ink stand in the Somersetshire Archaeological and Natural History Society's Collection, Somerset County Museum, Taunton.

9.1 **Ink Stand**

9.2 **Clock Case** In the form of a hollow-topped rectangle with a four centimetre diameter hole in the front face; the sides and top of the front and rear faces are of irregular rococo edging, and the rear face has a vertical slot for suspension of the clock. The side faces are decorated with imitation stonework, and the front with leafy motifs and tendrils, and with a cupid's face below the opening, with folded wings and a pendent tassel. The decoration in blue on a pale blue glaze.
Height 13.1cm, width 8.0cm
No. N.3077, purchased ex Hodgkin collection, 1947, ex Gautier collection
Perhaps London c. 1770

One other similar article of which we are aware is at Waddesdon Manor, Buckinghamshire. It is of the same general shape and size, with similar rococo edges, and is decorated largely in a trellis pattern on front and sides. It is inscribed on the back 'James Pickford Mason: at Roehampton 1768', and as a panel below the clockface appears to contain masonic emblems it probably refers to a Mr Pickford, who was a Mason. We do not illustrate it here, as it is being included in the catalogue of pottery and other earthenware at Waddesdon, now in preparation.
   There is also reference to a watch stand in a manuscript account of the Mortlake Potteries by J. E. Anderson (Victoria and Albert Museum Library ref. 96.JJ.Box II) which is there said to have been made by a Mortlake potter, and which sounds similar to the Bristol one. As Roehampton is not far from Mortlake, this must raise speculation that these rare articles were a speciality of that factory.

9.3 Bird Feeder Cylindrical, with four round holes of 2.5cm diameter in the sides. Decorated all over with a trellis diaper with, between the holes, four shaped reserves containing flower sprays, and below the neck with four lappet-shaped panels containing graffito motifs. Decorated in blue on an off-white glaze.
Height 10.4cm, diameter 10.5cm
No. N.5347, purchased 1952
Perhaps London *c.* 1780

Another is catalogued at no. 18.40. Compare also Victoria and Albert Museum no. C111–1935, Hall Warren collection no. 182 and Glaisher collection no. 1540. The openings in the sides of most bird feeders are shaped as tall arches, and Ray suggests that they might have been used to hold a night-light; the example we have here has small round holes suitable only for small caged birds.

9.4 Candlestick The shape copied from metalware, with double knopped stem. Decorated in blue-grey on a white glaze, with a stiff leaf border at the top, bands round the stem, and four leaf-shaped motifs round the base.
Height 17.3cm
No. N.3358, purchased ex Maddicks collection, 1936
Probably London *c.* 1730

9.5 Figurine Figure of a man in long jacket and boots standing on a stepped plinth. Much detail lost through chipping of the glaze. Decorated in blue on a white glaze.
Height 12.8cm
No. G.2004, purchased from T. Charbonnier, 1923
Perhaps Bristol *c.* 1720

9.6 **Figurine** The moulded figure of a Chinaman in long robe, the head, neck and beard in the pale bluish glaze colour, and the rest of the figure in powder blue. An oval hole in the top of the head suggests its use as a taper holder. The base inscribed '1753'.
Height 14.4cm
No. N.3772, purchased 1949
Probably Bristol 1753

9.7 **Pair of Shoes** Marked 'AH/92' on each high tongue. The toes elongated and cut off; the high heels are hollow; there are small bows on the front. Decorated in blue on a white glaze, with solid blue on the outside of the heels, and blue stripes elsewhere, the stripes containing a darker wavy blue line. The stripes down the front in chevron pattern.
Lengths 16.2 and 15.8cm, height 8.6cm
No. G.149, purchased ex Hodgkin collection, 1914
Perhaps London 1692

9.8 **A Shoe** Marked 'I/16' and 'R/86' on either side of the instep. With tall tongue and wide bow, and a high heel. Decorated on a pale blue glaze with a band of blue and yellow lines down the centre front and across the toe; the bow similarly striped, and lacy decoration either side of the frontal band, and also on the heel.
Length 12.5cm, height 8.5cm
No. G.150, purchased ex Hodgkin collection, 1914
Perhaps London 1686

9.9 **A Shoe** With high, buckled front and pointed toe. The decoration on a pale bluish glaze, with a solid blue coloured heel, and a trellis diaper pattern elsewhere, plus a Chinese scroll pattern band down the centre front and up the heel.
Length 13.7cm, height 8.7cm
No. N.6608, J. Stone Hodges bequest, 1961
Perhaps London c. 1700

9.10 **Sauce Boat** The shape copied from silverware of the period, pot-bellied, with a high canopied back carrying the handle with a snake twisted round it. Scenes on either side in rococo frames of (i) a sailing ship in a river with buildings beyond, and (ii) a ship alongside a quay. Leafy decoration inside rim and sides. The decoration in blue on a pale bluish glaze.
Length 21.5cm
No. G.2019, purchased from T. Charbonnier, 1923
Perhaps Bristol *c.* 1740

Compare Victoria Art Gallery, Bath, no. 57, which is also illustrated by Pountney in pl. XV and described on p. 88, with brief mention of this sauce boat as well. Pountney claims to have authenticated these pieces as the products of Thomas Cantle at the Temple Pottery, Bristol, but cites no evidence for this. They are both of the same size and shape, though differently decorated.

9.11 **Sauce Boat** With open bowl and shaped rim, standing on a pleated foot, and with a simple handle painted solid blue. Decorated in blue on a pale bluish glaze, with scenes either side of (i) a shepherd playing a flute to two sheep, and (ii) a house with trees by a stream with castle beyond. Inside, a delicate bunch of flowers, four rows of wave pattern up the lip, and a rim border of triangle pattern.
Length 20.1cm
No. N.6658, J. Stone Hodges bequest, 1961
Perhaps Liverpool *c.* 1750

9.12 **Coffee Pot** Of tin-glazed stoneware, with crabstock handle and spout at 90° to one another, between them a Chinaman seated on a bank, and round the rest of the body a man holding a balk of timber(?) erect in a garden with weeping willow from a tall rock. Decorated in smudged blue on a pale bluish glaze; the smudging is common on stoneware, the firing temperature being apparently very critical. No lid.
Height 15.8cm, maximum diameter 10.8cm
No. N.6392, purchased 1961
Probably Liverpool *c.* 1760

Compare Garner and Archer pl. 115A.

9.13 **Coffee Pot** With straight tapering sides, a strap handle and
beehive shaped lid. Decorated on both sides with a bunch of
flowers, and with top and bottom borders of trellis with Chinese
symbols in reserves. The lid similarly decorated. All decoration in
blue on a pale blue glaze.
Height with lid 22.0cm
No. N.7988, purchased 1970
Perhaps London *c.* 1750

Compare Hall Warren collection no. 124, which is of the same shape,
though with spout and handle at 90° to one another; that piece is
dated 1705 and the decoration is quite different. The somewhat
vulgar floral decoration on this piece suggests the later date.

9.14 **Teapot** With squat bulbous pear-shaped body, straight
conical spout and O-shaped handle. Dark blue glazed inside and
out. Lid with simple knob.
Height overall 10.9cm, maximum diameter 9.7cm
No. N.6655, J. Stone Hodges bequest, 1961
Perhaps London *c.* 1770, or Continental

9.15 **Teacup** Of conical shape curving in to footrim. Decorated in
blue on a pale bluish glaze with two leaf-shaped panels, one
containing houses, the other flowers behind a fence, and between
the panels a spray of flowers. The handle blue-banded.
Height 5.2cm
No. G.2003, purchased from T. Charbonnier, 1923
Probably Liverpool *c.* 1730

9.16 **Teacup** Cylindrical, curving in to the footrim. The
decoration in blue and manganese, with a Chinese house on a
rocky isle, with a bridge to another; weeping willows spring from
the rocks. The handle of flat oval section, blue-banded.
Height 5.5cm
No. N.3874, purchased 1949
Perhaps London *c.* 1760

9.17 Coffee can Of cylindrical shape curving out slightly to the flat base. Decorated in blue on a pale bluish glaze, with houses, rocks and cactus-like trees. The handle of oval section, blue-banded.
Height 6.0cm
No. N.5546, gift of Miss Nesbitt, 1955
Probably Bristol c. 1750

9.18 Cup and Saucer The cup has no handle and is fused to the saucer. Inside the cup is a Chinese leaf symbol within two circles, surrounded by four quadruple dots. Outside the cup and within the saucer are Chinese floral motifs embellished with scrolls. The decoration in blue on a pale blue glaze which has run. Under-rim marking of noughts and crosses.
Overall height 5.4cm, saucer diameter 12.1cm
No. N.6645, J. Stone Hodges bequest, 1961, ex Freeth collection
Probably Bristol c. 1710

Compare Victoria and Albert Museum no. C7–1963, described as a butter dish, for which this article might have been intended. Early cups or tea bowls did not necessarily have handles, and as the article has clearly been over-fired one cannot be certain whether they are fused together intentionally or accidentally. However, cups would not normally be placed on their saucers in the kiln, but would be fired separately. No other saucer is known with an under-rim marking.

9.19 Tea Caddy Of upright rectangular shape with chamfered corners, the two sides with twining sprays of flowers, the two ends with different flowers, and the chamfered surfaces with trellis diaper. On the top an all-over pattern of snail curls, and four trefoil-shaped reserves with little flowers. The decoration in blue on a pale blue glaze.
Height overall 9.4cm
No. G.2310, gift of T. Charbonnier, 1928
Probably Liverpool c. 1760

9.20 Tea Caddy Of upright rectangular shape with chamfered corners, the sides and ends with floral sprays with shaded petals and leaves, the four chamfered surfaces overlapping the others, and decorated with trellis pattern with reserves of leafy sprays. The tall neck painted blue. Decoration in blue on a white glaze.
Height 9.0cm
No. N.6600, J. Stone Hodges bequest, 1961
Probably Bristol c. 1760

9.21 Tea Caddy Of upright rectangular shape with chamfered corners, on one side a lady, and on the other a gentleman with tricorn hat under his arm, drawing his sword. On both ends a tall-stemmed plant from a rock. On the four chamfered surfaces, bunches of grapes(?), and on the top two bunches of grapes and two flowers. The decoration in blue on a pale blue glaze.
Height overall 10.3cm
No. N.6601, J. Stone Hodges bequest, 1961
Probably Bristol *c.* 1760

Note the similarity of the bunches of what may be intended as grapes, to those on the matching basin and bottle nos. 18.8 and 18.9. Those two pieces have figures in a landscape in the 'Bowen' style of decoration associated with Bristol.

9.22 Tea Caddy Of upright rectangular shape with chamfered corners, the sides and ends with sprays of flowers and leaves, and the four chamfered surfaces, which overlap the others, with acanthus leaf scrolls. The top with two sprays of flowers within bordering lines. The base shows a reddish body. The decoration in blue on an off-white glaze.
Height 8.1cm
No. N.5543, gift of Miss Nesbitt, 1955
Probably London *c.* 1740

9.23 Salt In damaged condition, but presumed to have had three scrolls standing up round the top. Decorated in blue, red and green on a white glaze, with lines, loops and chevrons.
Base diameter 9.1cm
No. G.2061, purchased from T. Charbonnier, 1922
Probably Bristol *c.* 1700

An illustration accompanying a note concerning this salt in *The Connoisseur*, (vol. LXV, no. 259) March 1923, p. 161, confirms its original form.
   Compare Morgan collection no. 18, which shows the same shape, and Rijksmuseum exhibition catalogue nos. 31 and 54, which show some variations of the shape.

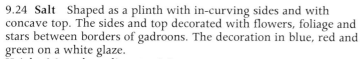

9.24 Salt Shaped as a plinth with in-curving sides and with concave top. The sides and top decorated with flowers, foliage and stars between borders of gadroons. The decoration in blue, red and green on a white glaze.
Height 6.9cm, base diameter 8.0cm
No. G.2229, purchased from T. Charbonnier, 1925
Probably Bristol *c.* 1730

Compare Glaisher collection no. 1660: this shape is of later date than the previous example, though still copied from silverware.

9.25 Fish Strainer Circular, with two heavy handles and standing on three little feet. Decorated with four fish and with a border of a stylized running vine. The dish perforated irregularly to act as a strainer. The decoration in blue on a pale bluish glaze.
Diameter 32.0cm
No. N.3368, purchased ex Maddicks collection, 1936
Perhaps Bristol *c*. 1700

These are sometimes called *mazarines*. There is an article like this one in the Victoria and Albert Museum no. 3863-01. This is probably the same as that in the catalogue of the old Jermyn Street Museum of Practical Geology no. Y.30. It is inscribed on the back 'V H M 1673'.

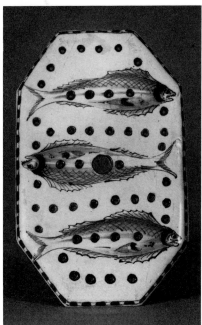

9.26 Fish Strainer Of long octagon shape perforated with one larger central hole and many others, and decorated with three fish and a narrow border ribbon. The decoration in blue on a pale bluish glaze.
Length 30.8cm
No. G.2513, gift of T. Charbonnier, 1930
Perhaps Bristol *c*. 1700

9.27 Char Pot Decorated with five fish round it, with manganese head and spine, blue-green lower body and red fins and tail, all on an off-white glaze.
Diameter 24.0cm
No. N.5349, purchased 1952
Liverpool mid-eighteenth century

The following quotations from the *Journeys of Celia Fiennes*, describing a visit to the Lake District in 1698, show that char were being potted long before delftware pottery began in Liverpool:

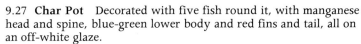

> At the King's Arms (Kendall) one Mrs Rowlandson she does pott up the charr fish the best of any in the country, I was curious to have some and so bespoke some of her, and also was as curious to see the great water which is the only place that fish is to be found in . .
> . . the water (of Lake Wiandermer) is very clear and full of good fish, but the Charr fish being out of season could not easily be taken so I saw none alive, but of other fish I had a very good supper; the season of the Charrfish is between Michaelmas and Christmas, at that tyme I have had of them which they pott with sweet spices, they are as big as a small trout rather slenderer and the skinn full of spotts some redish, and part of the whole skinn and the finn and taile is red like the finns of a perch, and the inside flesh looks as red as any salmon; if they are in season their taste is very rich and fat tho' not so strong or clogging as the lampreys are, but its as fatt and rich a food.

A recipe book by Mrs Elizabeth Raffeld, published in 1769, gives a recipe for their potting, concluding with 'lay them close into broad thin Pots for that Purpose', which indicates that it was the custom to make special pots for them. Mrs Hemming, in an article on Liverpool delftware in *The Connoisseur* in April 1918, says that Zachariah Barnes was the largest maker of char pots, though she quotes no evidence to support the assertion.

9.28 Meat Dish Of long octagon shape with octagonal
depression. Decorated in the centre with flowers from rocks with
many tendrils and dots embellishing the stems. On three points of
the rim are sprays of similar flowers, and at the top centre a crest
of a mermaid looking in a handglass. Decorated in blue, red, pale
green, yellow and manganese on a clear pale blue glaze.
Length 36.2cm, width 26.2cm
No. N.5963, found at the Red Lodge and accessioned 1959
Glasgow *c.* 1750

A similar, though smaller, meat dish is in the Burnap collection
no. 158, and other articles which appear to be from the same
service are Victoria and Albert Museum no. C103-1965, Liverpool
Museum nos. 50.45.17 and 50.60.52 and a plate at Rous Lench. The
crest was used by both Murray of Polmaise and by Rutherford.
However the Rutherford peerage became dormant before the
Glasgow delftware factory started, and Murray has the better
claim. The founder of the family was alive at the correct period
and living at Touchadam, Stirlingshire, which is only a few miles
from Glasgow.

9.29 Jar and Cover Of squat cylinder shape with no handles,
the lid flat with simple knob. Decorated with a spill vase in front
of a shallow basket; sprays of flowers twine from the basket, and
herringbone fern from the vase; a cock on the reverse side. The lid
similarly decorated. The decoration in blue, red and green on a
pale bluish glaze. The figure '7' marked inside jar and lid.
Height overall 13.9cm, diameter 11.2cm
No. N.3228, Sir Gilbert Mellor bequest, 1947
Probably Bristol *c.* 1740

9.30 Jar Of cylinder shape, without lid. Decorated in blue, red
and green on a pale bluish glaze, with eight pendent semi-circles of
trellis diaper from the top rim, and four floral motifs, with blue
lines encircling the base. Under the base the figure '4'.
Height 8.7cm, diameter 10.3cm
No. N.6647, J. Stone Hodges bequest, 1961
Probably Bristol *c.* 1740

9.31 Jar The body cylindrical, curving in to the base and top.
Small applied twisted handles. Decorated in an overall pattern
including a bunch of fruit, a bird and many quadruple spots.
Marked on the base with the letter 'H'. The decoration in blue on a
pale blue glaze.
Height 10.7cm, maximum diameter 13.5cm
No. G.2223, gift of T. Charbonnier, 1925
Perhaps Bristol *c.* 1740

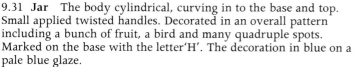

In Mr Charbonnier's records he suggests that the 'H' stands for
Henry Hobbs of Limekiln Lane Pottery; if this were so the date
would have to be a little earlier, for Hobbs retired in 1724.

9.32 Jar and Cover Of double ogee shape with applied twisted handles, the knob missing from the domed lid. Decorated overall in blue on an off-white glaze, with bunches of fruit on stems with perched birds, amid quadruple dots and many-pointed stars. The top and bottom borders of Chinese crude *ruyi* head and scroll pattern. The cover similarly decorated.
Height (without knob) 13.8cm, maximum diameter 17.5cm
No. G.1982, purchased from T. Charbonnier, 1923
Perhaps Bristol *c.* 1730

9.33 Sweetmeat Dish An oval dish with pointed ends and irregular curved sides, standing on four horseshoe feet. Decorated with a rock with sprouting tree, with a field and buildings beyond. The border with blue-washed trellis diaper and floral motifs. The decoration in blue on a pale blue glaze.
Length 15.9cm
No. N.7155, Ernest Blatch bequest, 1964
Probably Bristol *c.* 1750

9.34 Sweetmeat Dish Of irregular oval shape, decorated with a Chinaman fishing in a boat, off an island with castle, house and trees. Narrow border of trellis and floral motifs. Decorated in blue, red, green and manganese on a pale bluish glaze.
Length 15.5cm
No. N.3231, Sir Gilbert Mellor bequest, 1947
Probably Bristol *c.* 1760

9.35 Sweetmeat Dish An oval dish with pointed ends and irregular curved sides, standing on four horseshoe feet. Decorated with a house in garden with shrubs and trees. The border of blue-washed trellis and floral motifs. The decoration in blue, yellow, green and manganese on an off-white glaze.
Length 15.5cm
No. N.3232, Sir Gilbert Mellor bequest, 1947
Probably Bristol *c.* 1760

9.36 **Sweetmeat Dish** A single dish with three compartments on three fluted conical feet (one applied upside-down). Each compartment with a peony flower and leafy stems hatched, and a continuous vine pattern round all the edges. Decoration in blue on a pale bluish glaze.
Diameter 18.2cm
No. G.2006, purchased from T. Charbonnier, 1923
Probably Liverpool *c.* 1750

9.37 **Sweetmeat Dish** A single dish with three compartments on three waisted feet, the rim wavy. Each compartment decorated with flowers and leaves, and a running vine pattern round all edges with flowers at intersections. The decoration in blue on a pale blue glaze.
Diameter 18.2cm
No. N.6580, J. Stone Hodges bequest, 1961
Probably Liverpool *c.* 1750

Note that the same shape and diameter of this and the previous dish suggest that they were made on the same mould. The style of decoration is also similar.

9.38 **Sweetmeat Dish** A single dish with three compartments on three waisted feet; lobed rim. Decorated with three different scenes of flowers in gardens, and the edges bordered with various leafy patterns, all in blue on a pale bluish-greenish glaze.
Diameter 18.3cm
No. N.6582, J. Stone Hodges bequest, 1961
Probably Liverpool *c.* 1750

9.39 **Sweetmeat Dish** A single dish with four quadrantal compartments, standing on four flattened knobs. The rim symmetrically lobed. Decorated with the same floral motif in each quadrant, and a running vine pattern round all edges. The decoration in blue on a pale blue glaze.
Diameter 16.5cm
No. N.6579, J. Stone Hodges bequest, 1961
Probably Liverpool *c.* 1750

9.40 Sweetmeat Dish A set of five dishes, one central and four fitting round it. All with the same floral decoration and a narrow band of diagonal hatching. The decoration in blue on a pale blue glaze.
Diameter 18.8cm across the set as mounted
No. G.1983, purchased from T. Charbonnier, 1923
Probably Liverpool *c.* 1760

9.41 Sweetmeat Dish A single dish with five compartments. The central one lozenge-shaped with a winged putto; the four surrounding compartments decorated with a variety of country scenes. The rim symmetrically lobed; the dish standing on four flat disc feet. Borders of linked buds. Decorated in blue on an off-white glaze.
Diameter 20.1cm
No. N.6583, J. Stone Hodges bequest, 1961, ex Hall Warren collection
Probably London *c.* 1740

9.42 Sweetmeat Dish A single dish with five compartments, the rim with irregular convex and concave arcs. All compartments with floral decoration including lotus flowers; the centre square bordered with floral pattern, the rim border of lace pattern. The decoration in blue on a pale blue glaze. No feet.
Diameter 23.3cm
No. N.6584, J. Stone Hodges bequest, 1961
Probably London *c.* 1740

9.43 Sweetmeat Dish A single dish with five kidney-shaped compartments around a central five-pointed star, and standing on five flat knob feet. In the centre a sailor, and in surrounding compartments scenes of ships at sea. The edges decorated with floral motifs. All decoration in blue on a pale blue glaze.
Diameter 19.5cm
No. N.6581, J. Stone Hodges bequest, 1961
Probably Bristol *c.* 1760

In the eighteenth century one could buy sets of prints of shipping with titles such as 'Calm', 'Engagement', 'A Ship on Fire' and 'Shipwreck', which would fit the scenes on this dish; but it has not been possible to find a set that fits exactly.

COMMEMORATIVE AND
ALLUSIVE PIECES

Fig 10 'A View of Mr
Lunardi's Balloon':
aquatint by F. Jukes
published in 1784.

10   Personal and historical attributions

Many pieces of English delftware were made to commemorate people or historical events. In chapter 3 of the catalogue section we have already seen a number of chargers portraying royalty or other distinguished persons, and the first group of articles in this chapter also do so, but, at the smaller scale at which the figures appear on plates and in bowls, little attempt is made at accurate portraiture, and were it not for the inclusion of initials, we would often be at a loss to identify the intended subject. In a few cases we find merely initials, a crown and the rose and thistle, or an inscription such as 'Long live King George the 3d'.

Other heroes of their day were commemorated, such as John Wilkes and Admiral Keppel; while the practice also arose of producing bowls or plates to promote the candidates for election to Parliament. Of these we are able to illustrate three; but there is also a plate in the Bristol collection, damaged during the war, inscribed 'Cresswell Esq For Ever', referring to Thomas E. Cresswell, who was M.P. for Wotton Bassett, Wiltshire, from 1754 to 1774, during which time he contested elections in 1754, 1761 and 1768. This plate was recorded by Theodore Charbonnier as '$9\frac{1}{4}$" diam Grey blue enamel, marbled edges in manganese'.

There follows, in this chapter, a group of pieces inscribed variously with names, initials, dates and coats of arms, on which genealogical and other researches have enabled us to make attributions to the persons and events to which they may have referred. Most notable among all these is perhaps the 'Hen and Chickens' bowl, which we believe to be the only authenticated case of a piece of English delftware of which copies exist that were made in Chinese porcelain.

We also include six pieces in the 'Ann Gomm' style of decoration, including one eponymous example, another differently inscribed, and, for convenience, four uninscribed pieces of the same pattern.

Next we have some notable examples of delftware illustrating events and places, including three balloon plates which commemorate the earliest ascents of balloons in England. The first was by Lunardi on 15 September 1784 from Moorfields Artillery Ground in the City of London, which he followed by flights with a larger balloon in 1785, some of which started from St George's Fields, Southwark, There were also ascents by Blanchard in 1785, some of which were from Stockwell Road, South Lambeth. These south bank flights would have been within less than a mile from the riverside delftware factories, so that it is no wonder that the potters made these contributions to their commemoration. The contemporary print which we reproduce (fig. 10) shows the paddles by which it was supposed that the course of their flights could be controlled, and which are evident on all three plates.

We conclude with three specimens of Liverpool punch bowls illustrating ships, all of which were made around the middle of the eighteenth century, for ships trading with that port. As the manufacture of delftware takes at least a week from start to finish, it is presumed that such articles were ordered during one visit, and collected during a later visit. The one Bristol ship dish in the collection, which is decorated with *bianco-sopra-bianco*, has been catalogued at no. 16.32.

10.1 **Plate** 'WMR' inscribed over the head and shoulder portraits of William (on right) and Mary (on left), both of whom are depicted in blue, but crowned and sashed in yellow on a pale blue glaze.
Diameter 21.8cm, height 2.7/3.5cm, shape E
No. N.3177, Sir Gilbert Mellor bequest, 1947
Probably Bristol *c.* 1690

10.2 **Plate** 'W M R' with head and shoulder portraits of William and Mary interposed, both crowned and he robed in ermine. The decoration in blue on a white glaze.
Diameter 22.5cm, height 2.5cm, shape E
No. N.3175, Sir Gilbert Mellor bequest, 1947
Probably London *c.* 1690

10.3 **Plate** 'W MR R' inscribed over the head and shoulder portraits of William (on right) and Mary (on left). Decorated in blue and yellow on a pale greenish-blue glaze. The figures crowned and sashed.
Diameter 20.8cm, height 1.7cm, shape E
No. G.2052, purchased from T. Charbonnier, 1923
Probably London *c.* 1690

10.4 **Plate** 'W R M' with head and shoulder portraits of William and Mary interposed, both crowned and in robes, his of ermine. The decoration in blue on a pale blue-green glaze.
Diameter 21.0cm, height 4.4cm, shape: saucer with small footrim
No. N.6481, J. Stone Hodges bequest, 1961, ex Maddicks collection
Probably Bristol *c.* 1690

10.5 **Plate** 'W M R' with head and shoulder portraits of William and Mary interposed, crowned and in robes. The decoration in blue and yellow on a pale blue-green glaze.
Diameter 21.4cm, height 2.1cm, shape D
No. N.6520, J. Stone Hodges bequest, 1961
Probably London *c.* 1700

10.6 **Bowl** Marked 'A R' either side of a portrait of Queen Anne, crowned and wearing a necklace, surrounded by border of arcs. The rim everted with twenty crimps in the edge each marked with a stiff leaf, and with triple lines between. No outside decoration. Decorated in blue, red, green and yellow on an off-white glaze.
Diameter 16.1cm, height 6.4cm
No. G.1820, purchased from T. Charbonnier, 1921
Probably Bristol *c.* 1710

10.7 **Plate** 'A R' either side of a head and shoulders portrait of Queen Anne, uncrowned, surrounded by a broad blue band and three circles. The decoration in blue, red and green on a pale bluish glaze.
Diameter 22.4cm, height 2.9cm, shape B
No. N.6473, J. Stone Hodges bequest, 1961, ex Maddicks collection
Probably Bristol *c.* 1705

10.8 **Plate** 'A R' either side of a head and shoulders portrait of Queen Anne, crowned, between two curtains. Rim border of arcs and crescents. Decorated in blue, red and yellow on a pale bluish glaze, which is pitted.
Diameter 20.8cm, height 2.4cm, shape D
No. G.2029, purchased from T. Charbonnier, 1923
Probably Bristol *c.* 1705

10.9 Plate 'A R' either side of a head and shoulders portrait of Queen Anne, crowned and robed. The rim border of interlocking arcs and crescents. The decoration in blue on a white glaze.
Diameter 22.3cm, height 2.3cm, shape A
No. N.6464, J. Stone Hodges bequest, 1961
Probably London c. 1710

10.10 Plate 'A R' either side of a crown, with a rose and thistle growing together from a mound, surrounded by circles. Decorated in blue, green and yellow on a white glaze.
Diameter 22.2cm, height 2.7cm, shape A
No. N.3174, Sir Gilbert Mellor bequest, 1947
Probably Bristol 1707

This commemorates the Act of Union between England and Scotland in 1707, as does the mug no. 6.1 inscribed 'Union'.

10.11 Dish 'P G' either side of a head and shoulders portrait of Prince George, in ermine robes between two curtains. The rim border of twelve floral motifs. Decorated in blue on a white matt glaze.
Diameter 34.8cm, height 4.9cm, shape I
No. G.2490, purchased 1929
Perhaps London c. 1705

Queen Anne married Prince George of Denmark in 1683, and on her accession he was created generalissimo and Lord High Admiral. He died in 1708.

10.12 Bowl In the centre 'D M' either side of a head and shoulders portrait of the Duke of Marlborough, surrounded by six panels divided by columns, each containing a flower with leaves and curlicues. The rim with thirty-four crimps each marked with a stiff leaf. Decorated in blue, red, green and yellow on an off-white glaze. Outside the bowl, noughts and crosses under-rim marking.
Diameter 29.0cm, height 8.9cm
No.N.3248, Sir Gilbert Mellor bequest, 1947
Probably Bristol c. 1720

Compare Hall Warren collection no. 23, which is a plate of George I, utilizing roughly the same portrait, as also does Glaisher collection no. 1663.

10.13 **Plate** 'G R' either side of a crown, with a rose and a thistle rising from level ground below. All in blue on a white glaze.
Diameter 23.0cm, height 2.9cm, shape A
No. N.6508, J. Stone Hodges bequest, 1961
Probably London *c.* 1720

Compare Glaisher collection no. 1464 and Morgan collection no. 52, which is a similar plate in polychrome. Sherds matching this polychrome plate have recently been found by the Southwark and Lambeth Archaeological Society at the site of the Vauxhall Pottery.

10.14 **Small plate** A crown in the centre above 'G R', surrounded by a border of stiff leaf pattern emphasizing the twenty flutes in the edge. Decorated in blue on a thin pale bluish glaze.
Diameter 7.7cm, height 1.5cm
No. G.2143, gift of L. Gautier, 1924
Perhaps Bristol *c.* 1715

10.15 **Plate** 'P C' either side of a half length portrait of Princess Caroline, crowned, and with a rim decoration of interlocking arcs. The decoration in blue on an off-white glaze.
Diameter 21.7cm, height 3.1cm, shape A
No. N.6484, J. Stone Hodges bequest, 1961
Probably Bristol *c.* 1705

It was Princess Caroline of Anspach, who in 1705 married Prince George of Hanover, later to become George II. This plate is thought likely to have commemorated her marriage. The next plate, presumed to commemorate the coronation in 1727, suggests that she had put on a bit of weight in the meantime!

10.16 **Plate** 'C R' either side of a head and shoulders portrait of Queen Caroline, wife of George II, crowned and robed. The decoration in blue, red and yellow on a crazed white glaze.
Diameter 22.0cm, height 2.9cm, shape A
No. N.6503, J. Stone Hodges bequest, 1961
Probably Bristol *c.* 1727

10.17 Bowl Inside, 'Long live/King George/the 3d' inside a narrow zig-zag band, with a rim border of floral motifs. Outside, Chinese fences, large peonies, rocks and leaves. The decoration in blue on a clear pale blue glaze. The edge yellow.
Diameter 19.7cm, height 8.7cm
No. N.6782A, J. Stone Hodges bequest, 1961
Probably London *c.* 1770

10.18 Plate 'K P' either side of a head and shoulders portrait of the King of Prussia. Decorated in blue on a pale bluish glaze.
Diameter 20.0cm, height 2.8, shape E
No. G.2917, purchased 1931
Perhaps Bristol *c.* 1760

This commemorates the alliance of England with Frederick the Great, King of Prussia, during the Seven Years' War of 1756 to 1763. This is the actual plate illustrated in Mundy, pl. XXX.

10.19 Bowl 'WILKES, AND, LIBERTY, No 45' encircling a portrait of John Wilkes, surrounded by four sprays of flowers. On the outside, a bold design of spreading chrysanthemums. Decorated in blue on an off-white glaze.
Diameter 29.5cm, height 10.8cm
No. G.1147, purchased 1918
Perhaps London *c.* 1765

The publication of a satire on the speech from the throne in no. 45 of *The North Briton* in 1763, led to the arrest of John Wilkes, then Member of Parliament for Aylesbury. The print from which this portrait was copied may be found in the British Museum, and is the only print which shows the correct profile as well as the silken bag for the hair at the back of the neck.

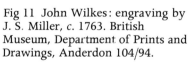

Fig 11 John Wilkes: engraving by J. S. Miller, *c.* 1763. British Museum, Department of Prints and Drawings, Anderdon 104/94.

The engraver J. S. Müller (see fig 17) anglicized his name to J. S. Miller after settling in England in 1744.

10.20 **Plate** 'I W' either side of a head and shoulders portrait of
John Wilkes. Outside the surrounding circle are 'Esq.' at the top
and '45' at the bottom. Decorated in blue on a pale bluish glaze.
Diameter 22.3cm, height 2.6cm, shape A
No. N.6475, J. Stone Hodges bequest, 1961
Probably Bristol *c.* 1765

See the remarks on the previous entry.

10.21 **Plate** 'ADMIRAL KEPPEL FOR EVER' below a head and
shoulders portrait of the Admiral surrounded by a scroll and shell
border. Round the rim a narrow band of trellis and debased
Chinese symbols. Decorated in blue and manganese on a pale blue
glaze, the edge painted brown.
Diameter 23.3cm, height 2.6cm, shape F
No. N.6490, J. Stone Hodges bequest, 1961
Probably Bristol *c.* 1780

This refers to the First Viscount Keppel who became Commander in
Chief of the British Grand Fleet in 1778 and First Lord of the
Admiralty in 1782. A copy of the print from which this portrait is
taken may be found in the British Museum.

Fig 12 Admiral Keppel:
engraving published 1779.
British Museum, Department of
Prints and Drawings
no. 53.1.12.1873.

10.22 **Dish** 'ADMIRAL KEPPEL FOR EVER' on the bottom rim;
in the centre a head and shoulders portrait of the Admiral,
surrounded by a leafy border, and with decoration in similar style
on the rim. The decoration in shades of blue on a pale blue-grey
glaze, the edge brown.
Diameter 31.2cm, height 4.1cm, shape G
No. G.2232, purchased from T. Charbonnier, 1925
Probably London *c.* 1780

10.23 Bowl 'Southwell For/Ever/1739' inside the bowl, and on the outside six shaped panels divided by columns with scroll decoration enclosing floral motifs with rhomboidal leaves. The decoration in blue, red, green and yellow on an off-white glaze. Within the footrim P/3.
Diameter 29.2cm, height 15.3cm
No. N.8194, purchased 1972
Probably Bristol 1739

This is the first of several electioneering pieces in the collection, and is in fact the earliest such article known. Edward Southwell was first elected as M.P. for Bristol in 1739 on the death of one of the sitting members. A privateer was named after him in 1744, he retired from parliament in 1776, when he was created Lord Clifford, and there is a memorial to him in Henbury church, Bristol. For yet another piece which may be connected with an election, see no. 6.20.

10.24 Bowl 'Success to/Geo: Fox: Lane/Esq.ʳ' within the bowl, surrounded by a narrow border, and with another border within the rim. On the outside a Chinese fence and rocks with chrysanthemums and other flowers. The decoration in blue on a pale bluish glaze.
Diameter 22.4cm, height 9.3cm
No. G.2060, purchased from T. Charbonnier, 1923
Probably Bristol 1754

George Fox was elected as member for York City in 1742 in an uncontested election on the death of a sitting member. He was re-elected in 1747, and during his second term took the name Lane. As George Fox Lane he was re-elected in 1754 and sat in the House of Commons until 1758. He was created Baron Bingley in 1762. As the only election in his full name took place in 1754, it is assumed that this bowl was made for that occasion.

10.25 Plate (centre only) Inscribed 'NUGENT./.ONLY./.1754.' on what appears to have been a plate with powdered ground with central woolsack reserve. The ground powdered manganese, and the lettering in blue on a pale bluish glaze.
No. G.1699, purchased 1921
Probably Bristol 1754

Compare Hall Warren collection no. 30, which is of similar type. See also Owen, p. 336, who comments on this plate, saying 'a novel mode of canvassing was adopted. Delftware plates bearing the inscription 'Nugent Only 1754' were made and distributed.' However, the Southwell bowl antedates these plates by fifteen years, though the bowls may not have been made in any numbers for handing out to prospective voters. See also the comments in Ray, *English Delftware Pottery*, pp. 127–8.

Robert Nugent was an Irishman with a talent for marrying rich widows so marked that Horace Walpole invented the word 'nugentise' for this practice. Nugent sat for St Mawes, Cornwall, from 1741 to 1754, and was re-elected at the general election that year, but preferred to sit for the City of Bristol. He had become controller of the Prince of Wales' household in 1747, in return for which George III saw that he obtained influential positions, pensions and peerages.

10.26 **Plate** Inscribed 'ER/1681' within a central wreath. The rim decorated with naturalistic bunches of flowers and butterflies. The decoration in blue on an off-white glaze.
Diameter 21.3cm, height 2.4cm, shape E
No. N.7977, found in store, and accessioned 1970
Probably Bristol (Brislington) 1681

One cannot help being reminded by the rim decoration of the King William charger no. 3.41, and of other Brislington pieces in Michael Archer's *Connoisseur* article in 1969. Unfortunately there is no obvious solution as to the identity of 'ER'. Garner and Archer, in pl. 47A, suggests a Lambeth attribution.

10.27 **Bowl and Cover** Outside, the arms of the Worshipful Company of Carpenters in mantling, with the intitials 'IT' at the top corners, the date '1709' below and 'HON/OUR/GOD' inscribed on a ribbon. The arms are in blue, with six polychrome floral panels round the bowl, half of flowers in vases, and half of sprays of flowers painted upside-down. The cover similarly decorated with the arms and seven panels, with serrations round the top, within which is a border of embellished cloud scrolls. The knob was surmounted by a crown(?) which is broken. Inside the bowl a man with a sack on his back walks along a road bordered with bushes and a tree with sponged foliage. The decoration in blue, red, green and yellow on an off-white glaze.
Diameter 25.1cm, height to rim of bowl 19.8cm
No. G.3170, purchased ex Revelstoke collection, 1934
Bristol 1709 COLOUR PLATE, p. 31

The arms of the Carpenters' Company are *Argent a chevron engrailed between three pairs of compasses sable*.

Pountney discusses this bowl on pp. 80–81 and 169–170, and also illustrates it twice, in his frontispiece in colour and at pl. XIII. He suggests that 'I T' stands for Isaac Territt, who was a Master of the London Coachmakers and Harnessmakers Company in 1707 and again in 1713. Unfortunately their records were lost in the war, but their Masters are listed in their published history, and the only other evidence surviving is a microfilm of apprentices made in 1936, in which Territt's names does not appear.

The London Carpenters' Company records are complete in the Guildhall Library. Isaac Territt was not an apprentice, nor a freeman, nor a liveryman, nor did he ever pay quarterage. There was nobody in the livery with the initials 'IT' or 'JT' over the relevant years. Isaac Territt's will is in the Public Record Office, and shows that he had properties in Ilkeston, Derbyshire; The Hyde, Hendon; Putney; Golden Square, and a house and business in the Haymarket. The will discloses no Bristol connection, and Territt is not a name that occurs in that locality.

Why then should a Carpenters' Arms bowl have been made in Bristol, as it certainly was, for a London Coachmaker with no connection with Bristol or with the Carpenters' Company?

Now Latimer's *Annals of Bristol in the Seventeenth Century* (Bristol, 1900) mentions the existence of a Carpenters' Company there in 1667, and there exist in the Bristol Record Office two ordinances of 1693 and 1729 between the City Commissioners and the Carpenters. These latter contain many names, but none with the initials 'IT' or 'JT'. However, the Burgesses records between 1650 and 1709 disclose the following carpenter candidates:

 1660 John Tucker, son of James Tucker, Cooper.
 1699 Jonathan Tucker, appt to his father John Tucker, Carpenter.

1707 Joseph Taylor, son of Nicholas Taylor, House Carpenter.
1708 John Tucker jnr, son of John Tucker, Carpenter.

John Tucker senior must have been just about seventy years old in 1709. He lived and worked in premises in Whitsun Court, and was an elder of the Church of Christ, which met in an upstairs room of Whitsun Court. He died in 1722, and in his will, preserved in the Bristol Record Office, left his working tools equally between Jonathan and John, and the premises and other bequests to them and a third son, Thomas. John Tucker senior could well have been Master of the Bristol Carpenters' Company in 1709, and he could have retired from active business in that year. He might then have been presented with this bowl, or alternatively he might have given it to them.

Joseph Taylor was the youngest of three brothers, the others William and Nicholas junior, who were all apprenticed to their father as House Carpenters, and became Burgesses in 1691, 1698 and 1707 respectively. Why the third of three sons might have had such a notable gift as this bowl is not immediately obvious. However, *The Inhabitants of Bristol in 1696*, published by the Bristol Record Society (vol. XXV 1968), shows 'Nicholas Tayler & Mary wf John Joseph Nicholas & Sarah ch' in St Thomas Street, Redcliff, which means that they were within a couple of hundred yards of the Redcliff Pottery. This entry suggests that John was the eldest son, whereas it was William who became a Burgess in 1691.

Now, there was a Thomas Taylor who was apprenticed to Thomas Frank of Redcliff as a potter in 1708 – the first of a family which was to provide the Bristol delftware industry with no fewer than nine potters over the next thirty years – and it is possible that these Taylor families were related to one another, and that the young apprentice potter was able to get the bowl made to mark some special occasion in Joseph Taylor's life.

But we can take matters no further than this, and must leave it that a more likely attribution for the initials 'IT' on this fine bowl is either John Tucker senior, or Joseph Taylor, of the Bristol Carpenters' Company.

10.28 **Bowl** Inside, the arms of the Worshipful Company of Coopers with the motto 'Love As Brethren' below and the initials 'R^{D}M' with a heart under the centre initial. Two spotted horses as supporters, and a crest of a bird holding a flower in its beak. The border within the rim of many English flowers. The inside decoration in blue, manganese and yellow on a pale greenish-bluish glaze. Outside decoration in blue only of a continuous scene of a cooper making barrels against a landscape with sponged-foliage trees and ships at sea. Within the footrim 'Augt 22 1763'. Diameter 26.5cm, height 11.0cm
No. N.3753, purchased 1949
Probably London 1763

The arms of the Coopers' Company are *Gyronny of eight gules and sable, on a chevron between three annulets or a royne between two broad axes azure, a chief vert thereon three lilies argent.* The royne is an instrument specific to the cooper's trade.

The crest is *On a wreath or and azure a demi-heathcock the body azure semee of annulets gold the wings argent semee of annulets sable holding in the beak a lily silver slipped and leaved vert, the mantling azure doubled argent.* The supporters should be *On either side a camel gules semee of annulets bridled or.* Apart, then, from a few inaccuracies there is little doubt that these are intended as the Coopers' arms.

A Richard Day junior, son of Richard Day who was Master of the Coopers' Company in 1769, himself became a freeman of the Coopers' Company on 2 March 1762, and took on four apprentices between that date and 1787. He worked at Brooks Wharf, Upper Thames Street, and lived in Garlick Hill, where the Coopers' Company owned property, on the north bank of the Thames.

He was married at the age of twenty-one, on 28 July 1762 in St Saviour's Church (Southwark Cathedral), on the south bank of the river, to Mary Hitchman, a spinster aged nineteen, Robert Hitchman, pewterer, of St Saviour's, her natural father, consenting. Richard Day senior and Robert Hitchman signed the register. The latter was then Deputy Master of the Pewterers' Company, but died in 1763.

Garner and Archer, p. 47, state that the Montagu Close delftware pottery, adjacent to the walls of Southwark Cathedral, was run by Richard Day and Son in 1754 and 1755, and that they then moved to Joiners' Hall, Upper Thames Street, where they were listed as merchants. Richard Day junior is described as 'Merchant' in the Surrey Marriage Licence allegation.

Richard Day junior, and his wife Mary, had four children between June 1763 and May 1766, all baptized in St James' Garlickhythe. Only two survived infancy, their eldest son, Richard, and the youngest son Robert Hitchman Day. The date under the bowl does not therefore tally with that of the birth of a child.

It does seem probable that this bowl was associated with Richard Day, Cooper and Merchant, and that he was the 'Son' of 'Richard Day and Son' who owned Montagu Close pottery. This belief is strengthened by his marriage to a lady from St Saviour's, whose father was an eminent pewterer, in which trade many delftware potters served their apprenticeships, and by the fact that Richard Day lived in the same Upper Thames Street area as Joiners' Hall.

However, the significance of the date under the bowl remains a mystery. The fact that the date is within the footrim and not adjacent to the initials within the bowl, may suggest that it was a date of more significance to the potter than to Richard Day. Montagu Close is believed to have closed down soon after 1762; is it possible that this bowl was one of the articles in the final firing of the kiln?

10.29 Plate Inscribed on the back 'Rosco Bristol'. On the front a coat of arms surmounted by a helm, and a crest of an embowed arm holding a rose. The dexter side of the coat of arms appears to be *Or three roses gules*, and the sinister side *Ermine three cat-a-mountain passant regardant*. On the rim are three groups of peonies with leaves and grasses. The decoration in blue on a pale bluish glaze. The edge madder brown.
Diameter 23.4cm, height 2.2cm, shape F with a footrim
No. N.8806, purchased at Christie's sale London, 2 June 1975, lot 272
Probably Liverpool *c.* 1765

This plate presents us with a few problems. It bears all the evidence of a Liverpool provenance – glaze, colour of blue pigment, and decoration on the rim – moreover there were several Rosco potters in Liverpool. Yet we find the word 'Bristol' on the back.

Turning to the coat of arms, it should represent a marriage, with the husband's arms on the dexter side, and the wife's arms on the sinister side. It has taken a diligent search to discover in a book on the Rosco family privately printed by F. W. Dunston in 1946, 'Sir Isaac Heard made a search for our family, but found no trace of us, except a branch of Roscoe related to Sir Willoughby de Broke. On calling to see Sir Isaac Heard . . in the Herald's Office . . I found a claim for the arms of Roscoe about the year 1760: *Or, three roses gules.*'

Thus it would seem that we are justified in attributing the dexter side of the shield to Rosco. The sinister side appears likely to be the arms of Adams; and it happens that there are no fewer than four known Chinese porcelain services bearing these arms, and attributed to dates between 1745 and 1780. They are illustrated by David Howard in his *Chinese Armorial Porcelain* (London 1974). If the Adams family was accustomed to have china decorated with their arms, what more natural than that when one of them marries into a delftware potter's family, we should find a delftware plate bearing the joint arms?

We cannot discover the marriage to which this plate must refer. We can only assume that perhaps it occurred in the Bristol area, thus explaining 'Bristol' on the back. There were, however, a Thomas and Agnes Roscow who had children baptized at St Mary's Roman Catholic Church in Liverpool in 1767 and 1772, but whose marriage we have been unable to trace.

10.30 Bowl Inside, a hen with a chicken on its back and eleven others, surrounded by an acanthus leaf scroll extending round the bowl and including the inscription 'W^{B}M/1759'. Outside, a country scene with a church and parents leading twelve children in pairs, walking in procession; the trees with sponged foliage. The decoration in blue on a pale blue glaze.
Diameter 38.7cm, height 16.3cm
No. G.2155, gift of Mr and Mrs Hall Warren, 1924
Probably Bristol 1759   COLOUR PLATE, p. 32

The scene of the hen and chickens inside the bowl is copied from a print by Francis Barlow (1626–1702), which we show in fig. 13. His engravings were so popular that sets were still being offered for sale in Sayer and Bennett's catalogue of prints issued in 1775. The hen and chickens print is marked no. 43 in a series of sixty-seven plates illustrating birds and beasts 'in a neat folio volume'. The scene on the outside appears to depict no recognizable church, and the family of twelve in procession may be a reflection of the size of the hen's brood inside the bowl.

But the most notable thing about this bowl is that in 1972 a copy of it, made in China, passed through the hands of a London dealer, and this is believed to be the only authenticated instance of any

English delftware article having been copied in China. That bowl was bought by an American who wishes to remain anonymous.

It is true that Hugh Owen, p. xiii, stated 'The officers of the East India Company's ships were accustomed to take out English delft bowls and get them reproduced in common porcelain, in China, for their merchant friends; and many a relic now prized as of home manufacture, was produced in this manner'. But it is unfortunate that he does not quote us an example.

The Chinese bowl has been variously stated to be of 38.7cm and 40.0cm diameter. It was said to be decorated in blue *over* the glaze, and to have the interior scene picked out in other colours. And in addition to conforming otherwise with the description of the delftware original, it was inscribed within the footrim 'F ROYLE'.

Now, apparently the owner of this bowl, who sold it to a country dealer before it reached London, also had a second one, identical in all respects, except that it was marked within the footrim 'GOD ALMING'. The Chinese potters copying these words could hardly have been expected to know that Godalming is a small town in Surrey, and that there is a village called Froyle in Hampshire, fourteen miles away.

But we inquired of the vicars of these two places for a marriage in 1759 to match the initials in the bowl, and the vicar of Froyle kindly obliged with that of William Bliset to Mary Whiteland on 25 July 1759. But, alas, the pair signed the register with a cross, which makes it unlikely that they could have ordered such a bowl to be made in the first place, let alone have arranged for it to be copied in China.

So it occurred to us that they might have been valued servants of the Lord of the Manor, and that he might have had the bowl made through some Bristol connection as a wedding present. Following up this theory, we found that the Lord of the Manor was then William Draper, and we also found that there was a Draper family in Bristol, headed by Ingleby Draper, a customs officer. We then discovered in the India Office Library that there was a William Henry Draper, who entered the East India Company in 1714, was supra-cargo on a ship to Canton in 1738, and was then resident supra-cargo there until 1745. Although William Henry retired from the East India Company in 1746, his son Daniel followed him, joining in 1748, and serving almost continually in Bombay until 1782, by which time he was a senior member of the Council there. Daniel Draper married a lady of East Indian birth, who is best know to us as the 'Eliza' of Laurence Sterne's *Letters of Yorick to Eliza* (1775). In any case this branch of the family would have enjoyed the privilege of ordering private commissions to be undertaken for them at any of the Company's overseas factories.

Now, William Henry Draper was a brother of Ingleby Draper, and they were descendants of William Draper of Nether Worton, Oxfordshire. William Draper of Froyle was directly descended from William Draper of Crayford, Kent, who in his will speaks of William Draper of Nether Worton as 'my cozen'. So the family relationship is established. Thus there is good reason to suppose that Ingleby Draper had the original bowl made in Bristol, for William Draper of Froyle to give to the bridal pair, and that the William Henry Draper family then sent out to China to get copies made there.

As for the Froyle and Godalming markings, it seems probable that they refer to the families of the bride and groom. There was a Whiteland family in a village six miles south of Froyle, whence the bride could have come; while there were several Blissets at Horsell, near Woking, ten miles north of Godalming, whence the groom could have come.

The bowl is illustrated in Garner and Archer pls. 76 and 77, and also in the Bristol Art Gallery booklet on *Delftware*, and one of the Chinese copies is illustrated in fig. 14.

Fig 13 'Hens and chickens': engraving by Francis Barlow published *c.* 1658. British Library no. 433.b.13

Fig 14 Chinese porcelain bowl dated 1759 and decorated with the same subjects as those on the English delftware bowl in the Bristol collection no. 10.30.

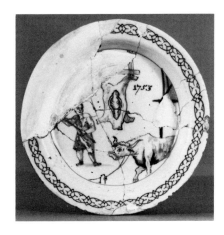

10.31 Plate Decorated with a scene in an abattoir of a butcher wielding an axe, while a carcass hangs beyond, marked '1753'. The rim border of interlocking ovals and lozenges. Damaged during the war and repaired. The decoration in blue on a glossy white glaze.
Diameter 22.8cm height 3.0cm, shape A
No. G.1998, purchased from T. Charbonnier, 1923
Probably London 1753

This plate, like the bowl no. 77 in the Hall Warren collection, and a plate at Rous Lench, was marked with the initials 'S ^H E' as well as the date before it was damaged. All these must refer to Samuel Hall, butcher, who married Elizabeth Audsley on 14 October 1750, at St Luke's, Old Street, London. Samuel was son of Nathaniel Hall, a butcher of Newgate Market, who himself married the daughter of a butcher. Samuel became a Freeman of the Worshipful Company of Butchers by patrimony on 5 April 1753, and the delftware was no doubt made to celebrate that occasion. He became a Liveryman in 1762, and took on six apprentices between that year and 1780.

10.32 Plate A lady and gentleman in eighteenth-century costume perhaps singing a duet together. The rim border of ten acanthus leaves. On the back, in large figures '1764'. Decorated in blue, manganese and yellow, on a pale greenish-blue glaze. The whorls of the acanthus leaves have a spot of yellow on them, which has largely worn off.
Diameter 23.1cm, height 2.7cm, shape A
No. N.3200, Sir Gilbert Mellor bequest, 1947
Perhaps London 1764

A plate similar to this was exhibited in London at the Festival of Britain in 1951, and illustrated on a coloured postcard issued by the Greater London Council, inscribed 'Plate of Lambeth delftware dated 1764 with the figures of Polly Peachum and Macheath from the *Beggars' Opera*. By kind permission of Colonel S. Rogers.' That plate is now in the possession of Colonial Williamsburg, no. 1958–276.

The figures are dressed similarly to those of Polly and Macheath in a print by J. McArdell after a painting by R. Pine published in 1752, though they are in a different pose. We have been unable to find an engraving to tally with the figures on the plate.

The glaze on the plate and the colours of its decoration are consonant with a London origin, and one might therefore suppose that it was produced by a London factory to commemorate some event, such as the performance of the *Beggars' Opera*, at a nearby south bank theatre. But there was no such event that we can discover. The shape of the plate is interesting, in that it was more fashionable fifty years earlier; however this would be of no practical consequence if the plate was purely for display purposes.

Now, if we turn to Bristol, we immediately note that the foundation stone of the Theatre Royal was laid on 30 November 1764, and that it was founded by a subscription list opened in May that year, of some fifty persons, each of whom subscribed fifty pounds. What more likely than that each subscriber was presented with a plate to commemorate his patronage?

Pountney, on p. 153, states that Joseph Flower and Michael Edkins were great friends and brother artists, both in music, ceramics and painting. Edkins is known to have joined with theatre companies from London in their Bristol productions at the Jacobs Wells Theatre in the 1750s, which included several performances of the *Beggars' Opera*. Moreover, Owen, on p. 332, quotes Michael Edkins' son as saying 'William Powell introduced Edkins to the stage in Bristol and Covent Garden. He would probably have settled in the latter place, but for a dispute between Powell and other proprietors; but he quitted the theatre in disgust and returned to his business in Bristol.'

Thus it appears that Edkins spent some time in London at just about the time when the Theatre Royal project in Bristol was germinating. It would be only natural that, while there, he should have had contacts with the London delftware potters, and this might explain the production of the *Beggars' Opera* plates on out of date moulds from a London factory. On his return to Bristol, Edkins took on responsibility for the interior decoration of the Theatre Royal, and his account books, now in the Central Reference Library, indicate that he worked from this time onwards very much as a freelance.

In sum, we believe that this plate was made to commemorate the foundation of the Theatre Royal, Bristol, that it does probably represent Polly Peachum and Macheath, and that it could well have been made at a London pottery. But it must be emphasized that this belief rests entirely on circumstantial evidence.

10.33 **Plate** A three-storey Chinese house with trellis walls, among trees, one of which arches over. Two flying insects. Inscribed 'L ^{E} M/1733'. The rim border of trellis and floral motifs. Decorated in blue on an off-white glaze.
Diameter 21.6cm, height 3.2cm, shape F
No. G.1959, purchased from T. Charbonnier, 1923
Bristol 1733, by Joseph Taylor of Redcliff Pottery

Bristol Marriage Bonds show that Lot Evans, bachelor of the parish of St Mary Redcliff, shipwright, married Mary Bayly, spinster of the same parish on 18 August 1733. The bondsman was Joseph Taylor, potter, of St Mary Redcliff. The records show that Joseph Taylor was apprenticed to Thomas Frank, of the Redcliff Pottery, in 1714, and became free in 1721. On 9 August 1756, John, son of Lot Evans, late of Bristol, shipwright, was in his turn apprenticed to Joseph Taylor. With all this evidence, this is one of the very few cases where we feel justified in attributing, not only to a factory, but to a specific workman. The plate itself is alas of no great merit. Compare Hall Warren collection no. 149 which appears to be a duplicate.

10.34 **Plate** Decorated with a lamb, marked below 'Jos. Hosken Esqr/Carines/1771', and with a border of four shaped panels of trellis diaper and four flowers suspended on swags. Decorated in blue on a pronounced blue glaze.
Diameter 22.8cm, height 2.8cm, shape F
No. G.2114, gift of Alderman J. F. Eberle, 1923
Probably Bristol 1771

Carines is a house in Cornwall, a few miles south of Newquay in the parish of St Cuthbert, in land no doubt suitable for sheep farming. The Hosken family were reported in 1870 to be the wealthiest farmers in those parts, and to have occupied the nearby Ellenglaze House for four generations. Joseph Hosken was born in 1698 and was living at Carines up to his death in 1780, when the estate passed to a cousin. He would have been seventy-three years old in 1771, and one knows of no special event which this plate might have been intended to commemorate. Perhaps a member of the family, or a friend, visiting Bristol, arranged to have the plate made.

10.35 Plate Decorated with a coat of arms of the Worshipful Company of Pewterers, on a shield held by two sea horses, with crest and motto. The rim border of a running vine with hatched leaves. The decoration in blue on a pale bluish glaze. On the back the inscription 'B ^{T} M' 1750'.
Diameter 22.6cm, height 2.5cm, shape F
No. G.172, purchased 1914
Probably London 1750

The arms of the Pewterers' Company are *Azure on a chevron or between three strykes argent, as many roses gules, stalked, budded and leaved vert*. The crest *On a wreath of the colour a mount vert, thereon two arms embowed vested argent, holding in both hands erect proper a pewter dish argent*. The supporters *On either side a sea horse or with tail proper*. And the motto *'Tota Me Fiducia Est In Deo'*.

A Benjamin Townsend was bound to William Hitchins as apprentice pewterer in 1736, and became free in 1744. He married Margaret Field at St Mary Aldermary on 23 December 1750, both being of the parish of St Thomas Apostle. Both these parishes were on the north bank of the Thames, across from the Southwark delftware factories, most easily accessible by ferry before Southwark Bridge was built. There was an association between delftware and pewterers, because potters were often apprenticed in the Pewterers' Company. One presumes that this plate was made to commemorate Benjamin Townsend's marriage. A duplicate of this plate is in the Hall Warren collection, no. 39.

10.36 Covered Bowl The outside of the bowl decorated with six panels each containing fruit and stylized leaves among quadruple dots and multi-point stars; the cover with an all-over decoration of the same nature, and surmounted by two handles (one broken) of twisted serpents with diminishing curls attaching to the lid. The lid carries a sampling cup in place of the centre knob, the foot of the bowl with a border of Chinese *ruyi* heads and the base with a stiff leaf border. Inside the bowl the silhouette of a man carrying a branch, and the inscription 'I ^{S} E' 1711'.
Diameter 26.8cm, height to rim 21.2cm
No. G.139, gift of A. M. Hale, 1914
Probably Bristol 1711

This is illustrated by Pountney in its undamaged condition in pl. XV, and discussed on p. 35. It may refer to the marriage of John Stokes of Sutton, butcher, and Elizabeth Pool of East Harptree, at Chew Magna church on 15 December 1711. All these places are between five and ten miles south of Bristol. The marriage was authorized by a Bath and Wells Marriage Bond.

The picture within the bowl is, at first sight, baffling, until one is reminded that the arms of the Butchers' Company include *two bunches of holly vert*. This is not true holly, but knee-holly or butcher's broom, which Philip Miller, in *The Gardeners Dictionary* of 1733, says 'is very common in the Woods in divers Parts of England . . . the green Shoots are cut and bound into Bundles, and sold to the Butchers, who use it as Besoms to sweep their Blocks'. Surely, then, the picture is of Mr Stokes with his butcher's broom?

10.37 **Plate** A spray of flowers and two insects, encircling the initials and date 'T W S/1736', and surrounded by a narrow chequered band. The rim border of five floral motifs with rhomboidal leaves. The decoration in blue on a pale bluish glaze.
Diameter 22.0cm, height 3.0cm, shape G
No. G.1999. purchased from T. Charbonnier, 1923
Probably London 1736

Thomas West, widower, fifty-five, and Sarah Turner, spinster, thirty, both of St James' Piccadilly, obtained a Bishop of London Licence on 10 July 1736 to get married in St James' Church. There is, however, no record of their marriage in the church register. It does seem probable that they were married, for the register of baptisms of St Leonard's Shoreditch shows the birth of a daughter Sarah to Thomas and Sarah West on 21 April 1739, and her baptism on 27 April. Their residence is given as Cold Harbour, which was a sizeable house with a garden up the Hackney Road, in what must then have been pleasant country fields.

10.38 **Plate** Inscribed 'R H A/1728' in the centre encircled by two bands of lozenges and one of blue and white squares. The rim border of eight cactus motifs and eight twin rhomboidal leaf motifs. On the back the letter 'A' within footrim. Decorated in blue on a pale bluish glaze.
Diameter 20.7cm, height 2.8cm, shape C
No. N.6436, J. Stone Hodges bequest, 1961
Probably Bristol 1728

This is thought to refer to the marriage of Robert Hart to Ann Mason, which was authorized by a Bristol Marriage Bond dated 26 March 1729. In those days the last day of 1728 would have been 24 March, the New Year commmencing on Lady Day. The plate would have had to be ordered a little time in advance, when the precise date of the marriage might not have been known. The Bondsman was Joseph Gould, Vintner, and the bond for the unusually large sum of £1000. The parties were both of St Werburgh's parish, but there is no record of the event in the parish registers.

10.39 **Plate** Inscribed 'ANN; GOMM/1793' in the centre of an octagonal spider's web, embellished with flower buds. The rim border with four fragments of spider's webs and four sprays with triple buds. The decoration in blue, manganese, red, green and yellow on a pale blue-green glaze.
Diameter 22.9cm, height 2.8cm, shape F
No. G.2000, purchased from T. Charbonnier, 1923
Probably London 1793

Sherds of this pattern are illustrated in Garner's article 'Lambeth Earthenware', *English Ceramic Circle Transactions* 1937, pl. XIV(C). Gomm was not a common name. An Ann Gomm did however marry a Robert Jones in St Marylebone Church on 31 March 1797, where they are stated to be both of this parish. A search of the rate books for the parish for the period does not show anyone of either name paying rates in the parish.

   This is a fairly common pattern, which has come to be known as the Ann Gomm pattern, although, as we see from the next entry, other names appeared on them. The earliest known dated example is one decorated in blue only, inscribed 'R G A 1749' and sold in the second Garner Sale at Sotheby's on 2 March 1965, lot 57. It will be seen, therefore, that this pattern survived for at least forty-four years; for a pattern that does not strike one as very attractive, such a long life is surprising.

10.40 Plate   Inscribed in the centre 'JOHN, SARAH/BOWLES/ 1792' in the centre of an octagonal spider's web, embellished with buds. The rim border of four part-spider's webs and four sprays with triple buds. Decorated in blue, manganese, red, green and yellow on a pale bluish-greenish glaze.
Diameter 23.0cm, height 3.0cm, shape F
No. N.8456, found in store, and accessioned 1974
Probably London 1792

The registers of St Giles Cripplegate show that 'John Bowles of this parish, bachelor, and Sarah Jupe of ye parish of St Luke's spinster, were married in this church by licence this 18th day of September 1759, by me E. Warneford curate. This marriage was solemnised between us (signed) John Bowles, Sarah Jupe, in the presence of Thos Holloway & Wm Ayscough.' The London Diocese Licence was sworn by Sarah Jupe on 17 September 1759, but contains no additional information.

A John Bowles witnessed the marriage of a Sarah Bowles, presumably his daughter, to Thomas Kimber at Rotherhithe on 8 November 1804; assuming this to be the same person, it shows that he was still alive in 1792, when the plate was obtained, but does not explain any significance of that date.

10.41 Plate   Decorated in the 'Ann Gomm' style with a rosette in the centre of the spider's web. The colours blue, manganese, red, green and yellow on a pale bluish-greenish glaze.
Diameter 22.5cm, height 2.6cm, shape F
No. N.6478, J. Stone Hodges bequest, 1961
Probably London c. 1780

10.42 Dish   Decorated in the 'Ann Gomm' style with a rosette in the centre of a decagonal spider's web, and with five repeats of the rim decoration. The decoration in blue, manganese, red, green and yellow on a pale bluish glaze.
Diameter 34.7cm, height 3.6cm, shape H
No. N.3141, Sir Gilbert Mellor bequest, 1947
Probably London c. 1790

10.43 Dish   Decorated in the 'Ann Gomm' style with a rosette in the centre of an octagonal spider's web, and five repeats of the rim pattern. The colours blue, manganese, red, green and yellow on a pale bluish glaze.
Diameter 30.2cm, height 3.6cm, shape G
No. N.6768, J. Stone Hodges bequest, 1961
Probably London c. 1790

10.44 Bowl Decorated on the outside with six part-spider's webs with sprays of triple buds between, and with stylized buds round the lower part embellished with curls. Above the foot a border of twisted cable design. Inside, in blue only, a floral spray surrounded by a circle of a leafed vine. The decoration in blue, manganese, red, green and yellow on the outside, on an off-white glaze.
Diameter 26.2cm, height 11.3cm
No. N.6798, J. Stone Hodges bequest, 1961
Probably London *c.* 1790

The outside decoration is clearly of 'Ann Gomm' style. There is a small bowl of 12cm diameter, similarly decorated, in the Victoria Art Gallery, Bath, no. 85.

10.45 Dish The central scene of Joshua standing on a rock, with a baton in his outstretched hand, wearing a breastplate and plumed helmet, and with his sword sheathed. Two enemy swordsmen creep up behind; the battle rages in the valley below. The scene encircled by a quotation from the Book of Joshua, ch. 10. v. 12, in which Joshua commands the sun and the moon to stand still. The rim decorated with four sprays of carnations on vines. The edge brown. On the back an under-rim marking of four leafy stems with flower buds. All decoration in light blue on a pale bluish glaze.
Diameter 33.9cm, height 4.5cm, shape I
No. G.3241, gift of Mrs E. M. Openshaw 'from the collection of Flower's great grand-daughter Mrs E. J. Swann', 1936
Probably Bristol *c.* 1750

Pountney illustrates this dish in pl. XXXVI and mentions it on pp. 142 and 174, attributing it to Joseph Flower. Ray illustrates it in fig. 7 of his *English Delftware Pottery*, and discusses it among other pieces attributed to Joseph Flower, casting doubt on his authorship. The design source for the biblical scene is elusive, though there are such circular engravings with circumferential inscriptions among the work of Cornelis Galle, the Dutch engraver, 1576–1656. This dish should perhaps be compared to the 'Ascension' dish in the Victoria Art Gallery, Bath, no. 78, which their catalogue attributes to Joseph Flower, and which comes from a known engraving after Martin de Vos, 1532–1603.

10.46 Plate Inscribed 'A View of y[e] Hot Well/near BRISTOL' with four large sailing ships and eight boats, and houses on the shore with hills rising behind. The edge brown. On the back the letters 'I S F' and the date '1741/2', and the noughts and crosses under-rim marking. Decorated in blue on an off-white glaze.
Diameter 22.5cm, height 2.6cm, shape G
No. N.7461, purchased 1966
Bristol 1741/2

This piece is illustrated by Ray in fig. 3 of *English Delftware Pottery*, and discussed on pp. 56–63. It is also the subject of an article by J. K. D. Cooper in the *Burlington Magazine*, August 1966.

Fig 15 'A View of the Hot Well':
engraving by J. Mynde after a
drawing by W. Halfpenny published
in 1731. British Library.

The plate is decorated with a scene taken from an engraving by J.
Mynde after a drawing by W. Halfpenny (fig. 15), which was
published by him in 1731, in *Perspective Made Easy*, 'With the
draughts of several remarkable places in and about the cities of
Bristol and Bath; in 26 copper plates'. Halfpenny was a Bristol
architect, and was responsible for the Coopers' Hall in King Street,
which was opened in 1744. The engraving of the Hot Well has
been adapted to fit the plate, and the ships have been rearranged,
while the little boat in the foreground has been added from the
print of the Capture of Chagres. There are two identical dishes of
the Capture of Chagres, taken from the print of which there is a
copy in the National Maritime Museum, Greenwich, and of which
we show a photograph in fig. 16.

The initials and date on the back of this plate almost certainly
belong to Joseph Flower and his wife Sarah, née Lamb who were
married at St James' Church, Bristol, on 29 January 1741/2. The
initials should more properly have been arranged 'J F S', but, as
Ray points out, Joseph Flower appeared to have been careless
about such matters.

Fig 16 'An exact Account of Vice
Admiral Vernon's taking the Castle &
Town of Chagre in ye West-Indies':
engraving published in 1740.
National Maritime Museum.

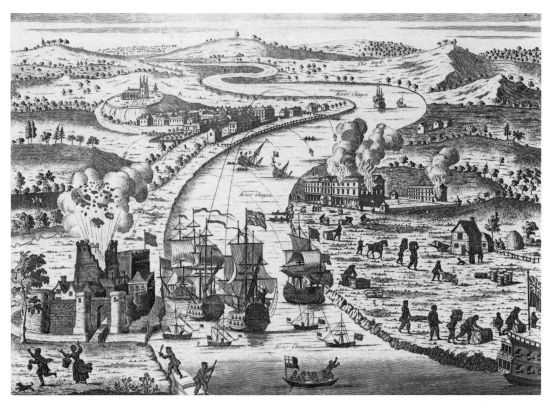

Fig 17 'A View of the Grand South Walk in Vaux Hall Gardens': engraving by J. S. Müller after Canaletto, published in 1751. British Museum, Department of Prints and Drawings Crace collection xxxv/140.

10.47 **Dish** A scene of a colonnaded garden with an avenue of trees, and a statue in a rotunda, painted from rim to rim. The decoration in blue on a pale blue glaze.
Diameter 42.3cm, height 5.9cm, shape F
No. N.3781, found in store and accessioned 1949
Probably London 1760

The scene is of Vauxhall Gardens and is taken from J. S. Müller's engraving after Canaletto, published in 1751, of which we reproduce a copy in fig. 17. The painting on the dish is an exact scale of the print, which makes it fairly certain that the print was pricked through and transferred by pouncing. The detail and the figures in the foreground have been drawn in freehand. The rotunda on the right contains the statue of Handel by Roubiliac, now in the Victoria and Albert Museum. The pleasure gardens were opened in 1732 and continued to the middle of the nineteenth century.

10.48 **Dish** Decorated from a scene of the capture of Portobello showing three ships attacking, the fort at the left, a church(?) against the hill to the right, and the town beyond. The rim with a border of leaves and berries painted from the edge inwards. The edge red-brown. The decoration in soft blue on a pale blue glaze.
Diameter 34.9cm, height 3.7cm, shape H
No. N.6745, J. Stone Hodges bequest, 1961
Probably Liverpool *c.* 1740

Compare Hall Warren collection no. 28 where it is fully discussed. Admiral Edward Vernon captured Portobello, in the Panama isthmus, in 1739 with five ships, and instantly became a national hero. Descriptions of the event refer to the fort on the left of the entry, the church on the right, and the town on the right of the inlet beyond, but no print has come to light which shows all these features in the way presented. Vernon went on to capture Chagres the following year, and his eventual return to Bristol is described by John Latimer in his *Annals of Bristol in the Eighteenth Century* (Bristol 1893) thus:

> *Admiral Vernon landed at Bristol on the sixth of January 1743 and was greeted with great acclamations in proceeding to Small Street to partake of the hospitality of the Mayor. A week later thirty chests of silver bullion, containing about 900,000 pieces-of-eight were taken out of his ship and despatched to London.*

10.49 **Dish** Similar to the previous dish, though the detail stands out better against a paler glaze.
Diameter 35.2cm, height 5.3cm, shape H
No. G.2924, purchased 1931
Probably Liverpool *c.* 1740

10.50 **Plate**   A balloon with two people in bonnet hats rowing in a boat-shaped gondola, and two houses among sponged-foliage trees below. Decorated in blue on a pale bluish glaze.
Diameter 23.1cm, height 3.0cm, shape F
No. G.2914, purchased 1931
Probably London c. 1785

See the remarks in the chapter introduction about the early balloon flights. However, the Lunardi and Blanchard flights in England all appeared to have baskets for the crew, and the boat-shaped gondola was more used by the French. This was probably copied from a popular print, by a delftware potter to whom a balloon was a balloon.

10.51 **Plate**   A balloon over a house with fence and trees with combed foliage. The rim decorated with floral swags, and with radial brush marks on the edge. The decoration in blue, manganese, green and yellow on a pale bluish-greenish glaze.
Diameter 22.8cm, height 2.9cm, shape F
No. N.6466, J. Stone Hodges bequest, 1961, ex Hall Warren collection
Probably London c. 1785

10.52 **Dish**   A balloon over a house with fence and combed-foliage trees. The rim decorated with floral swags, the edge painted blue with lighter brush marks radially inwards. The decoration in blue, manganese, green and yellow on a pale bluish glaze.
Diameter 25.9cm, height 3.5cm, shape F
No. G.128, purchased 1910
Probably London c. 1785

10.53 **Bowl**   Inside 'Succefs to The Two Sisters' over a two-masted ship, with the union flag at the bow, ensign from the stern and a pennant from the mainmast. Within the rim a border of trellis on blue-painted ground. Outside, four daisy flowers with leaves on twining stems, and a rim border of trellis and floral motifs. The decoration in blue on a clear pale blue glaze, the edge madder brown. Within footrim 'Christophar Bowen 1747'.
Diameter 26.1cm, height 11.0cm
No. G.2218, gift of T. Charbonnier, 1926
Probably Liverpool 1747

This ship does not appear in the first *Lloyd's Register* of 1764, and Lloyds Lists for 1747 only disclose a *Two Sisters* trading between Pool and London, with the master Burrell. As Pool was a source of clay, it is conceivable that this same ship made some trips to

Liverpool. The Chester Port Books in the Public Record Office, which covered the port of Liverpool, do not disclose any ship of this name visiting the port between 1747 and 1751.

10.54 Bowl Inside, 'Success to the Livley of ~/Emsworth Robart ~/Randell Master' under a ship in full sail with a red ensign at the stern, the union flag at the bow, and a pennant from the top mast. Ringlets of cloud in the sky. A rim border of trellis on a blue ground and reserves of floral motifs. Outside, a similar border and two floral vines from rocks. The decoration in blue with yellow deck lines and red in the flags, all on an off-white glaze.
Diameter 27.0cm, height 11.1cm
No. G.2115, gift of Alderman J. F. Eberle, 1923
Probably Liverpool 1747   COLOUR PLATE, p. 32

In the first *Lloyd's Register* of 1764, this ship can be identified with the following entry:

> 'LIVELY, Master W. Hicks, Trading London-Dublin, 80 tons, SDSI (=Single Deck, ? ?), M.5 (Number of crew?) Built Emsworth, First Registered 1747, Owner R. Randell, Class EM.'

The Bristol Merchant Venturers Society's anchorage and wharfage books show port dues of 1s 3d paid by the *Lively* of Emsworth on 22 August 1746, arriving from Kinsale, Ireland. This suggests she was built in 1746, but not registered until the following year. Lloyd's List for 1747 shows a *Lively* arriving in Liverpool from Cork, Ireland, on 1 June, with Doran as Master.

The Bristol Port Books in the Public Record Office show the *Lively* of Emsworth, Robert Randall Master sailing for Southampton and Portsmouth with a mixed cargo, including twenty-six crates of earthenware on 12 September 1755; and making a similar voyage with John Wright as Master, with seventeen crates of earthenware included, on 5 May 1756.

Emsworth, where the ship was built, is not far from Portsmouth. These entries show, first, that the *Lively* did use the port of Liverpool, and second, that she was accustomed to carrying earthenware among her cargo, probably implying contact with the delftware factories.

See also the next entry.

10.55 Bowl Inside, 'God Preferve the Providence/Piter Emmet Master/1751' under a two-masted ship with union flag from the bows, red ensign from the stern, and a pennant from the top mast. Clouds in the sky of triple ringlets. Within the rim, a border of trellis on a blue ground and floral motifs. Outside, a large-scale man down to his waist, pointing his right arm, with two exotic birds, foliage and a Chinese fence. The decoration in blue, with red in the flags, and a brown edge, all on a pale bluish glaze.
Diameter 26.5cm, height 11.3cm
No. G.2227, purchased from T. Charbonnier, 1925
Probably Liverpool 1751

Lloyd's Register of 1764 includes forty-six *Providences*. Of these nine were built before 1751, but none shows Peter Emmet as Master. Lloyd's List for 1751 has two entries associating a *Providence* with Liverpool; on 16 April one is recorded as having arrived in St Christophers from Liverpool, and on 22 November one is shown arriving in Liverpool from Malaga. The Masters are recorded as Taylor and Scot respectively.

The Customs Office for Liverpool was Chester, and in the Chester Port Books in the Public Record Office, a *Providence* is shown sailing for Dublin on 24 October 1751, with Henry Hughes as Master and Merchant. None of these facts provides evidence that the *Providence* referred to is that for which the bowl was made.

However, the Bristol Port Books for 16 October 1755 show the *Providence of Emsworth*, William Randall Master, sailing for Exeter, with a mixed cargo including four crates of earthenware and four crates of glassware from Chester; and the same ship on 20 April 1756, under William Randall, sailing for an undisclosed destination. These entries are interesting in that they suggest she was a sister ship to that in our previous entry, built in Emsworth, and captained by another Randall, who must surely have been related to the captain of the *Lively*. Research in fact shows that a Robert Randel of Walberton (probably a mistake for Warblington, the Emsworth parish church), Mariner, married Elizabeth Coleman in Rogate, Sussex, on 27 August 1727, and that their sons Robert and William were baptized at Warblington in 1728 and 1733. It seems probable that this was the family concerned. 'Thomas Coleman of Warblington, marriner' was one of the sureties at the wedding, so evidently both parents were of seafaring stock.

Attention should be drawn to the triple ringlets of cloud in the sky, as these may almost be said to constitute a 'signature' of the Liverpool ship bowls.

DECORATIVE STYLES

11.45 Dish

11   Chinoiserie I

In the course of the seventeenth century the manufacture of tin-glazed earthenware in Europe was undoubtedly stimulated by the realization that its white glaze and blue underglaze decoration could imitate Chinese blue-and-white porcelain, which Europeans were beginning to see and marvel at for the first time. It is not surprising, then, that English delftware potters also began to copy Chinese decorative styles. This was also the case in Holland, and though the influence was simultaneous, its effects differed between the two countries, and it is not true to say that the influence in England came to us from Holland.

The effects of this fashion for Chinese art are best described by the term *Chinoiserie*, which the *Encyclopaedia Britannica* defines as 'seventeenth and eighteenth century Western style' (including 'pottery design') 'that represents fanciful European interpretation of Chinese styles. In the first decades of the seventeenth century, English and Italian and later other craftsmen began to draw freely on decorative forms found on cabinets, porcelain vessels and embroideries imported from China. Chinoiserie, used mainly in conjunction with Baroque and Rococo styles, featured . . . much use of blue-and-white (e.g. in Delftware); asymmetrical forms; disruption of orthodox perspective; and Oriental figures and motifs.' All these characteristics can be detected in the specimens illustrated in this and the next chapters.

Probably the earliest Chinese decorative influence found in English delftware is the 'bird perched on a rock' motif, which we associate with articles produced by Christian Wilhelm's factory at Pickleherring Quay, Southwark, soon after its foundation in 1615. Examples may be found in Garner and Archer pls. 7 and 8B. We have not got any early examples in the Bristol collection, but basically the same motif is still to be found in the products of other factories well on into the eighteenth century, and such examples may be found at nos. 13.3 and 13.8.

Another Chinese decorative influence, which we find in the last quarter of the seventeenth century, is a Chinaman sitting among rocks with moss or cactus-like growths. This is often repeated several times; for instance, in the centre of a plate, and again round the rim. The Bristol collection contains a good number of examples of the style, and in this chapter we are able to illustrate some of the variations on the theme, both in details of the decoration, in the different two-colour combinations, and in the articles decorated.

Both the decorative styles we have so far mentioned come from Chinese porcelain of the Ming Dynasty, which ended in 1644, after which there was a decline in Imperial patronage from which the industry suffered for several decades. How did these styles reach England?

The English East India Company was founded by Queen Elizabeth I in 1600, and in the course of a few years had established its easternmost Presidency in Bantam, Java, where it found itself side by side with the Dutch Company. It remained in Java until the last quarter of the century, when it began to get a toehold in China. But it was not until the very last year of the century that a 'factory' had been established in Canton and that regular and direct trading took place.

There is no doubt that considerable quantities of Chinese porcelain and other goods were reaching England and causing this cultural influence, and we must assume that it mostly came via Bantam, to which Chinese traders brought their wares, before direct trading with China was permitted, although there is a probability that some came via Portugal and Holland, who were also active in this trade.

In the catalogue entries which follow, our first example which shows the Chinaman among rocks is the largest known dish in English delftware, and it is decorated round the rim with twelve panels in the Ming style, giving a wide variety of Chinamen in rocky landscapes and of cactus-like plants. The centre of this dish is a combination of several such scenes put together, though, in typical *chinoiserie* manner, with little attempt at integration or perspective.

We then show a group of seven plates, of which the first three are octagonal and the rest round. The first five of this group have basically the same decoration, but the other two, being saucer-shaped plates with no flat rim, have in each case one enlarged scene covering the whole plate. We also find that there is a variety of colour combinations, from two shades of blue, to blue and manganese, to blue and yellow, and to manganese and yellow.

The theme of the Chinaman in a rocky landscape was used without change over at least a quarter of a century, so that precise dating is difficult. Similar Chinamen appear on other shapes of articles, such as mugs, posset pots, bowls and bottles. In many such cases there is not the same variety of colour combinations, but only blue, sometimes in the normal manner of decoration, and sometimes with the outlines in manganese or dark blue, and shades of blue wash then used to fill in these outlines. Such outlining is known to the Dutch as *trek*, and was much used by them.

These designs were still influenced by the Ming Dynasty, as witness the three examples of a seated Chinaman in a landscape in nos. 11.11 to 11.13, which are very much like the decoration on a flask in the Mottahadeh collection, illustrated by David Howard and John Ayers in *China for the West* (London 1978) vol. I, no. 8, which is attributed to the late sixteenth century. A Chinaman, with slight changes, is then to be found in Chinese decoration of the Transitional period and of the Qing Dynasty, with different settings, such as fenced gardens, country landscapes, and among different Chinese versions of flowers, shrubs and trees; and also engaged in different pursuits, conversing with others, walking under a parasol, playing with birds on a string, and fishing. The full palette of colours available to the English delftware potters was also employed, together with a freehand interpretation of the subject, thus conveying a very different impression from the original Chinese inspiration.

11.1 **Dish** Across the centre, two Chinese ladies in a garden, and above and below, garden landscapes with buildings. A border round the well of eight pairs of acanthus leaves. The rim decorated with twelve panels of scenes of Chinamen, houses, gardens and cactus plants. The back marked within the footrim 'W ^H M/1703', and with noughts and crosses under-rim markings both under the curvature and under the rim. The decoration in blue with dark blue outlines, on a white glaze.
Diameter 59.6cm, height 7.9cm, shape I
No. N.3354, purchased 1936
Probably Bristol 1703   COLOUR PLATE, p. 33

This is believed to be the largest known English delftware dish, and although it is also remarkably flat there is no significant warping or cracking, which demonstrates a high degree of technical skill in its manufacture and firing. It must also be one of the most admirable examples of *chinoiserie* decoration in English delftware. One would expect that such a fine article was made for a distinguished lady and gentleman, probably to commemorate their marriage, but research has not yielded a solution.

11.2 **Plate** A Chinaman seated in a moss-covered rocky landscape, with the marking 'W ^D D/1679' and the rim decorated with a Chinaman at the bottom and top, and four other groups of similar rocks. The decoration in shades of blue on a pale bluish glaze.
Diameter 21.2cm, height 2.0cm, shape E octagonal
No. G.1866, purchased from T. Charbonnier, 1922
Probably Bristol 1679

This actual plate is illustrated in Rackham and Read pl. 109, and discussed on p. 53, where it is given a Bristol provenance. It is, however, very difficult to detect any difference between these plates, which were made in both London and Bristol.

But research shows that in Bristol, on 14 February 1679/80, a William Davis of Castle Precincts, Grocer, aged twenty-seven, married Dursabella Horne of All Saints, aged twenty-seven, at All Saints' church. The bondsman was John Horne, Bristol Mercer. It happens that an Isaac Davis appears in the apprentices' roll as taking on an apprentice in 1694, when he is described as 'educated in arte pro le Potter'. It is therefore possible that there was a family relationship here, and that Isaac made the plate to celebrate the occasion of a kinsman's marriage.

11.3 **Plate** In the centre, a Chinaman sitting in a rocky landscape. On the rim, the same Chinaman top and bottom, and four more groups of rocks. The decoration in blue and manganese on a white glaze, tinged with grey on the back.
Diameter 20.6cm, height 2.4cm, shape D octagonal
No. N.3187, Sir Gilbert Mellor bequest, 1947
Probably London *c*. 1690

11.4 **Plate** In the centre a Chinaman seated among mossy rocks, and on the rim two similar Chinamen top and bottom, and four more groups of rocks. The decoration in manganese and yellow on a white glaze.
Diameter 21.5cm, height 2.9cm, shape E
No. N.6442, J. Stone Hodges bequest 1961, ex Hall Warren collection
Probably London *c.* 1690

11.5 **Plate** In the centre a Chinaman seated among mossy rocks, and on the rim the same Chinaman top and bottom, and four more groups of rocks at the sides. Decorated in blue and pinky manganese wash on a pale bluish glaze.
Diameter 20.9cm, height 1.9cm, shape E octagonal
No. N.6494, J. Stone Hodges bequest 1961, ex Hall Warren collection
Probably London *c.* 1690

11.6 **Plate** In the centre a Chinaman seated among mossy over-hanging rocks, and on the rim the same Chinaman, with four more groups of rocks at the sides. Decorated in manganese *trek* with two shades of blue on a pale blue glaze.
Diameter 24.9cm, height 3.3cm, shape E
No. N.2242, gift of Mrs Hall Warren, 1946
Probably Bristol *c.* 1690

11.7 **Saucer Dish** A rim-to-rim scene of a Chinaman walking in a landscape of mossy rocks, some overhanging. The decoration in blue and yellow with manganese *trek*, on a white glaze with pinky tinge.
Diameter 20.0cm, height 4.1cm, shape J shallow
No. N.3186, Sir Gilbert Mellor bequest, 1947
Probably London *c.* 1690

11.8 Saucer Dish A rim-to-rim scene of two Chinamen standing among mossy and overhanging rocks. Decorated in blue and manganese on a crazed, white glaze.
Diameter 24.4/24.9cm, height 5.1cm, shape J shallow
No. N.3172, Sir Gilbert Mellor bequest, 1947
Probably London *c.* 1690

11.9 Dish In the centre a Chinaman seated in a rocky ravine among cactus-like plants, and on the rim a hunch-backed Chinaman running on either side, and seated Chinamen with flags at top and bottom. The decoration in blue on a pale blue glaze. On the back a herbal sprig under-rim marking and the figure '7' within the footrim.
Diameter 26.7cm, height 3.4cm, shape F
No. N.6496, J. Stone Hodges bequest, 1961
Probably Liverpool *c.* 1750

The same theme as on the previous plates will be recognized, but with more sophistication.

11.10 Plate In the centre a stag among shrubs and rocks, and on the rim Chinese ladies(?) sitting at top and bottom, and standing on either side in similar background. The decoration in blue on a pale blue glaze. The edge brown. Ribbon under-rim marking.
Diameter 21.8cm, height 2.2cm, shape G
No. N.3237, Sir Gilbert Mellor bequest, 1947
Probably Bristol *c.* 1750

Compare Hall Warren collection no. 154 which appears to be a duplicate.

11.11 Dish In the centre a Chinaman seated on a rocky promontory and round the rim five repeats of leaf and flower decoration. The colours blue, red, green and yellow on a pale bluish glaze.
Diameter 34.8cm, height 3.7/4.4cm, shape F
No. N.3169, Sir Gilbert Mellor bequest, 1947
Probably London *c.* 1740

11.12 **Plate**   In the centre a Chinaman seated on a rocky promontory and round the rim four repeats of leaf and flower decoration. The colours blue, red, green and yellow on a pale blue glaze.
Diameter 23.0cm, height 2.7cm, shape F
No. N.6434, J. Stone Hodges bequest, 1961, ex Mellor collection
Probably London *c.* 1750

11.13 **Plate**   In the centre a seated Chinaman in a hilly landscape with daisy flowers, surrounded by a narrow band, and on the rim four repeats of leaf and flower decoration. The colour blue on a pale blue glaze.
Diameter 19.8cm, height 3.8cm, shape F deep
No. N.3063, purchased ex Hodgkin collection, 1947
Probably London *c.* 1750

11.14 **Mug**   A Chinese garden scene with rocks and cactus, a Chinaman leaning against a rock, the sun in the sky and an inverted bird. The strap handle with chevron bands and a curled up tail. The base partly glazed. Decorated in blue on an off-white glaze.
Height 18.4cm, diameter 10.3cm
No. G.123, purchased 1908
Bristol or London *c.* 1720

11.15 **Jug**   With spherical bowl, parallel neck and no spout. Decorated with two Chinamen in a rocky landscape with fern-like trees and hanging orchids. The top border of scroll pattern. The handle of oval section, flattened inside, and blue banded. The decoration in blue on a pale bluish glaze.
Height 18.0cm, maximum diameter 13.9cm
No. N.6618, J. Stone Hodges bequest 1961, ex Maddicks collection
Probably London *c.* 1730

11.16 **Jug** With flattened spherical body on slight foot, and parallel neck with no spout. The handle of oval section with a few broad blue bands and curled up tail. Decorated with a Chinaman seated by two urns with sprouting flowers, and plants sprouting from rocks beyond. The decoration in grey-blue on a pale grey-blue glaze.
Height 10.0cm, maximum diameter 8.3cm
No. N.6622, J. Stone Hodges bequest, 1961
Probably London *c.* 1700

11.17 **Jug** With pear-shaped bowl, wide parallel neck and no spout. The handle of heavy oval section, flattened inside, and with broad blue bands and the tail pointed. Decorated in blue on a white glaze with a Chinaman seated among rocks with cactus-like plants.
Height 9.8cm, maximum diameter 8.5cm
No. G.2145, purchased 1924
Probably London *c.* 1700

11.18 **Posset Pot** With round body on flattened base, and short parallel neck. No lid. The heavy round section handles curled in at the top and out at the bottom, and with blue bands. Decorated with a Chinaman on a stool with low table and an urn of flowers, another seated Chinaman, and a rock sprouting bamboo. The rim decorated with pendent arcs, and the spout with a scroll pattern. All decoration in blue outlines with two shades of blue wash on a pale greenish glaze. The figure '3' on base.
Height 15.1cm, maximum diameter 17.6cm
No. N.3078, purchased ex Hodgkin collection, 1947
Probably London *c.* 1690

11.19 **Posset Pot** With rounded body curving into very short neck. The heavy handles flattened inside, curled in at the top and out at the bottom, and blue banded. Decorated in blue on a pale bluish glaze with a seated Chinaman on a garden terrace. No lid.
Height 14.4cm, maximum diameter 18.4cm
No. G.2007, purchased from T. Charbonnier, 1923
Probably London *c.* 1700

11.20 Posset Pot Squat round body on a flattened base, with neck widening slightly to rim. The heavy round section handles curled in at the top, and out at the bottom. Both handles and spout with blue bands. The body decorated with three scenes of a Chinaman seated in a garden, or in a house with potted plants. The lid, with a simple knob, decorated with a lady, trellis and flowers. The decoration outlined in blue, with two shades of blue wash, on an off-white glaze. The figure '2' on the base.
Height 12.9cm to rim, maximum diameter 15.1cm
No. N.6627, J. Stone Hodges bequest, 1961
Probably London *c.* 1690

11.21 Bowl Inside, in large figures, '1683' within blue circles. Outside, three scenes of a Chinaman in a rocky garden with cactus-like shrubs. The decoration in manganese *trek* washed smudgily with blue, on a clear pale blue glaze.
Diameter 24.6cm, height 12.4cm
No. N. 5950, found at the Red Lodge and accessioned 1959, ex Alderman J. F. Eberle collection
Probably Bristol 1683

Illustrated in Pountney pl. VI with Brislington attribution.

11.22 Bowl Of flattened bulbous shape with two curled handles standing erect from the outer part of the bowl. The handles with blue dashes, the bowl decorated with scenes of a Chinaman seated in a garden with hollyhock and other flowers. The decoration in blue outline with two shades of blue wash on an off-white glaze.
Maximum diameter 16.5cm, height to rim 7.8cm
No. N.5548, gift of Miss E. Nesbitt, 1955
Possibly London *c.* 1700

This bowl is of unique shape for which we can find no parallel. It probably had a lid, and it may have been copied from a metalware original with taller and more slender handles.

11.23 **Bowl** Inside, a single leaf surrounded by three heart-shaped leaves and three Chinese scroll motifs. Outside, three shaped panels of Chinamen (i) pointing to a heron, (ii) watching a boat on a river from a terrace, and (iii) offering a plate heaped with food to an animal. Decorated in blue on an off-white glaze.
Diameter 26.4cm, height 12.4cm
No. N.7455, gift of Mrs Snow, 1966
Probably Bristol *c.* 1760

11.24 **Tazza** Standing on three feet mounted on shaped brackets with Chinese scroll pattern decoration. On top, a Chinaman dancing on a fenced terrace with screens, within a border of a meandering thorny vine in white on a blue ground. All decoration in blue on an off-white glaze.
Diameter 13.0cm, height 4.2cm
No. N.6651, J. Stone Hodges bequest, 1961
Probably London *c.* 1750

11.25 **Tazza** Standing on a pedestal foot, the top decorated with two ladies seated on rocks, with buildings across a stretch of water. The stem with pendent stiff leaf design, and the foot with three leafy sprays. Decorated in blue *trek* with two shades of blue wash on a pale blue glaze.
Diameter 12.5cm, height 6.2cm
No. N.7153, Ernest Blatch bequest, 1964
Perhaps London *c.* 1720, or Continental

11.26 **Vase** Of urn shape, the bell-shaped mouth with seventeen crimps, the twisted handles daubed with blue. The body decorated with a seated Chinaman holding a small parasol in a garden; the same scene repeated on both sides. The decoration in blue on a pale bluish glaze.
Height 17.0cm, rim diameter 15.5cm
No. N.2244, gift of Mrs Hall Warren, 1946
Probably Bristol *c.* 1750

11.27 **Bottle** Of globular shape with flat cup-shaped mouth. A Chinaman seated on a stool turns to another in a coolie hat and points to the garden with rocks, shrubs, trees and houses. Random leaves on the neck; scrolling leaf pattern inside the rim. Decorated in blue on a pale bluish glaze.
Height 23.4cm, maximum diameter 13.0cm
No. N.6626, J. Stone Hodges bequest, 1961
Probably London c. 1770

This appears identical to Hall Warren no. 183, which is also illustrated in the Rijksmuseum exhibition catalogue no. 159. A similar example is in Garner and Archer pl. 117A.

11.28 **Bottle** With globular body (neck broken off), decorated all round with a scene of a Chinaman meeting another with a staff in a fenced garden with rectangular rocks, bamboos and willow trees. Above is a beaded ring with two pendent rococo reserves of trellis diaper. On the neck, scrolls of leaves. The decoration in blue on a pale bluish glaze.
Height c. 25.0cm, maximum diameter 14.3cm
No. N.3047, purchased ex Hodgkin collection, 1947
Bristol or Liverpool c. 1740

11.29 **Plate** A Chinaman in a garden holds a parasol between his legs, while another leans on the fence behind. Bamboo and cactus plants grow in the garden. Decorated in blue on a pale blue glaze, the scene stretching from rim to rim.
Diameter 22.6cm, height 3.1cm, shape F, scalloped edge
No. N.6421, J. Stone Hodges bequest, 1961
Probably Liverpool c. 1750

11.30 Dish Rim-to-rim decoration of a Chinaman seated in a garden with a fence and flowers. Decorated in manganese outline with colour wash, in pale blue, red, green and yellow on a pale bluish glaze.
Diameter 33.2cm, height 5.4cm, shape I
No. N.3165, Sir Gilbert Mellor bequest, 1947
Probably Liverpool *c*. 1750

11.31 Plate A Chinaman with a parasol, walks in a fenced garden, the rim decorated with trellis diaper containing three reserves with stylized flowers. The decoration in blue on a pale blue glaze.
Diameter 22.7cm, height 3.2cm, shape F
No. N.7119, Ernest Blatch bequest, 1964
Probably Liverpool *c*. 1760

11.32 Dish A Chinaman in a barren rocky landscape with sparse vegetation, and hills beyond. Round the inner edge of the rim, a narrow band of floral motifs. Decorated in blue and manganese on a pale blue glaze.
Diameter 29.9cm, height 3.9cm, shape G
No. N.7123, Ernest Blatch bequest, 1964
Probably Liverpool *c*. 1760

Compare with no. 8.26, a saucer dish with similar decoration.

11.33 Plate A rim-to-rim scene of a Chinaman with right arm upheld, reclining on a terrace by the sea, with a rocky island and overhanging cliffs. A narrow rim border of lines and crosses. Decorated in heavy blue on a pale blue glaze.
Diameter 22.7cm, height 3.9cm, shape F deep
No. N.7116, Ernest Blatch bequest, 1964
Perhaps London *c*. 1770

11.34 **Dish** In the centre a Chinese lady balancing a flag on her head beside a fenced garden. On the rim four hollow rocks sprouting plants. Decorated in blue, red, green and yellow on a pale bluish glaze. Noughts and crosses under-rim marking.
Diameter 29.6cm, height 4.5cm, shape I
No. G.2514, gift of T. Charbonnier, 1930
Probably Bristol *c.* 1740

11.35 **Dish** Similar to the preceding one, but in blue only.
Diameter 33.9cm, height 4.4cm, shape I
No. G.1955, purchased from T. Charbonnier, 1923
Probably Bristol *c.* 1740

11.36 **Dish** A rim-to-rim scene of a pagoda on a rocky island, with flowers, and a man on a bridge. Two aerobatic birds in the sky. Decorated in blue, manganese and yellow on a pale bluish glaze.
Diameter 30.8cm, height 4.7cm, shape I
No. N.3164, Sir Gilbert Mellor bequest, 1947
Probably Liverpool *c.* 1740

11.37 **Mug** Decorated with a lady with a bird perched on her outstretched arm, another seated with a bird on a string, and a third person between them, all in a garden. The strap handle and swelling foot with floral decoration, and the rim border of trellis with floral motifs. The rim edge painted blue. All decoration in blue on a pale bluish glaze.
Height 18.6cm, diameter of top 13.6cm
No. G.114, purchased 1903
Perhaps Bristol *c.* 1760

11.38 **Dish** A rim-to-rim scene of a Chinaman on a landing stage with a vertical pole on which a bird is perched. Trees with pansy flowers, and an island with houses beyond. The decoration in heavy blue on a pale bluish glaze.
Diameter 30.7cm, height 4.4cm, shape G
No. N.6782, J. Stone Hodges bequest, 1961
Probably London c. 1770

11.39 **Brick** The top perforated with four rows of three holes and a large square hole in the centre. On each side a Chinaman fishing with a pail and bottle beside him and a clump of tall grasses; on each end a clump of the same grasses. Decorated in blue on a pale bluish glaze. The flat hollowed base marked '88'.
Length 12.0cm, width 5.3cm
No. N.5598, purchased 1955
Probably Bristol c. 1760

11.40 **Dish** A rim-to-rim scene of a Chinaman in a coolie hat sitting fishing beside a rock and cactus-like plants. Decorated in blue outlines and blue wash on a pale blue glaze.
Diameter 33.5cm, height 4.6cm, shape I
No. N.6773, J. Stone Hodges bequest, 1961
Probably Bristol 1730

11.41 **Dish** A rim-to-rim scene of a seated Chinaman with a fishing rod; a tall rock behind him and some flowers. Decorated in blue on a pale bluish glaze.
Diameter 33.5cm, height 5.1cm, shape I
No. N.2250, gift of Mrs Hall Warren, 1946
Probably Bristol c. 1730

11.42 Dish A rim-to-rim scene of a Chinese lady in a fenced park with trees with manganese sponged foliage, and a high cliff. The decoration in blue, red, manganese, green and yellow on a pale blue-grey glaze.
Diameter 33.2cm, height 4.4cm, shape I
No. N.6738, J. Stone Hodges bequest, 1961, ex Maddicks collection
Probably Bristol *c.* 1730

11.43 Dish A rim-to-rim scene of a Chinese lady seated among hillocks and stylized trees, with an ornate bird flying over. The decoration roughly drawn in blue, red, green and yellow on a pale bluish glaze.
Diameter 33.2cm, height 5.2cm, shape I
No. N.3163, Sir Gilbert Mellor bequest, 1947
Probably Bristol *c.* 1740

11.44 Dish A rim-to-rim scene of a Chinese lady standing and pointing in a garden with stylized shrubs, and another garden scene above. The decoration in blue, green, yellow and 'sealing-wax' red on a pale bluish glaze.
Diameter 30.3cm, height 4.3cm, shape I
No. N.3162, Sir Gilbert Mellor bequest, 1947, ex Gautier collection
Probably Bristol *c.* 1740

11.45 Dish A rim-to-rim scene of a Chinaman skipping, against three transverse landscapes in heavy blue and green, with yellow foregrounds; the trees of stylized shapes. The colours blue, green, yellow, with red shading, on a pale blue glaze.
Diameter 33.6cm, height 4.4cm, shape I
No. N.3161, Sir Gilbert Mellor bequest, 1947
Probably Bristol *c.* 1740

Illustrated in Garner and Archer pl. 70C, and discussed on p. 41.

11.46 Bowl Inside, some bullrushes surrounded by four Chinese motifs in red, tied with blue, and four sprigs in blue. Outside, five panels each of a Chinaman seated among flowers, beside a vase, the panels separated by trellis and floral motifs; and a lower border of trellis with Chinese symbols in reserves. The decoration in blue, red, green and yellow on a pale bluish-greyish glaze.
Diameter 30.5cm, height 15.7cm
No. N.3243, Sir Gilbert Mellor bequest, 1947
Probably Bristol c. 1750

11.47 Plate A rim-to-rim scene, boldly drawn, of a Chinaman in a fenced garden, with flowers taller than he is, and a giant flying insect. Decorated in blue, red, green and yellow on a bluish grey glaze.
Diameter 19.8cm, height 2.2cm, shape B
No. N.6446, J. Stone Hodges bequest, 1961, ex Freeth collection
Probably Bristol c. 1770

11.48 Dish A rim-to-rim scene of a countryman seated on a bank with flagon in hand and clay pipe in mouth, the landscape dotted with *chinoiserie* stylized trees. The decoration in blue, red, green and yellow on a pale blue glaze.
Diameter 33.4cm, height 5.2cm, shape I
No. G.2916, purchased 1931
Probably Bristol c. 1740

Here, in the same *chinoiserie* landscape that we have seen before, is the seated Chinaman converted back to an English countryman.

12   Chinoiserie II

The Chinese style influencing English delftware decoration from about 1720 onwards springs mainly from ceramics of the Qing Dynasty, following the resurgence of the production of fine porcelain after the doldrums of the Transitional period.

The first section of this chapter deals with Chinese symbols. These were the emblems of Buddhism, Taoism or of legend[1]. We illustrate them on thirteen plates from the collection, on which the symbols are in nearly every case round the rims. That most frequently encountered is the scroll, which symbolizes either painting, which was one of the Four Scholarly Accomplishments, or the sacred scriptures, because such early writings were on scrolls. Another symbol is the Castanets, whose portrayal has become debased so that they resemble two planks of wood nailed together to form a cross; but they are in fact the emblems of one of the Eight Immortals of Taoism. We also find a pair of Rhinoceros Horns, looking like cornucopiae, one of the Eight Precious Things, denoting happiness. One more favourite is the Chinese Artemisia Leaf, another of the Eight Precious Things, and a symbol of felicity. Thus, to the Chinese, most of this decoration had a symbolic meaning; we do not know if it had any meaning to the delftware potters, but in any case they copied it.

Pieces of red cloth are always tied round symbols, such as these, which are believed to have the efficacy of a charm, and they are supposed to represent the rays or aura of the charm. They are, in fact, to the charm what a halo is to a god or goddess[2].

In the second section of this chapter we start with a dish inscribed on the back with initials said to be those of John and Esther (Hester) Niglett, and with the date 1733. Niglett served his apprenticeship as a potter at Brislington, becoming free in 1722[3]. Little is known of him before this; Niglett is a very rare name, and we have only found it to occur in some villages in the extreme north of Gloucestershire, near Newent, but have been unable to trace his birth there. His wife died in 1755, after which we lose all trace of him in Bristol; however, some sherds with decoration on them, similar to what is believed to be his work at Bristol, have been dug up at Vauxhall in London[4]. Did he perhaps move there?

Some of the work attributed to Niglett, purely on the evidence of his dish, is illustrated among the group of nine pieces in this section. This so-called Niglett style seems to include tall Chinese ladies known as 'long Elizas' (after the Dutch *lange lijzen*), or somewhat similar seated figures or dancing boys, all of whom have bright red loose jackets. We also find included Chinese fences, rhomboidal leaf forms and other Chinese decorative motifs. We include at the end of this section some pieces which seem to be related to the Niglett style, perhaps decorated by other artists influenced by it.

In the third section we show a number of pieces decorated with flowers springing from a hollow rock. This is a favourite design, but if we did not know the hollow rock motif we would perhaps not recognize it in the debased forms to which it descends in the later examples. For a Chinese original we may refer to *China for the West* or to *Later Chinese Porcelain*[5]. The flowers concerned vary somewhat, but are probably intended to show three species representing the Three Friends of Chinese symbolism, affording shelter from the weather and pleasure to the eye in winter.

The last section shows first several plates which illustrate Chinese legend. Two of these can clearly be interpreted, one as the Eight Horses of King Mu, who ascended the throne in 1001 BC, and the other as the Paragon of Filial Piety, from the time of the ruler who came to the throne in 2356 BC. We also notice some 'cracked ice' patterned plates, derived from a Chinese decoration which denotes the coming of spring, and of which a Chinese porcelain example may be found of the Kangxi period (1662–1722)[6]. An example of the *chinoiserie* drawings of Jean Pillement occurs with no. 12.55, where we find a lady fishing copied from the work of the French artist who produced a wealth of such designs.

There were available to the ceramic artist many Drawing Books which were much influenced by the Chinese taste. The earliest is probably Stalker and Parker's *Treatise of Japanning and Varnishing* of 1688. Other notable ones were Edwards and Darly's *New Book of Chinese Designs Calculated to Improve the Present Taste*, published in 1754, and Carrington Bowles' *Drawing Book for Ladies or Complete Florist* of 1785. However the most famous must be *The Ladies' Amusement or the Whole Art of Japanning Made Easy* published by Robert Sayer in 1760, and described in Sayer and Bennett's print catalogue of 1775 as 'illustrated in upwards of two thousand different designs on 300 copper plates, consisting of flowers, shells, figures, birds, insects, landscapes, shipping, vases, borders, &c all adapted in the best manner for joining in groupes, or being placed in single objects, drawn by J. Pillement and other masters, and excellently engraved,' There follows a footnote: 'NB the above work will be found extremely useful to the porcelane, and other manufacturers depending on design.'

Although these drawing books no doubt gave many ideas to delftware artists, we very rarely find decoration taken from them directly. The Lady Fishing is reproduced in the *Ladies' Amusement*, but is there reversed, suggesting that the decoration on that plate was in fact taken from the original print, which we reproduce later.

The remaining examples in this chapter show many varieties of Chinese flowers and trees, pagodas and houses, all of which may be called *chinoiserie*; and if we revert to the *Encyclopaedia Britannica*'s definition of the term, we will note the 'asymmetrical forms; disruption of orthodox perspective; and Oriental figures and motifs' in profusion. We also note several debased versions of *chinoiserie*, suggesting that the English delftware artist was often a long way removed from the Chinese original which we suppose to have been influencing his work.

Notes
1 See C. A. S. Williams *Encyclopaedia of Chinese Symbolism*, New York, 1960
2 W. G. Gulland, *Chinese Porcelain*, London 1898, vol. I, p. 32.
3 See Anthony Ray, *English Delftware Pottery*, pp. 63–64.
4 D. Cockell, 'Some Finds of Pottery at Vauxhall Cross', *English Ceramic Circle Transactions*, vol. 9, part 2, p. 230 and pl. 128.
5 D. S. Howard and John Ayers, *China for the West*, London 1978, vol. I, no. 175, and Soame Jenyns, *Later Chinese Porcelain*, London 1951, pl. XXV(1C).
6 Soame Jenyns, op. cit., pl. XIX (1).

Section i

12.1 Plate In the centre a crane with a flower in its beak among peonies by a garden shrine, and round the rim three Chinese scrolls tied with ribbons among sprigs of flowers. The decoration in blue on a pale bluish glaze. On the back herbal sprig under-rim markings, and the letter 'Q' inside the footrim.
Diameter 23.1cm, height 2.1cm, shape F indented edge
No. G.2918, purchased 1931
Probably Liverpool *c.* 1760

12.2 Dish A very similar decoration to the previous example, though with four repeats of scroll symbols and sprigs of flowers round the rim. Decorated in blue on a pale bluish glaze. On the back whiplash under-rim markings and 'T' within the footrim.
Diameter 35.0cm, height 5.2cm, shape I
No. G.1956, purchased from T. Charbonnier, 1923
Probably Liverpool *c.* 1760

12.3 Plate In the centre a basket of flowers surrounded on the curvature by a band of double curl pattern, and round the rim four floral sprigs with Chinese symbols tied with ribbons. On the back herbal sprig under-rim markings. The decoration in blue on a pale bluish glaze.
Diameter 23.2cm, height 3.0cm, shape F octagonal
No. G.1165, purchased 1918
Probably Liverpool *c.* 1750

12.4 Plate The decoration similar to the previous entry, both on the front and on the back.
Diameter 23.5cm, height 4.2cm, shape F deep octagonal
No. N.6480, J. Stone Hodges bequest, 1961
Probably Liverpool *c.* 1760

12.5 Dish In the centre a chrysanthemum and a peony with foliage from a shallow basket, surrounded by a narrow scroll pattern border on the curvature. Round the rim four Chinese symbols tied with ribbons with floral sprigs. The decoration in blue on a pale blue glaze. On the back, herbal sprig under-rim markings.
Diameter 34.6cm, height 4.2cm, shape F
No. G.122 purchased 1907
Probably Liverpool *c.* 1750

12.6 Dish In the centre a lady, bird in hand, among flowers in a fenced garden with two more birds and insects. Round the rim a band of trellis diaper with seven reserves containing symbolized Chinese scrolls. The decoration in shades of blue, red and green on a white glaze. On the back noughts and crosses under-rim markings.
Diameter 33.6cm, height 4.2cm, shape I
No. N.6688, J. Stone Hodges bequest, 1961
Probably Bristol (Temple Back) *c.* 1740

A sherd of this pattern is illustrated in the forthcoming publication of 'Pottery Kiln-Waste from Temple Back, Bristol' by R. H. Price in the *City of Bristol Museum and Art Gallery Research Monograph* no. IV.

12.7 Plate In the centre a tower at the end of an arcaded causeway, with a small sailing boat passing by, and a tree and fence in the foreground. The rim decorated with trellis diaper and four reserves containing Chinese artemisia leaf symbols. On the back noughts and crosses under-rim markings, and the figure '5' within the footrim. The decoration in blue on a white glaze.
Diameter 22.6cm, height 7.2cm, shape F deep
No. G.1984, purchased from T. Charbonnier, 1923
Probably Bristol *c.* 1750

12.8 Dish In the centre a boat sailing and two slipper-shaped boats moored by a rocky outcrop from which flowers sprout; one bird perched and another flying. On the rim a trellis pattern with six reserves containing Chinese artemisia leaf symbols. On the back noughts and crosses under-rim marking, and a 'WP' monogram within the footrim. The decoration in blue, red, green and yellow on a pale bluish glaze.
Diameter 33.3cm, height 4.8cm, shape I
No. N.3158, Sir Gilbert Mellor bequest, 1947
Probably Bristol *c.* 1740

12.9 Dish In the centre a basket of flowers with many striped red daisies, and a bird's head emerging from the ground either side, surrounded by a band of overlapping lozenges. On the rim a trellis pattern with six reserves containing Chinese artemisia leaf symbols. The edge dark brown. On the back noughts and crosses under-rim markings and the figure '4' within the footrim. Decorated in blue, red and green on an off-white glaze.
Diameter 33.5cm, height 5.5cm, shape F
No. N.6758, J. Stone Hodges bequest, 1961
Probably Bristol *c.* 1730

12.10 Plate A rectangular Chinese urn containing flowering plants, surrounded by a band of trellis with four Chinese artemisia leaf symbols in reserves. On the rim three sprigs of flowers. On the back herbal sprig under-rim markings, and 'B' within the footrim. The decoration in blue on a pale blue glaze.
Diameter 17.5cm, height 2.5cm, shape F
No. N.3064, purchased ex Hodgkin collection, 1947
Probably Liverpool *c.* 1750

12.11 Dish A central daisy face, surrounded by a curl pattern, and with four sprigs of flowers beyond. On the rim a band of trellis with eight Chinese artemisia leaf symbols interposed. Decorated in blue, red and green on a white glaze; the back having a greyish tinge.
Diameter 30.4cm, height 3.9cm, shape I
No. N.6726, J. Stone Hodges bequest, 1961
Perhaps London *c.* 1740

12.12 Plate In the centre bamboo and peonies with shaded petals springing from a hollow rock. On the rim a band of trellis diaper with four debased Chinese scroll symbols in reserves. Decorated in blue, red, pastel green, manganese and yellow on a pale blue glaze.
Diameter 21.8cm, height 4.2cm, shape F
No. N.6472, J. Stone Hodges bequest, 1961
Probably Liverpool *c.* 1750

Compare this and the next plate with Garner and Archer pl. 78A, which, as explained on their p. 42, is one of a group of four plates of this pattern all inscribed for people living in the vicinity of Liverpool and bearing the date 1749 or 1750.

12.13 **Plate**   Decorated very similarly to the preceding one, but with a slightly different palette of blue, blue-green, manganese and yellow.
Diameter 22.3cm, height 3.0cm, shape F
No. N.6452, J. Stone Hodges bequest, 1961
Probably Liverpool *c.* 1750

Section ii

12.14 **Dish**   Rim-to-rim decoration of many Chinese figures, mostly in fenced gardens among trees, rocks and shrubs. Five figures standing, two jumping, three sitting and one lying down. The Chinese figures all with red jackets and with spotted skirts or trousers. The decoration in blue, red, green and yellow on an off-white glaze. Inscribed on the back within the footrim 'J N E/1733'.
Diameter 36.8cm, height 6.3cm, shape I
No. G.140, purchased ex Pountney collection, 1914
Bristol 1733   COLOUR PLATE, p. 33

See, Pountney pp. 47 and 171–2 and pl. XXX; Garner and Archer pp. 25 and 40, and pl. 95A; Ray, *English Delftware Pottery*, p. 64 and fig. 9; and Rackham and Read p. 58.
   The labels on the back of the dish read:

   This dish was exhibited at the Annual Meeting of the Archaeological Institute of Great Britain and Ireland held in Bristol, August 1851. See Catalogue of the temporary Museum, page 94.

and

   Old Brislington Ware. Landscape with figures in 4 Colors.

   The initials on the back of this dish are thought to refer to John Niglett and his wife Hester (Esther). John Niglett, son of James Niglett, yeoman, was apprenticed to Thomas Dixon of the Limekiln Lane Pottery, Bristol, on 13 November 1714, and became a free Burgess in 1722. He married in 1721, and the significance of the date 1733 on the dish is not known. His wife died in 1755 after which he seems to have 'disappeared'.
   There can be no certainty that the initials on this dish do belong to John Niglett and his wife; still less that it is to Niglett that we are justified in attributing the authorship of, or inspiration for, a considerable number of articles decorated in a similar style. However Niglett was apprenticed at Limekiln Lane and there is strong evidence that one of the dishes in this section of the chapter was made there. We are therefore prepared to accept the Niglett attribution for this dish until such time as any other more plausible attribution is offered. We shall refer therefore to 'Niglett' style, and leave the reader to make his own decision.

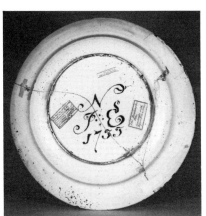

12.15 Dish In the centre a seated Chinaman by a boulder on a terrace overlooking a lake. On the rim a stylized floral pattern repeated six times. The decoration in blue, red, green and yellow on a white glaze with slight pink tinge. On the back noughts and crosses under-rim markings.
Diameter 25.9cm, height 4.0cm, shape I
No. N.3229, Sir Gilbert Mellor bequest, 1947
Bristol (Limekiln Lane) *c.* 1740

This dish is similar to Hall Warren collection no. 145, and as explained by Ray (*English Delftware Pottery*) on p. 64, a batch of five kiln wasters of this pattern was recovered from the Limekiln Lane pottery site. The seated Chinaman wears the red jacket of 'Niglett' style, the fence is of similar design and the palette of colours the same.

12.16 Dish In the centre a tall Chinese lady stands on a terrace between mounds from which grow shrubs. The rim contains forty-seven flutes each decorated with a flower bud. Decorated in blue on an off-white glaze with slight pinky tinge on the back. Noughts and crosses under-rim markings.
Diameter 34.0cm, height 5.6cm, shape J shallow
No. N.3138, Sir Gilbert Mellor bequest, 1947
Bristol *c.* 1730

The lady and the fence behind her are similar to the decoration in the centre of the 'Niglett' dish. These tall ladies are taken from Chinese ceramics, and the Dutch called them *lange lijzen* ('long stupids') corrupted in English to 'long Elizas'.

12.17 Bowl Inside, a flower and foliage, surrounded by seven quadruple dots and seven single dots. Outside, seated, standing and jumping Chinese figures among mounds, fences and trees. The top border of *ruyi* heads, and the bottom border of twisted cable. The decoration in blue, red, green and yellow on an off-white glaze.
Diameter 29.8cm, height 16.3cm
No. N.3216, Sir Gilbert Mellor bequest, 1947
Bristol *c.* 1730

The seated and the jumping figures are taken from the 'Niglett' dish, as are the fence and the landscape.

12.18 Posset Pot The rounded body curves gently into a slightly widening neck. The strap handles are blue-dashed and have the tails neatly curled. The lid is shallow domed with a mushroom knob. There is no spout. Decorated with a Chinese lady and jumping boy in fenced gardens, and the neck border of *ruyi* heads. The lid similarly decorated. The colours blue, red, green and yellow on a white glaze.
Height to rim 15.1cm, maximum diameter 17.4cm
No. G.2031, purchased from T. Charbonnier, 1923
Bristol *c.* 1730

This was listed by Charbonnier as 'Painted by Niglett *c.* 1733', an obvious reference to the 'Niglett' dish, and it must be the posset pot referred to by Pountney on p. 171 which he also attributed to Niglett.

12.19 **Bowl** A flower bowl with convex top pierced with one large centre hole and twelve others decorated with two rings of Chinese scroll pattern and radial red lines. The body has two identical scenes of a Chinese lady seated on a cushion between shrubs. The decoration in blue, red, green and yellow on a white glaze.
Height to rim 8.6cm, diameter 15.7cm
No. N.3220, Sir Gilbert Mellor bequest, 1947
Bristol *c.* 1730

The seated Chinese lady has come from the right-centre of the 'Niglett' dish, the rest of the decoration is in *chinoiserie* style and the palette repeats the same 'Niglett' colours.

12.20 **Plate** In the centre a multi-coloured flower with fruit and leaves, and round the plate a pair of twining stems with flowers and leaves. In the centre bottom stands a Chinese lady in a red jacket. Decorated in blue, red, green and yellow on a pale blue glaze.
Diameter 22.8cm, height 2.6cm, shape F
No. N.3183, Sir Gilbert Mellor bequest, 1947
Bristol *c.* 1730

A very attractive plate on which the 'long Eliza' and the palette at once suggest 'Niglett' even in the absence of any other decorative similarities with the 'Niglett' dish.

12.21 **Dish** A Chinese island scene in the centre with a tall building and a man fishing from a small boat off shore. The rest of the plate covered with a trellis diaper pattern with six shaped reserves containing floral motifs with rhomboidal leaves, and six small round reserves with smaller motifs. On the back noughts and crosses under-rim markings. The decoration in blue, red, green and yellow on an off-white glaze, with a pinky tinge on the back. The figure '4' within the footrim.
Diameter 34.1cm, height 4.8cm, shape I
No. N.6732, J. Stone Hodges bequest, 1961
Probably Bristol *c.* 1740

12.22 **Dish** A pair to the previous example both on the front and on the back; in fact it is hard to detect any significant points of difference.
Diameter 34.0cm, height 4.4cm, shape I
No. N.3140, Sir Gilbert Mellor bequest, 1947
Probably Bristol *c.* 1740

These last two dishes retain the 'Niglett' palette and are decorated in the *chinoiserie* style; moreover the glaze has similar characteristics. They probably represent a later development from the same pottery.

Section iii

12.23 **Dish** Rim-to-rim decoration of three sorts of flower sprouting from a hollow rock, with a small temple in the midst. Marked 'R E/1752'. Decorated in blue on a pale blue glaze.
Diameter 34.1cm, height 4.2cm, shape I
No. G.1730, gift of T. Charbonnier, 1921
Probably Liverpool 1752

This style of decoration is clearly traceable to a Chinese origin as pointed out in the chapter introduction. The hollow rock is a 'tufa' rock of volcanic origin, which got more and more debased by potters who were not familiar with it.

12.24 **Dish** In the centre three flowers sprouting from hollow rock, and round the rim six sprigs of flowers. The decoration in blue on a pale bluish glaze. On the back noughts and crosses under-rim markings, and the letter 'X' within the footrim.
Diameter 33.3cm, height 5.5cm, shape I
No. N.6760, J. Stone Hodges bequest, 1961
Probably Bristol c. 1760

12.25 **Plate** marked 'SARAH BEUFIELD.'. In the centre three kinds of flowers sprouting from hollow rock, and round the rim four sprigs of flowers. An outer rim border of lozenges and crosses. The decoration in blue on a pale blue glaze.
Diameter 23.0cm, height 2.9cm, shape F
No. G.2324, purchased 1928
Probably Bristol c. 1760

No trace has been found of the name 'Beufield'.

12.26 **Dish** In the centre three kinds of flowers sprouting from hollow rock, and round the rim six sprigs of double or triple flowers. The decoration in blue, red, manganese, green and yellow on a blue glaze.
Diameter 34.1cm, height 4.7cm, shape I
No. N.6742, J. Stone Hodges bequest, 1961
Probably Bristol c. 1760

12.27 Plate In the centre three kinds of flowers sprouting from hollow rock, and round the rim four sprigs of flowers. Decorated in deep blue on a pale bluish glaze. On the back the figure '4' in the footrim.
Diameter 23.5cm, height 2.5cm, shape F
No. N.6806, J. Stone Hodges bequest, 1961
Probably Liverpool *c.* 1770

12.28 Dish A rim-to-rim scene of chrysanthemum and peonies sprouting from hollow rock, and a flying insect. Decorated in blue, red, green, manganese and yellow on a pale bluish glaze. Edge grasses under-rim markings.
Diameter 33.2cm, height 4.4cm, shape I
No. N.7124, Ernest Blatch bequest, 1964
Probably Bristol *c.* 1760

12.29 Plate A rim-to-rim scene of chrysanthemum and peonies sprouting from hollow rock, and butterfly in flight. Decorated in blue, manganese, green and yellow on a pale bluish glaze. On the back the letter 'R' within the footrim.
Diameter 21.6cm, height 2.9cm, shape F 16-scalloped edge
No. N.3252, Sir Gilbert Mellor bequest, 1947
Probably Bristol *c.* 1760

12.30 Plate A rim-to-rim scene of chrysanthemum, peony and other flowers sprouting from hollow rock, and an insect in flight. Decorated in blue, manganese, green and yellow on a bluish-grey glaze.
Diameter 21.3cm, height 2.8cm, shape F 16-scalloped edge
No. N.6423, J. Stone Hodges bequest, 1961, ex Freeth collection
Probably Bristol *c.* 1760

12.31 Dish In the centre a Chinese garden with fence and hollow rock from which peonies sprout, and on the rim five sprays of flowers. Decorated in blue, manganese black, manganese pink, green and yellow on a pale blue glaze. On the back whiplash under-rim markings and the letter 'F' within the footrim.
Diameter 30.6cm, height 3.5cm, shape I
No. G.1427, purchased 1919
Probably Liverpool *c.* 1760

This is referred to by Pountney on p. 149, with the suggestion that 'F' indicated Frank's Bristol pottery.

12.32 Plate A rim-to-rim scene of a Chinese fenced garden with flowers sprouting from hollow rock, and a yellow bird perched on the fence. Decorated in blue, manganese, green and yellow on a pale blue glaze. On the back the letter 'h' within the footrim.
Diameter 22.6cm, height 3.0cm, shape F 24-scalloped edge
No. N.3363, purchased ex Maddicks collection, 1936
Probably Liverpool *c.* 1760

12.33 Plate In the centre a thicket of bamboo and two large flowers sprouting from flat ground, and surrounded by a band of floral motifs. On the rim a border of dots in connected arcs. The decoration in blue, manganese and yellow on a pale blue glaze.
Diameter 22.6cm, height 2.7cm, shape F
No. N.7121, Ernest Blatch bequest, 1964
Probably London *c.* 1770

12.34 Dish In the centre flowers sprouting from hollow rock, and on the rim four sprigs of flowers. The decoration in blue, green and yellow on a pale bluish glaze.
Diameter 31.3cm, height 4.0cm, shape I
No. N.4075, Hugh V. Smith bequest, 1949
Probably Liverpool *c.* 1770

12.35 **Plate** In the centre flowers sprouting from hollow rock on which sits a crested bird, and round the rim three sprigs of flowers. The decoration in blue, manganese, green and yellow on a pale blue-green glaze.
Diameter 22.4cm, height 2.6cm, shape F
No. N.5702, purchased 1957
Probably London *c.* 1750

12.36 **Dish** In the centre peonies sprout from hollow rock on which stands a rooster, with a hen and two chickens below. Round the rim four sprays of flowers. On the back whiplash under-rim markings and the letter 'h' within the footrim. The decoration in blue, manganese outlines, green and yellow on a pale blue glaze.
Diameter 30.7cm, height 4.0cm, shape I
No. N.6756, J. Stone Hodges bequest, 1961
Probably Liverpool *c.* 1760

12.37 **Plate** In the centre flowers sprouting from a hollow rock, and a vase containing poppies, surrounded by a band in the curvature of multiple lozenges. Round the edge of the rim a narrow border of trellis alternating with stylized floral patterns. The decoration in blue on a pale blue glaze. On the back the figures '11' within the footrim.
Diameter 23.8cm, height 3.0cm, shape F
No. N.6807, J. Stone Hodges bequest, 1961
Probably Liverpool *c.* 1770

12.38 **Dish** In the centre two kinds of flowers sprout from a lozenge-shaped hollow rock, and round the rim four repeats of a floral group centred on a half-sunflower face. Decorated in blue, red, manganese, green and yellow on a pale bluish-grey glaze.
Diameter 33.9cm, height 4.5cm, shape F
No. N.3146, Sir Gilbert Mellor bequest, 1947
Probably London *c.* 1750

12.39 Dish In the centre a lozenge-shaped hollow rock sprouting flowers and leaves outlined in blue and shaded red. Round the rim four groups of flowers centred on a sunflower face. The decoration in blue, red, green and yellow, on a pale blue glaze.
Diameter 30.7cm, height 3.9cm, shape F
No. G.3497, purchased ex Vassall collection, 1938
Probably London *c.* 1750

A sherd of this pattern is illustrated in Garner's article on 'Lambeth Earthenware' pl. XIV(b).

12.40 Dish A pair to the previous entry; the only difference:
Diameter 30.6cm, height 4.4cm
No. G.3498, purchased ex Vassall collection, 1938
Probably London *c.* 1750

12.41 Dish A Chinese garden scene with trapezoid rocks and peony, pine, bamboo and other flowers. Round the rim three long sprigs of cherry. On the back herbal sprig under-rim markings. The decoration in blue on a pale blue glaze.
Diameter 30.7cm, height 3.8cm, shape I
No. N.6675, J. Stone Hodges bequest, 1961
Probably Liverpool *c.* 1760

Section iv

12.42 Plate In the centre a lady with a fan reclines against a tree stump from which one branch arches over her, and on the rim trellis diaper and shaped panels with twin tree branches between. Decorated in blue and blue wash on a pale blue glaze.
Diameter 22.5cm, height 3.3cm, shape D indented edge
No. N.2252, gift of Mrs Hall Warren, 1946
Probably Bristol (Temple Back) *c.* 1750

Compare Garner and Archer pl. 100A, Victoria and Albert Museum no. C 92–1940, and Glaisher collection no. 1680. Sherds of this pattern are illustrated in R. H. Price, 'Pottery Kiln-Waste from Temple Back, Bristol'; *City of Bristol Museum and Art Gallery Research Monograph* no. IV, (forthcoming publication).

12.43 **Plate** The decoration as on the previous example.
Diameter 22.7cm, height 3.4cm, shape F 24-scalloped edge
No. N.6420, J. Stone Hodges bequest, 1961
Probably Bristol *c.* 1750

12.44 **Plate** The decoration as on the last two examples, but
more roughly painted and on an off-white glaze.
Diameter 22.8cm, height 4.7cm, shape F
No. N.6506, J. Stone Hodges bequest, 1961
Probably Bristol *c.* 1750

12.45 **Dish** Eight Chinese horses in a field with a central tree
among hills, with three birds flying over, and round the rim five
repeats of new leaves sprouting from dead tree stumps. The
edge brown, the decoration in blue on a pale bluish glaze. On the back
concentric circles under-rim markings.
Diameter 30.5cm, height 3.9cm, shape H
No. N.6771, J. Stone Hodges bequest, 1961
Probably Liverpool *c.* 1760

D. F. Lunsingh Scheurleer, in *Chinese Export Porcelain* (London
1974) p. 200, notes that the eight horses of King Mu, famous for
speed and staying power, became subjects in favour with the
porcelain painters. The interesting implications of the under-rim
markings are discussed on pp. 310–12.

12.46 **Dish** The decoration as described on the previous
example, though with detailed differences, and only four repeats
of the border design. The decoration in shades of blue on a pale
bluish glaze, and the edge painted brown. Concentric circles
under-rim markings.
Diameter 27.3cm, height 2.7cm, shape H
No. N.6778, J. Stone Hodges bequest, 1961
Probably Liverpool *c.* 1760

12.47 Dish Two Chinese ladies under a parasol in a fenced garden with a figure holding a baby standing on a cloud. The rim with four repeats of a fence with three posts and sprouting flowers. The decoration in manganese and blue on an off-white glaze, the edge brown. On the back concentric circles under-rim markings.
Diameter 32.3cm, height 3.5cm, shape H
No. N.6707, J. Stone Hodges bequest, 1961
Probably Liverpool *c.* 1760

The subject is explained by W. H. Edmunds in *Pointers and Clues to the Subjects of Chinese and Japanese Art* (London 1934): Yao, last but one of the Rulers of China, ascended the throne in 2356 BC and reigned ninety-eight years! He debarred his unworthy son from heirship to the throne and appointed Shun, a Paragon of Filial Piety, to succeed, giving him his two daughters in marriage. Shun is said to have been nursed as a child by the Dragon Queen of Long Hou.

12.48 Dish The decoration as described on the previous example except that there are only three repeats of the border design on this somewhat smaller dish. The decoration in blue on a pale bluish glaze, the edge red-brown.
Diameter 26.5cm, height 3.8cm, shape H
No. N.5561, gift of Miss E. Nesbitt, 1955
Probably Liverpool *c.* 1760

12.49 Dish A robed lady with a fan is offered a crown(?) by a pigtailed servant in a garden with overhanging trees. The decoration in blue on a pale bluish glaze. On the back noughts and crosses under-rim markings.
Diameter 33.7cm, height 5.3cm, shape I
No. N.6668, J. Stone Hodges bequest, 1961
Probably Bristol *c.* 1760

Compare Mundy pl. IX, where it is suggested that it represents William offering the crown to Mary for which there seems little foundation. The trees are similar to those on the next two dishes, and their Chinese origins may be seen in Soame Jenyns' *Ming Pottery and Porcelain* (London 1953) pl. 111B.

12.50 Plate A rim-to-rim scene of a Chinese lady beneath a parasol under arching trees, with buildings – some ruined – in the background. Marked 'A·V/1748'. Decorated in blue on a white glaze. The lady with the parasol on this and the next piece also appears on brick no. 7.32.
Diameter 22.8cm, height 2.8cm, shape F
No. G.1996, purchased from T. Charbonnier, 1923
Probably Bristol 1748

Compare Hall Warren collection no. 153, and see comments on the previous entry.

12.51 Dish A rim-to-rim scene of a Chinese lady beneath a parasol under arched trees with buildings beyond and a 'long Eliza' standing in the background. Some of the buildings and trees are copied in the foreground. The decoration in blue on a pale bluish glaze. On the back edge grasses under-rim markings and a trefoil within the footrim.
Diameter 34.0cm, height 5.5cm, shape I
No. N.6749, J. Stone Hodges bequest, 1961
Probably Bristol *c.* 1750

12.52 Tray Of quatrefoil shape, with the rim standing up, the base flat without feet. Decorated with two Chinamen in a garden with hummocks and flowers under a weeping willow, with a house beyond. A rim border of trellis and floral motifs. The decoration in blue on a pale blue glaze, the edge brown.
Maximum diameter 20.2cm, height 1.4cm
No. N.6585, J. Stone Hodges bequest, 1961
Probably Liverpool *c.* 1750

12.53 Plate In the centre two deer among pine trees and two birds flying over. On the rim, trellis diaper with flowerheads and four shaped reserves with sprays of flowers. The decoration in pale blue on a pale bluish glaze. On the back noughts and crosses under-rim markings and the letter 'X' within the footrim.
Diameter 23.0cm, height 2.5cm, shape F
No. G.143, purchased 1911
Probably Bristol *c.* 1750

Compare the Chinese plate in Soame Jenyns' *Later Chinese Porcelain* (2nd. edn., London 1971) pl. XXX(2).

12.54 Plate In the centre two Chinamen on a rocky shore under a willow tree with catkins, and a ship in full sail at sea. On the rim trellis diaper with flowerheads and shaped reserves with flowers. On the back ribbon under-rim markings. Decorated in blue on a pale bluish glaze.
Diameter 22.4cm, height 3.1cm, shape F
No. G.2011, purchased from T. Charbonnier, 1923
Probably Bristol *c.* 1750

Fig 18 A lady fishing: engraving by
P. C. Canot from a drawing by Jean
Pillement.

12.55 Plate A Chinese lady sitting fishing, watched by another
from an arbour. A narrow border in the curvature and another at
the edge of the rim, both with trellis and floral motifs. On the back
herbal sprig under-rim markings. Decorated in blue on a pale blue
glaze.
Diameter 22.7cm, height 2.7cm, shape G octagonal
No. N.7108, Ernest Blatch bequest, 1964
Probably Liverpool *c.* 1760

The scene is copied from the '*Livre de Chinois, Inventé et Dessiné par
Jean Pillement et gravé par P.C. Canot,* London. Published
according to Act of Parliament Jany 2nd 1758' in which it appears
as plate 19. A copy is reproduced at fig. 18 from the British
Museum Department of Prints and Drawings, no. 161.b.6 p. 21.
This same print appears in *The Ladies' Amusement* but reversed.
Compare Mundy pl. XX. The author has a French faience plate
similarly decorated.

12.56 **Plate** A Chinese house under a weeping tree, surrounded by a wide border of 'cracked ice' pattern with three reserves containing similar houses in miniature. The decoration in blue and manganese on a pale blue glaze.
Diameter 23.8cm, height 2.7cm, shape F
No. N.6455, J. Stone Hodges bequest, 1961
Probably Bristol *c.* 1750

Cracked ice is the Chinese symbol for spring. For a Chinese example see Soames Jenyns' *Later Chinese Porcelain* pl. XIX(L) which bears the mark of the Kangxi period (1662–1722).

12.57 **Plate** Similar to the previous example, except that the decoration is less distinct.
Diameter 23.0cm, height 3.1cm, shape F
No. G.192, purchased 1916
Probably Bristol *c.* 1750

12.58 **Dish** Similar to the previous two examples, but the scene in the centre of the plate is much enlarged, while the houses in the four reserves are of a different design to that in the centre. Decorated in blue, red, manganese and yellow on a pale bluish glaze.
Diameter 35.0cm, height 4.0/4.8cm, shape I
No. G.1957, purchased from T. Charbonnier, 1923
Probably Bristol *c.* 1760

12.59 **Plate** A Chinese pagoda on an island with a twisted tree in the foreground, and a Chinaman crossing a bridge; two birds fly overhead. The rim border of a trellis band with flower motifs at the corners. Decorated in blue on a pale bluish glaze.
Diameter 23.3cm, height 3.0cm, shape F octagonal
No. N.3780, found in store and accessioned 1949
Probably Liverpool *c.* 1750

12.60 Plate A Chinaman sitting under a weeping willow sprouting from a rock, surrounded by an arcade-pattern band in the curvature. On the rim a border pattern of heavy scrolls. The decoration in blue on a pale blue glaze.
Diameter 22.7cm, height 2.6cm, shape F
No. N.6437, J. Stone Hodges bequest, 1961
Probably London *c.* 1760

12.61 Plate A Chinaman standing fishing on an island, with other islands beyond with a weeping tree and a house. The rim with ten swags of leaves, and the edge with radial brush marks. Decorated in blue on a pale blue glaze with greenish back.
Diameter 22.4cm, height 2.8cm, shape F
No. N.3238, Sir Gilbert Mellor bequest, 1947
Probably London *c.* 1780

12.62 Dish In the centre bamboo and flowers grow from level ground, surrounded by a band of stylized flowers. On the outer rim a border of blue dots in yellow arcs. The decoration in blue, manganese, green and yellow, together with red shading, on a pale bluish glaze.
Diameter 31.5cm, height 4.3cm, shape I
No. N.6753, J. Stone Hodges bequest, 1961
Probably London *c.* 1770

Compare no. 12.33, which is basically the same pattern on a plate, but is less colourful.

12.63 Dish A Chinese island with a pagoda among trees, and a long, low canopied hut. The rim with panels of trellis and of floral motifs. On the back noughts and crosses under-rim markings, and the letter 'X' within the footrim. Decorated in blue on a pale bluish glaze; the back slightly pinky.
Diameter 29.0cm, height 4.2cm, shape I
No. N.6780, J. Stone Hodges bequest, 1961
Probably Bristol *c.* 1750

12.64 **Plate** A Chinese island with a poplar tree and small bungalow, surrounded by a band of trellis on the curvature. On the outer rim another border of blue squares with red dots. The decoration in blue, red, manganese and yellow on pale bluish glaze.
Diameter 23.0cm, height 2.9cm, shape F
No. N.6516, J. Stone Hodges bequest, 1961
Probably London *c.* 1750

12.65 **Plate** A Chinese fenced garden with fern-like shrubs and a tree with slender stems, surrounded by a rim border of five floral swags and radial brush marks on the edge. Decorated in blue, red, green, manganese and yellow on a pale bluish glaze.
Diameter 22.9cm, height 2.1cm, shape F
No. N.7113, Ernest Blatch bequest, 1964
London *c.* 1790

The swags and brushed edge are typical of late London plates and may be found on balloon plates which celebrated the first ascents in 1784 and 1785, see nos. 10.50 to 10.52.

12.66 **Dish** A two-storey house on an island with trees, surrounded by a band of trellis with ten floral motifs in graffito on blue grounds. On the rim five more Chinese islands with houses or temples, and trees. The decoration in blue on a pale blue glaze. On the back three herbal sprig under-rim markings.
Diameter 35.7cm, height 5.0cm, shape I
No. N.6674, J. Stone Hodges bequest, 1961
Probably Liverpool *c.* 1750

12.67 **Plate** Of basically the same pattern as the previous entry, scaled down to size for a plate. Decorated in blue on a pale blue glaze with a greenish tinge to the back.
Diameter 22.4cm, height 2.1cm, shape F
No. N.4074, Hugh. V. Smith bequest, 1949
Probably Liverpool *c.* 1750

12.68 Plate A garden with fences and rectangular rocks, and sprouting bamboo and other flowers, surrounded by a continuous red wavy line. On the rim a border of scroll pattern with four floral motifs. Decorated in blue, red, green and yellow on a pale blue glaze.
Diameter 22.8cm, height 2.8cm, shape F
No. N.7115, Ernest Blatch bequest, 1964
Probably London *c*. 1780

12.69 Plate In the centre two huts on stilts and two weeping willows from rocks. The outer rim border a band of trellis and four floral motifs. Decorated in blue, manganese and yellow on a pale bluish-greenish glaze.
Diameter 22.1cm, height 2.3cm, shape F
No. N.7109, Ernest Blatch bequest, 1964
Probably London *c*. 1750

12.70 Plate Rim-to-rim decoration of a Chinese landscape with a two-storey pagoda among trees of stylized shape. Marked on the back 'Elizabeth Bridgman 1754'. The decoration in blue on a pale bluish glaze.
Diameter 22.0cm, height 3.0cm, shape F
No. N.6438, J. Stone Hodges bequest, 1961
Probably London 1754

Compare Victoria and Albert Museum no. C.6–1932, illustrated in Garner and Archer pl. 114B.
    An Elizabeth Bridgeman was baptized at St Mary, Rotherhithe on 10 August 1732, daughter of John and Margaret Bridgeman, but was buried on 14 June 1734. A second daughter, baptized on 1 August 1735, was similarly named, and survived. She would have been nineteen years old in 1754. The pottery at Rotherhithe had closed down before the end of the seventeenth century, but it is only a mile downstream from Southwark, where potteries were still active.

12.71 Plate In the centre a Chinaman crosses a bridge to an island on which are a tree and a house, with a sailing ship at sea. The rim decoration spreading into the curvature, with four bunches of grapes(?) and two groups of foliage. Decorated in blue on a pale blue glaze.
Diameter 23.8cm, height 3.0cm, shape F
No. N.6528, J. Stone Hodges bequest, 1961
Probably Liverpool *c*. 1750

12.72 Dish A Chinese house in fenced garden with lilies, and a weeping willow from an overhanging rock. The outer rim with a trellis border and four floral motifs. Decorated in blue, red, green and yellow on a pale blue glaze.
Diameter 35.7cm, height 4.8cm, shape G
No. N.3367, purchased ex Maddicks collection, 1936
Probably Liverpool *c.* 1750

12.73 Saucer Dish Decorated on the inside only with a Chinese pagoda on a island with fences and a willow tree, surrounded by a wavy circle. A trellis border round the inside rim. The decoration in blue on a pale bluish-greyish glaze.
Diameter 25.6cm, height 6.8cm, shape J
No. N.6801, J. Stone Hodges bequest, 1961
Probably Bristol *c.* 1770

12.74 Plate A Chinaman leaning on a stick in a garden, under a weeping willow, with house and tall rock. On the curvature a band of trellis interrupted by three blue painted panels with graffito markings. The whole rim decorated with three mounds growing shrubs with blue painted dividers. The decoration in blue on a pale blue glaze.
Diameter 23.2cm, height 2.9cm, shape F
No. N.7120, Ernest Blatch bequest, 1964
Probably Liverpool *c.* 1770

12.75 Plate A Chinese pagoda under a tree with fern-like foliage on an island, surrounded by a band of sketchy trellis and graffito designs on blue panels. The rim with three mounds from which ferns grow, and the edge with a wavy line. Decorated in blue, green and manganese on a pale blue-green glaze.
Diameter 22.8cm, height 2.9cm, shape F
No. N.3198, Sir Gilbert Mellor bequest, 1947
Probably London *c.* 1770

12.76 Dish A pagoda among trees on a promontory, and the rim with four scenes of stylized shrubs from a rocky fenced garden. On the back four whiplash under-rim markings, and the letter 'y' within the footrim. Decorated in blue on an off-white glaze.
Diameter 36.3cm, height 4.1cm, shape I
No. N.6696, J. Stone Hodges bequest, 1961
Probably Liverpool *c.* 1770

12.77 Dish With similar decoration to the preceding entry, and with similar under-rim marking, but the figure '7' within the footrim. The decoration in blue on a pale bluish glaze.
Diameter 35.7cm, height 3.2cm, shape I
No. N.6751, J. Stone Hodges bequest, 1961
Probably Liverpool *c.* 1770

12.78 Dish In the centre twin bungalows with trees sprouting up between them, and three other vignettes of hills with shrubs. Surrounded by a border of the 'three-brick' and whorl pattern. On the rim five twining stems from trefoils. On the back noughts and crosses under-rim markings and the figure '3' within the footrim. The decoration in blue on an off-white glaze, with a trace of pink on the back.
Diameter 32.9cm, height 4.9cm, shape I
No. N.6762, J. Stone Hodges bequest, 1961
Probably Bristol *c.* 1720

12.79 Meat Dish Of long octagon shape with octagonal depression, decorated with a Chinese house behind walls on an island, and with a bridge leading to a smaller island, the scene surrounded by a band of trellis and four panels with floral stems. On the rim four sprays of flowers. On the back four herbal sprig under-rim markings. The decoration in blue on a pale bluish glaze.
Dimensions 50.5cm × 37.5cm, height 5.4cm
No. N.3084, purchased ex Hodgkin collection, 1947
Probably Liverpool *c.* 1760

12.80 **Meat Dish** Of long octagon shape with indented corners, and an oval depression, decorated with a Chinaman poling a boat with a rattan shelter and a cat(?) on board, off a rocky coast with trees. A band in the curvature of trellis pattern with triangular inserts and flowers and on the rim many flowers from painted bands and fish-egg areas. The decoration in blue on a pale blue-green glaze.
Dimensions 51.8 × 34.2cm, height 4.5/5.4cm
No. N.5703, purchased 1957
Probably London *c.* 1770

12.81 **Dish** In the centre a pagoda behind a fence with tall trees overshadowing it on the right, surrounded by eight repeats of round panels stretching from the edge to the well, each of which contains a Chinese temple and flagmast. On the back noughts and crosses under-rim markings and the figure '5' within the footrim. The decoration in blue, red and green on an off-white glaze, the back greyish.
Diameter 34.0cm, height 4.6cm, shape I
No. N.3157, Sir Gilbert Mellor bequest, 1947
Probably Wincanton *c.* 1740

See Garner and Archer pl. 122A and p. 66, where it is explained that sherds of this design have been found in excavations at Wincanton. A greyish tinge to the glaze is often an indication supporting a Wincanton provenance.

12.82 **Dish** Two guinea hen by a steep bank with trees, surrounded by a border of double curl pattern. On the rim four repeats of a small house by a willow tree and flowers. On the back noughts and crosses under-rim markings. Decorated in blue, red and green on a pale bluish glaze.
Diameter 33.9cm, height 4.7cm, shape I
No. N.6721, J. Stone Hodges bequest, 1961
Probably Bristol *c.* 1730

12.83 **Dish** Chinese houses with a tree from a rock, and a fence in the foreground. Surrounded by shaped panels containing floral decoration. On the back noughts and crosses under-rim markings and a single brush stroke within the footrim. Decorated in blue, red, green and yellow on an off-white glaze.
Diameter 34.7cm, height 4.5cm, shape I
No. N.6750, J. Stone Hodges bequest, 1961
Probably Bristol *c.* 1740

12.84 Saucer In the foreground a hut by a rock from which a tree sprouts, with a small boat at sea from which a man is fishing. The rim decorated with floral motifs. The decoration in blue on a grey-white glaze. Within the footrim the figure '1'.
Diameter 12.1cm, height 2.0cm
No. N.5547, gift of Miss E. Nesbitt, 1955
Perhaps London *c.* 1780

12.85 Dish An urn of flowers on a table with a Chinaman standing by, and two flying insects, all within a shaped cartouche, inscribed above 'Jacob & Rebecca Anobas'. The rim with a band of trellis diaper and four floral motifs. On the back noughts and crosses under-rim markings. Decorated in blue on a pale bluish glaze.
Diameter 25.6cm, height 2.8cm, shape I
No. G.1991, purchased from T. Charbonnier, 1923
Probably Bristol *c.* 1740

The name 'Anobas' is so rare that we have found no mention of it anywhere; it is possible that the plate was made for some foreign visitor.

12.86 Plate A rim-to-rim scene of a small boat being rowed towards the shore, where there is a pagoda and spires. In the foreground rocks and trees with a perched bird. Inscribed 'Thomas Sarson/1749'. The decoration in blue on a glossy white glaze with a greyish back.
Diameter 22.4cm, height 2.6cm, shape F
No. G.753, Arthur Robinson bequest, 1917
Perhaps Liverpool 1749

No trace has been found of the name 'Sarson'.

12.87 Dish In the centre finely drawn flowers with twining stems and a perched bird, and on the rim similar floral decoration. The colours blue, red, green and yellow on a pale bluish glaze.
Diameter 29.7cm, height 2.6cm, shape F
No. N.6754, J. Stone Hodges bequest, 1961
Probably Bristol *c.* 1750

12.88 Dish Large blooms on a floral vine from a fenced garden, and round the rim five reserves of stylized floral decoration on a trellis background. The decoration in blue, red, green and yellow on an off-white glaze; on the back noughts and crosses under-rim markings.
Diameter 33.0cm, height 4.4cm, shape I
No. N.3168, Sir Gilbert Mellor bequest, 1947
Probably Bristol *c.* 1730

12.89 Plate A basket of flowers with hatched leaves and petals, surrounded by a border on the outer rim of trellis with four inset panels of scrolls. Decorated in blue on a white glaze with pinky tinge; the edge brown.
Diameter 19.2cm, height 4.1cm, shape J shallow
No. N.4930, purchased 1951
Probably Liverpool *c.* 1730

12.90 Plate In the centre a large pomegranate flower on a stem with buds, surrounded by a band of trellis pattern and three panels of floral decoration. On the rim four repeats of similar flowers. On the back noughts and crosses under-rim markings. Decorated in blue on an off-white glaze.
Diameter 22.4cm, height 3.0cm, shape G
No. N.6510, J. Stone Hodges bequest, 1961
Probably Bristol *c.* 1720

12.91 Plate In the centre two tall trees within a fence with peony and chrysanthemum flowers, and hills and a pagoda beyond, surrounded by a neat band of curl pattern in the curvature. On the rim a blue painted ground with floral motifs, and with four panels of trellis. Marked 'I·C/1764'. The edge dark brown, the decoration in blue on a pale bluish glaze. On the back two herbal sprig under-rim markings.
Diameter 22.1cm, height 2.5cm, shape G
No. G.184, purchased 1914
Probably Liverpool 1764

12.92 Plate In the centre a willow tree and peonies with graffito leaves and other flowers in a fenced garden, surrounded by a band of trellis in the curvature. Round the rim three repeats of prunus and peony. On the back two herbal sprig markings. Decorated in blue on a pale blue glaze.
Diameter 23.4cm, height 3.0cm, shape F octagonal
No. G.3106, gift of Mrs E. H. Lowe, 1932
Probably Liverpool *c.* 1750

12.93 Meat Dish Of long octagon shape with oval depression, decorated with peony and prunus from a fenced garden, surrounded by a band of trellis diaper. On the rim four sprays of flowers. On the back herbal sprig under-rim markings. Decorated in blue on a pale bluish glaze.
Dimensions 41.2 × 30.2cm, height 4.0/4.5cm
No. N.3083, purchased ex Hodgkin collection, 1947
Probably Liverpool *c.* 1760

12.94 Dish Rim-to-rim decoration with a house on an island of 'jam roll' appearance, a lanky Chinaman in the foreground, a sailing boat to the left, and clouds or foliage scattered over the whole area. On the back noughts and crosses under-rim markings. The decoration in blue, red and green on a pale blue glaze.
Diameter 34.0cm, height 4.7cm, shape I
No. N.6743, J. Stone Hodges bequest 1961, ex Vassall collection
Probably Bristol *c.* 1740

12.95 Meat Dish Of long octagon shape with indented corners, and oval depression, decorated with bamboo and flowers from a mound with geometrical rocks surrounded by a neat double curl pattern border. On the outer rim a trellis border with floral motifs at the angles. Decorated in blue on a pale bluish glaze; the edge brown. On the back the figure '11'.
Dimensions 56.0 × 25.0cm, height 2.3cm
No. N.5102, purchased 1951
Probably Liverpool *c.* 1770

13 Bristol blue-red-green

We devote this chapter to twenty-four examples we are able to assemble of a very pleasing Bristol decorative style of the early part of the eighteenth century. Two of the pieces are dated 1723 and 1724, and it is probable that they all fall within ten years or so either side of those dates.

The most typical examples of this style are all in rich blue, red and green colours on a glaze which is almost dead white. However, despite the title of the chapter, we have also included a few clearly related pieces in blue only, and three in which yellow occurs as an addition to the three basic colours. Often a blue ground is painted on, leaving floral decoration to stand out within it in the colour of the basic glaze, and forming shaped panels within which floral designs are depicted in all three colours of the palette. Other decorative motifs to be found are the bird-on-a-rock, the hollow rock, a chicken, a spill-shaped vase, a flower basket, flying insects and triple fish. All these derive from Chinese stylistic influences, with the sole exception of the last, which is a Christian symbol of the Holy Trinity. One bowl and one dish have vases of flowers in panels, such as are to be found on tiles. A common rim decoration on the dishes is of symbolized flower buds embellished with a Chinese scroll pattern.

There must be a reasonable presumption that all these pieces came from one Bristol factory. Pountney illustrates no. 13.1 in his pl. VI and attributes it to Temple Back. The catalogue of the Victoria Art Gallery, Bath, illustrates a bowl in pl. II which looks as though it belongs to this group, and attributes it to Brislington of the late seventeenth century; but another bowl – no. 53 – whose description makes it sound similar, is attributed to Temple Back *c.* 1730, which at least tallies with our own assessment of date. The evidence on which these authorities made their attributions to factories is not stated, and until archaeological evidence is forthcoming it is usually wisest not to nominate a factory of origin.

However, in this case the one anomalous decorative motif may provide a clue. If one looks around Bristol for the triple fish symbolizing the Holy Trinity, one does not have far to look. Bristol Cathedral is dedicated to the Holy and Undivided Trinity, and if one enters through the north transept, as one did in the eighteenth century, the triple fish may be seen in a boss of the roof vaulting over one's head, as shown in fig. 19. The possibility therefore arises that either this symbol was

Fig 19 Triple fish motif on a boss in roof vaulting in Bristol Cathedral.

Note
1 I am most indebted to Mrs Alwyn Harper of Bristol for her photograph of the vaulting.

seen by a potter and inspired him to include it in his decoration, or that the articles in question were made for a person connected with the cathedral. The closeness of the cathedral to the Limekiln Lane pottery would suggest that it was that pottery which was involved, soon after it had started up in the first decade of the eighteenth century, and the occurrence of the 'William Pottery' monogram on the back of no. 13.20 may lend some support to this theory, although there is no proof that the monogram is his. In any case this is an admirable style of decoration.

13.1 Bowl

13.1 Bowl Inscribed inside 'Drink Feair/Dont Swear/1724' flanked with Chinese scroll patterns and surrounded by eight lozenges round the bowl. Outside, six panels formed by blue ground containing white floral motifs, the panels containing polychrome flowers. Smaller medallions in the blue ground containing triple fish, and lozenges. Within the footrim an undecipherable mark. Decorated in blue, red and green on an off-white glaze.
Diameter 27.0cm, height 13.7cm
No. N.5949, found at the Red Lodge and accessioned 1959, ex Alderman J. F. Eberle collection
Bristol 1724

Compare Hall Warren collection no. 141, inscribed 'Drink faire Dont Sware 1728', but decorated in blue only with a quite different design outside, and with a bowl of different shape. Note also Hall Warren collection nos. 140 and 142 which may belong to this group.

13.2 Bowl Inside, in blue only, a sprig of chrysanthemums with a perched bird, surrounded by four flowing sprays of flowers and four double lozenges with diagonal cross marks. Outside, four shaped panels formed of blue painted ground containing floral motifs, the panels decorated with polychrome flower sprays. Smaller circular medallions containing flowers. Above the footrim a border of twisted cable. Decorated in blue, red and green on an off-white glaze.
Diameter 36.6cm, height 20.7cm
No. N.6809, J. Stone Hodges bequest, 1961
Bristol *c.* 1730

13.3 Bowl Inside, a polychrome bird on a rock among flowers, surrounded by a border of scroll pattern, and with four ornate scroll motifs round the bowl. Outside, trellis diaper with eight panels of pendent flower sprays; a double curl pattern border round the rim, and a pendent palmate leaf border on the footrim. Decorated in blue, red and green on a white glaze, somewhat crazed.
Diameter 35.4cm, height 20.3cm
No. G.131, purchased 1911
Bristol *c.* 1720

Mentioned by Pountney on p. 170 where he says that alternate panels of flowers are upside down; in fact they all are.

13.4 **Bowl** Inside, a three-masted ship in full sail, surrounded by a border of embellished scroll pattern, outside of which are alternate insects and florets and a ring of *chinoiserie* scroll pattern. Outside are six panels containing urns of flowers with a bird standing on either side and often another in the flowers. The panels divided by blue-painted columns with flower stems within them, and elaborate floral motifs on blue ground above. Decorated in blue on an off-white glaze. Within the footrim the date '1723'.
Diameter 29.4cm, height 16.7cm
No. G.3501, purchased 1939, ex Vassall collection
Bristol 1723

Although decorated in blue only, this bowl appears to belong to this group. Compare the panels of urns with tiles in Anthony Ray's *English Delftware Tiles* p. 49, and with the last dish in this chapter.

13.5 **Bowl** Inside, a floral bunch in blue only. Outside, a blue painted ground with eight large shaped reserves containing flowers with rhomboidal-shaped leaves, and small round reserves interspersed, with symbolic plant forms above and below them. Decorated in blue, red and green on an off-white glaze.
Diameter 30.5cm, height 14.3/14.6cm
No. G.1952, purchased from T. Charbonnier, 1923
Bristol *c.* 1730

13.6 **Bowl** Inside, in blue only, a tuft of grass surrounded by four crosses with empty centres and four circles with a bar through them. Outside, round the rim seven large pendent bud motifs and other floral decoration, four spreading sprays of flowers on the sides and other motifs round the base. Above the footrim, a twisted cable border. Inside the footrim the figure '7'. The decoration in blue, red and green on an off-white glaze.
Diameter 29.0cm, height 15.3cm
No. N.6815, J. Stone Hodges bequest, 1961
Bristol *c.* 1720

13.7 **Bowl** Inside, in blue only, a plant with fern-like leaves surrounded by five sprigs and five crosses with empty centres. Outside, profuse flowers sprouting from rocks, a bird and insects in flight. A rim border of blue painted ground with floral motifs set in triangles, and stiff leaf motifs round the footrim. Decorated in blue, red and green on a white glaze.
Diameter 29.4cm, height 15.0cm
No. N.3210, Sir Gilbert Mellor bequest, 1947
Bristol *c.* 1720

13.8 **Dish** In the centre a bird on a hollow rock among a profusion of flowers, surrounded on the rest of the dish by eight shaped panels on a blue ground each containing a spray of flowers, and by eight medallions containing triple fish, the remainder of the blue ground being embellished with floral motifs in the colour of the glaze. The decoration in blue, red and green on a white glaze. On the back noughts and crosses under-rim markings and the figure '2' within the footrim.
Diameter 36.5cm, height 5.8cm, shape I
No. N.3135, Sir Gilbert Mellor bequest, 1947
Bristol *c.* 1730   COLOUR PLATE, p. 34

Note the similarity of the floral decoration in the panels, and of the triple fish, to those in no. 13.1, and of the shape of the panels to those in no. 13.5.

13.9 **Dish** In the centre a spray of flowers and an insect. On the rim a border of symbolized flower buds embellished with scrolls. Decorated in blue, red and green on a pale bluish glaze.
Diameter 33.0cm, height 4.2cm, shape I
No. N.3149, Sir Gilbert Mellor bequest, 1947
Bristol *c.* 1730

13.10 **Dish** The centre filled with a bird on a rock among flower sprays, and two insects in flight. The rim with symbolized flower buds and scroll embellishment. Decorated in blue, red and green on a bluish glaze with greenish discoloration in places. On the back noughts and crosses under-rim markings and the figure '2' within the footrim.
Diameter 36.2cm, height 6.2cm, shape I
No. N.8466, found in store and accessioned 1974
Bristol *c.* 1720

13.11 **Dish** Three chrysanthemum flowers and buds on a twining stem, surrounded by a border of geometric motifs with rhomboidal leaves linked by curl pattern. On the rim floral and bud motifs embellished with scrolls. On the back noughts and crosses under-rim markings. Decorated in blue, red and green on a white glaze.
Diameter 32.7cm, height 5.3cm, shape F
No. N.6737, J. Stone Hodges bequest, 1961
Bristol *c.* 1730

13.12 **Dish** Two transverse landscapes of twin bungalows, trees and clouds(?), surrounded by a band of interlocking arcs. On the rim six panels each containing a symbolized bud with scroll embellishment, divided by trellis pattern. Decorated in blue, red and green on an off-white glaze, with some pink on the back. Also on the back, noughts and crosses under-rim markings and the figure '7' within the footrim.
Diameter 33.7cm, height 4.6cm, shape I
No. N.6759, J. Stone Hodges bequest, 1961
Bristol *c.* 1730

13.13 **Dish** A cock crowing and a vase by a basket of flowers with three flying insects among other sprigs of flowers. The rim border with eleven repeats of a flower face embellished with scrolls and unopened buds. The decoration in blue, red and green on a white glaze, pink and pitted on the back.
Diameter 34.5cm, height 5.4cm, shape I
No. N.3136, Sir Gilbert Mellor bequest, 1947
Bristol *c.* 1730

13.14 **Dish** A cock in front of a vase and basket of flowers with many flower sprays, surrounded by a linked border. On the rim ten triple buds with scroll embellishment with a cross-hatched band between. Decorated in blue only on an off-white glaze, the back pitted. On the back, noughts and crosses under-rim markings and the figure '8' within the footrim.
Diameter 32.3cm, height 4.8cm, shape I
No. N.6677, J. Stone Hodges bequest, 1961
Bristol *c.* 1730

Note that this is decorated in blue only, but the similarity of the central decoration to that of the previous example is self-evident, and the border of embellished bud motifs also links it to this group. A few other pieces in blue only are included for like reasons.

13.15 **Dish** In the centre a bird with long tail perched on a floral spray, surrounded by seven lotus-shaped panels of floral motifs with rhomboidal leaves, divided by herringbone patterns, with flying insects in medallions. The rest of the rim blue painted with some graffito scrolls. Decorated in blue, red and green on a white glaze, showing pink where it has thinned on the back. Noughts and crosses under-rim markings on the back, and the figure '5' within the footrim.
Diameter 33.2cm, height 4.5cm, shape I
No. N.6739, J. Stone Hodges bequest, 1961
Bristol *c.* 1730

13.16 **Dish** A profusion of flowers sprouting from a hollow rock, surrounded by a border of embellished floral motifs. On the rim a repeat of acanthus leaves. The decoration in blue, red and green on a white glaze with greyish back. Noughts and crosses under-rim markings on the back and the letter 'X' in the footrim.
Diameter 33.0cm, height 5.1cm, shape I
No. N.3139, Sir Gilbert Mellor bequest, 1947
Bristol 1730

13.17 **Saucer Dish** A profusion of flowers growing from the earth, and a perched bird, surrounded by a border of the 'three-brick' pattern. Round the rim six panels with embellished triple buds with rhomboidal leaves, against a blue painted ground. Decorated in blue, red and green on a pale bluish glaze, pinky on the back. The rim gently fluted.
Diameter 29.9cm, height 5.5cm, shape J
No. N.3156, Sir Gilbert Mellor bequest, 1947
Bristol *c.* 1740

13.18 **Jar** Of double-ogee shape with a pair of twisted handles applied just below the neck. No lid. Decorated on either side with a bird perched on a hollow rock among rather sketchy flowers. Debased *ruyi* pattern borders above and below. Decorated in blue, red and green on an off-white glaze. On the base the figure '2'.
Height 15.6cm, maximum diameter 15.7cm
No. G.110, purchased 1904
Bristol *c.* 1720

13.19 Deep Dish In the centre a bird perched on a fence post and a vine sprouting from the ground with stylized flowers. Round the rim a border of embellished bud symbols. Decorated in blue, red and green on an off-white glaze. Noughts and crosses under-rim markings and a heart within the footrim.
Diameter 22.8cm, height 8.1cm, shape I deep
No. N.6783, J. Stone Hodges bequest, 1961
Bristol *c.* 1740

13.20 Dish A four-panelled fence with profuse flowers beyond and a flying insect. On the rim a border of embellished bud symbols. Decorated in blue, red, green and yellow on a pinky white glaze. On the back noughts and crosses under-rim markings and 'WP$_2$' within the footrim.
Diameter 33.4cm, height 4.5cm, shape I
No. G.1191, gift of T. Charbonnier, 1918
Bristol *c.* 1730

Note the appearance of yellow as an added colour in this and the next two pieces. 'WP' is said to stand for William Pottery of the Limekiln Lane pottery in Bristol, and this is one of the only two pieces in the collection so marked.

13.21 Bowl Inside, blades of grass with flowers and a flying insect, surrounded by blue circles. Outside, the inside decoration repeated twice and two sprays of flowers. The rim border of lozenges in ovals, and a blue band above the footrim. Decorated in blue, red, green and yellow on a white glaze.
Diameter 29.8cm, height 15.0cm
No. N.3058, purchased ex Hodgkin collection, 1947
Bristol *c.* 1730

13.22 Jar Of double-ogee shape with twisted handles applied near the top, and a lid of domed shape. Decorated with four floral sprays with depending leaf patterns between, and with scroll pattern borders above and below. The lid with a bird on a hollow rock and flowers. The decoration in blue, red, green and yellow on a white glaze.
Height to rim 14.8cm, maximum diameter 14.1cm
No. G.2319, gift of T. Charbonnier, 1928
Bristol *c.* 1740

13.23 **Dish** In the centre a floral sprig, surrounded by six shaped panels containing similar decoration, divided by blue painted ground through which leaf patterns emerge shaded in lighter blue. All decoration in shades of blue on a white glaze with some pink on the back. Noughts and crosses under-rim markings and the figure '5' within the footrim.
Diameter 36.9cm, height 5.4cm, shape I
No. N.6717, J. Stone Hodges bequest, 1961
Bristol *c.* 1730

13.24 **Dish** An urn with flowers and a perched bird, and three flying insects, with draped curtains behind. A sketchy band of scroll pattern in the curvature, and a rim border of symbolized buds embellished with scrolls. On the back noughts and crosses under-rim markings and the figure '3' within the footrim. The decoration in two shades of blue on a pale bluish glaze.
Diameter 30.3cm, height 4.8cm, shape I
No. N.3081, purchased ex Hodgkin collection, 1947
Bristol *c.* 1730

See the comments on bowl no. 13.4, decorated with urns of flowers. The border decoration is almost identical with that of dish no. 13.19, and quite close to that on several others.

14.8 **Plate**

14   Farmyard and rural

In the early part of the eighteenth century the common sort of delftware plate was often decorated in a very fluent freehand style with birds of the farmyard and of the estate, familiar country animals, simple floral arrangements and country scenes. This style was able to depict its subject in a few lines, and often in bright colours, making it both charming and decorative, but above all giving it vitality.

The shapes of the earlier plates were as shown in appendix I, A to E, without footrims; but later plates with more sophisticated decoration adopted the more sophisticated shapes of F and G, with footrims. It is notable that the majority of the examples are attributable to Bristol, a minority to London, and only two to Liverpool. The first Liverpool pottery only started in about 1710, and Liverpool seems to have concentrated on a more sophisticated pattern of plate from the outset.

The most common subject for these plates, in the Bristol collection, is the farmyard rooster, of which there are eight examples. He was either shown in rim-to-rim decoration between manganese-sponged trees, setting off his brightly coloured plumage to best advantage, or under an arching flower-stem and with a rim decoration of arcs and crescents.

The peacock and pheasant appear with sponged trees with equal effect; while the heron is also pictured, but with less scope for colourfulness, and usually among stylized foliage, making full use of the area of the plate with artistic economy. The swan was another favoured subject.

Rabbits appear on plates nos. 14.19 and 20, among trees and shrubs typical of the style used in London factories, while nos. 14.21 to 23 will probably tax the powers of the best naturalist to identify: the first appears to be a squirrel with a hare's ears, while the other two are usually regarded as squirrels, even though they are obese and have mangy tails!

The dolphin was a popular subject in Bristol, it being the crest of Edward Colston, a Bristol merchant and noted benefactor of his native city, and also being the emblem of the Colston and Dolphin Societies founded in his memory.

Floral decoration starts with a somewhat formalized lily plant, whose development we can trace through several stages of elaboration, both in the lily plant itself and in its accompanying rim decoration. Some of these styles are reminiscent of tulip chargers. On later plates, and also on dishes, the floral decoration becomes much more profuse and blatant, and loses its naive charm.

Country scenes varied greatly, from an imposing castle to an enigmatic pylon-like structure, to small houses and figures among sponged-foliage trees. Among them we find a pottery kiln and a couple of windmills. We should not associate the latter with grinding corn, for many were owned by delftware factories and used for grinding the glaze materials and colours for their use.

We conclude with some simple geometric styles and with a delightful cupid defying the laws of gravity.

220 ENGLISH DELFTWARE

14.1 Plate A rim-to-rim scene of a cock among sponged-foliage trees, decorated in blue, red, yellow and manganese on a pale bluish glaze.
Diameter 18.1cm, height 2.2cm, shape B
No. N.5565, gift of Miss E. Nesbitt, 1955
Probably Bristol *c.* 1720   COLOUR PLATE, p. 35

14.2 Plate A rim-to-rim scene of a cock among sponged-foliage trees, decorated in blue, red, yellow and manganese on a greyish white glaze.
Diameter 22.3cm, height 3.2cm, shape B
No. N.6432, J. Stone Hodges bequest, 1961
Probably Bristol *c.* 1720

14.3 Plate A rim-to-rim scene of a cock standing among sponged-foliage trees, decorated in blue, red, yellow and manganese on an off-white glaze.
Diameter 17.6cm, height 1.7/2.2cm, shape B
No. N.3181, Sir Gilbert Mellor bequest, 1947
Probably Bristol *c.* 1720

14.4 Plate A rim-to-rim scene of a cock standing among sponged-foliage trees, decorated in blue, red, yellow and manganese on an off-white glaze.
Diameter 22.8cm, height 2.9cm, shape B
No. N.3179, Sir Gilbert Mellor bequest, 1947
Probably Bristol *c.* 1720

14.5 **Plate** In the centre a cock standing under an arching flower stem, and an insect in flight. The rim border of arcs and crescents. Decorated in blue, red and green on an off-white glaze with a pinky back.
Diameter 22.5cm, height 2.7cm, shape A
No. N.3197, Sir Gilbert Mellor bequest, 1947
Probably London *c.* 1730

A more carefully drawn version of this border appears on plate no. 14.42, where the design can be more clearly seen. It appears in the reign of Queen Anne, as may be seen from plate no. 10.9.

14.6 **Plate** Very similar to the previous example, though the flying insect has turned into a pair of leaves. Decorated in blue, red and green on an off-white glaze.
Diameter 21.7cm, height 2.8cm, shape A
No. N.5563, gift of Miss E. Nesbitt, 1955
Probably London *c.* 1730

14.7 **Plate** A cock walking with a flower stem arching over. The rim border of interlocking arcs. The decoration in blue, red and green on an off-white glaze.
Diameter 22.1cm, height 3.0cm, shape A
No. N.3196, Sir Gilbert Mellor bequest, 1947
Probably London *c.* 1730

This cock is a bit more stilted than the last two. The border can be found on the Princess Caroline plate no. 10.15.

14.8 **Plate** A rim-to-rim scene of a peacock by a fence among trees with sponged foliage, decorated in blue and manganese on an off-white glaze.
Diameter 22.1cm, height 3.1cm, shape B
No. N.3194, Sir Gilbert Mellor bequest, 1947
Probably Bristol *c.* 1720

COLOUR PLATE, p. 35

14.9 Plate A rim-to-rim scene of a peacock walking among trees with sponged foliage, decorated in blue, red, yellow and manganese on an off-white glaze.
Diameter 23.0cm, height 2.5cm, shape B
No. N.6440, J. Stone Hodges bequest, 1961, ex Maddicks collection
Probably Bristol *c.* 1730

14.10 Plate A rim-to-rim scene of a peacock among sponged foliage trees, decorated in blue, red, yellow and manganese on an off-white glaze with a pinkish tinge.
Diameter 22.7cm, height 3.2cm, shape B
No. N.3178, Sir Gilbert Mellor bequest, 1947
Probably Bristol *c.* 1740

14.11 Plate A pheasant flying over a pair of trees with sponged foliage, the decoration in blue, red, green, yellow and manganese on an off-white glaze.
Diameter 22.2cm, height 2.8cm, shape C
No. N.6433, J. Stone Hodges bequest, 1961, ex Maddicks collection
Probably Bristol *c.* 1740

14.12 Plate A rim-to-rim scene of a pheasant on a gate twisting its head to see an insect overhead; tall flowers on either side in a hedge of green rushes. The colours blue, red, green and yellow on a pale bluish glaze, the back partly bare.
Diameter 20.4cm, height 2.3cm, shape E
No. N.7117, Ernest Blatch bequest 1964, ex Freeth collection
Probably Bristol *c.* 1740

14.13 **Plate** The same decoration as in the previous example, but in blue only on a pale bluish glaze.
Diameter 22.2cm, height 3.3cm, shape E
No. N.6468, J. Stone Hodges bequest, 1961, ex Maddicks collection
Probably Bristol *c.* 1740

14.14 **Plate** A crested heron standing in water among roughly sketched plants, and with four repeats of similar plants round the rim. Decorated in blue on a pale blue glaze.
Diameter 20.4cm, height 2.7cm, shape E
No. N.6443, J. Stone Hodges bequest, 1961, ex Maddicks collection
Perhaps London *c.* 1740

14.15 **Dish** A heron standing in water among profusely flowering plants, with three repeats of similar flowers round the rim. Decorated in blue, red, green and yellow on a pale blue glaze.
Diameter 33.3cm, height 6.0cm, shape I
No. N.6706, J. Stone Hodges bequest, 1961
Probably London *c.* 1750

14.16 **Plate** A swan swimming between two fir trees set in a gourd-shaped frame, and on the rim a circular dashed border. The decoration in manganese and shades of blue on a pale blue-green glaze.
Diameter 22.5cm, height 2.3cm, shape A
No. N.3184, Sir Gilbert Mellor bequest, 1947
Probably London *c.* 1750

14.17 Dish In the centre two sketchily drawn swans swimming in front of Chinese buildings with tall trees, surrounded by a band of herringbone and floral motifs. The rim border of arcs with green ovals and triple dots. The decoration in blue, manganese, red-brown, green and yellow on a white glaze.
Diameter 34.0cm, height 3.8cm, shape I
No. N.6752, J. Stone Hodges bequest, 1961
Probably Liverpool *c.* 1760

14.18 Dish Two sketchy swans swimming in front of Chinese buildings among trees, surrounded by a band of herringbone and floral motifs. The outer rim with a border of arcs and triple dots. Decorated in blue on a pale bluish glaze.
Diameter 26.9cm, height 3.5cm, shape I
No. N.6779, J. Stone Hodges bequest, 1961
Probably Liverpool *c.* 1760

14.19 Plate Two rabbits facing each other either side of a fern-like tree, with similar foliage elsewhere, surrounded by a hooped border. On the outer rim a border of arcs with pendent trefoils. Decorated in blue, red, green and manganese on a white glaze.
Diameter 22.7cm, height 3.5cm, shape D
No. N.3189, Sir Gilbert Mellor bequest, 1947
Probably London *c.* 1770

14.20 Plate A similar example to the previous entry, but with only a double circle round the central scene. Decorated in blue, brown, green and manganese on an off-white glaze.
Diameter 22.9cm, height 3.8cm, shape D
No. N.3190, Sir Gilbert Mellor bequest, 1947
Probably London *c.* 1770

14.21 **Plate** A squirrel with long ears very sketchily drawn, surrounded by a scallop border, and on the outer rim a dashed border on three circular lines. The decoration in blue on a pale bluish glaze.
Diameter 22.6cm, height 2.4cm, shape B
No. N.6465, J. Stone Hodges bequest, 1961
Perhaps Bristol *c*. 1730

14.22 **Dish** In the centre a squirrel surrounded by a circle of leaf motifs and a border of interlocking arcs and crescents; on the rim a repeat of the inner circle of leaf motifs. The decoration in blue on a white glaze.
Diameter 33.2cm, height 5.5cm, shape I
No. G.2046, purchased from T. Charbonnier, 1923
Perhaps London *c*. 1730

14.23 **Dish** In the centre a vine with berries and tendrils, and round the rim similar decoration including two squirrels and intersecting rectangles. Decorated in blue on a pale bluish glaze. On the back noughts and crosses under-rim markings.
Diameter 33.6cm, height 4.8cm, shape I
No. N.6761, J. Stone Hodges bequest, 1961
Probably Bristol *c*. 1740

Compare bowl no. 8.7.

14.24 **Plate** Rim-to-rim decoration of a dolphin with its tail in the air, with its mouth open and apparently spouting water. The decoration in shades of blue on a pale blue glaze.
Diameter 22.9cm, height 2.5cm, shape B
No. N.6501, J. Stone Hodges bequest, 1961
Probably Bristol *c*. 1730

14.25 **Plate** A dolphin with its tail in the air, apparently spouting water, and with a very large eye; a sailing ship on either side. Round the rim four Chinese symbolic scrolls, and four crosses with quadruple dots. Decorated in blue on a pale blue glaze.
Diameter 19.7cm, height 3.0cm, shape A
No. N.5651, purchased ex Fripp collection, 1956
Perhaps London *c.* 1730

Dolphin plates are not uncommon; compare Glaisher collection nos. 1467 and 1521, Reading Museum no. 241.61.16 and Mundy pl. XXXVII. They are usually associated with Edward Colston, the Bristol merchant, though his crest was a dolphin naiant (i.e. swimming horizontally) whereas these seem to be dolphins urinant.

14.26 **Plate** In the centre a bunch of three lilies, surrounded by an indented line. On the rim seven repeats of geometric motifs. Decorated in blue on a pale bluish glaze.
Diameter 22.1cm, height 2.7cm, shape B
No. G.2483, gift of W. Strachan, 1929
Probably Bristol *c.* 1730

14.27 **Plate** Three red lilies on intertwining stems, set in a ring of dashes, and on the outer rim red brush marks. The decoration in blue and red on an off-white glaze.
Diameter 22.2cm, height 3.1cm, shape B
No. N.6814, J. Stone Hodges bequest, 1961
Probably London *c.* 1730

14.28 **Plate** In the centre three lilies, and round the rim fifteen panels with alternate blue and green trefoils. The decoration in blue, red and green on a pale bluish glaze.
Diameter 22.4cm, height 2.8cm, shape B
No. N.5562, gift of Miss E. Nesbitt, 1955
Probably Bristol *c.* 1730

14.29 **Plate** Three lilies in red and yellow from a tuft of green and blue leaves, and round the rim seven trefoils with interconnecting lines. The colours blue, red, green and yellow on an off-white glaze.
Diameter 20.3cm, height 3.2cm, shape E
No. N.7125, Ernest Blatch bequest, 1964
Perhaps Bristol *c.* 1740

14.30 **Dish** Three red and yellow lilies from blue and green leaves, and round the rim ten repeats of floral motifs linked with loops. Decorated in blue, red, green and yellow on an off-white glaze.
Diameter 33.7cm, height 5.7cm, shape I
No. N.3167, Sir Gilbert Mellor bequest, 1947
Probably Bristol *c.* 1750

14.31 **Plate** A central daisy flower flanked by eight blades of tulip leaves and two 'seed pods'. On the rim a border of interlocking arcs. Decorated in blue, red and green on an off-white glaze.
Diameter 21.8cm, height 2.9cm, shape A
No. N. 3185, Sir Gilbert Mellor bequest, 1947
Probably London *c.* 1730

14.32 **Dish** Three peonies among blades of leaves, surrounded by a border of yellow buds in blue and green foliage. The rim decorated with trellis with four reserves of peony buds. Decorated in blue, red, green and yellow on a pale bluish glaze.
Diameter 34.0cm, height 5.8cm, shape I
No. N.3148, Sir Gilbert Mellor bequest, 1947
Probably Bristol *c.* 1750

14.33 Plate A yellow flower and three buds among blue geometrical foliage, and round the rim three repeats of similar buds and stems. Decorated in blue and yellow on a pale blue glaze.
Diameter 19.6cm, height 2.7cm, shape B
No. N.6429, J. Stone Hodges bequest, 1961
Perhaps Bristol *c.* 1720

14.34 Plate Decorated in the centre and round the rim with five sprigs of a flower and rhomboidal leaves, and with other leaves and quadruple dots. The decoration in blue on a pale blue glaze.
Diameter 22.1cm, height 6.0cm, shape F deep
No. G.1194, gift of T. Charbonnier, 1918
Probably Bristol *c.* 1740

14.35 Plate A central spray of flowers and leaves, with quadruple dots scattered about, and on the rim a border of arcs and crescents. Decorated in blue on a pale blue glaze.
Diameter 22.5cm, height 3.0cm, shape B
No. N.6425, J. Stone Hodges bequest, 1961
Probably Bristol *c.* 1720

14.36 Plate Boldly drawn flowers and trees sprouting from behind a fence, and round the rim eight alternating floral motifs. The decoration in blue, red and green on a pale blue-grey glaze.
Diameter 22.3cm, height 3.2cm, shape E
No. N.8458, found in store and accessioned 1974
Probably Bristol *c.* 1740

14.37 **Dish** A rim-to-rim scene of a large peony plant with flower and buds, from a small fence, with bamboo and a flying insect. The decoration in blue, red, green and yellow on a pale blue glaze.
Diameter 33.4cm, height 5.3 cm, shape I
No. N.6710, J. Stone Hodges bequest, 1961, ex Vassall collection
Probably Bristol *c.* 1750

14.38 **Dish** Boldly drawn plants with flowers and rhomboidal leaves from a fenced garden, and insect in flight. Decorated in blue, orange-red, green and yellow on a pale blue glaze.
Diameter 34.1cm, height 6.1cm, shape I
No. N.3142, Sir Gilbert Mellor bequest, 1947, ex Gautier collection
Probably Bristol *c.* 1750

14.39 **Plate** A rim-to-rim scene of a castle among trees with sponged manganese foliage. Decorated in blue and manganese on a pale bluish glaze.
Diameter 19.3cm, height 2.3cm, shape A
No. N.3195, Sir Gilbert Mellor bequest, 1947
Probably Bristol *c.* 1730

14.40 **Plate** A rim-to-rim scene of a pottery kiln belching smoke. Decorated in blue on a pale blue glaze.
Diameter 22.6cm, height 3.1cm, shape B
No. G.1425, purchased 1919
Probably Bristol *c.* 1730

14.41 Plate A windmill in an open landscape with fern-like trees, and on the rim a broad manganese line and narrow blue one. The decoration in blue, red, green and manganese on a pale bluish glaze.
Diameter 23.3cm, height 3.3cm, shape A
No. N.3191, Sir Gilbert Mellor bequest, 1947
Probably London *c.* 1770

14.42 Plate A windmill by a pottery(?) building between two trees, the rim with an arcs and crescents border. Decorated in blue on an off-white glaze.
Diameter 22.6cm, height 2.7cm, shape B
No. N.6471, J. Stone Hodges bequest 1961, ex Maddicks collection
Probably London *c.* 1750

Mundy illustrates three windmill plates in pls. III(2) and V(1) and (3), and attributes them all to Bristol. However, the style of drawing the trees and other aspects of the decoration and glaze suggest London for both of these. Although of 'primitive' style they are not thought to be very early.

14.43 Plate A tower rising from a fence among sponged foliage. The outer rim with twenty-nine sponged half circles. Decorated in manganese and red on a pale bluish glaze.
Diameter 22.7cm, height 2.5cm, shape A
No. N.6439, J. Stone Hodges bequest, 1961
Probably Bristol *c.* 1740

14.44 Plate A futuristic pylon structure surmounted by a cross, rising from the middle of a fence, among sponged trees and foreground, surrounded by a band of lozenges. The rim sponged in blue. The decoration in blue, red and manganese on a pale bluish glaze.
Diameter 22.6cm, height 2.4cm, shape B
No. N. 6461, J. Stone Hodges bequest, 1961
Probably Bristol *c.* 1740

The designs in the centres of these last two plates appear to be related to one another, but what they represent is a mystery. The blue sponging on the rim of this last plate is very rare; for some reason manganese was almost invariably used for this technique.

14.45 **Plate** Trees with sponged manganese foliage with a house to the right, the rim with red dashes on triple blue circles.
Decorated in blue, red, green and manganese on an off-white glaze.
Diameter 22.0cm, height 2.8cm, shape C
No. N.3173, Sir Gilbert Mellor bequest, 1947
Probably Bristol *c.* 1720

14.46 **Plate** A small house with a streamer flying from the flagpole, and trees of 'scaffolding' either side. The rim decorated with six floral swags. The decoration in blue, red and manganese on a white glaze.
Diameter 23.0cm, height 3.3cm, shape A
No. N.6458, J. Stone Hodges bequest 1961, ex Revelstoke collection
Probably London *c.* 1750

Compare Mundy pl. III(1) with the same central scene but a different rim decoration.

14.47 **Plate** A building with streamers flying, among fern-like shrubs, and on the rim six floral swags. The decoration in blue, red, green and manganese on an off-white glaze.
Diameter 22.7cm, height 3.5cm, shape A
No. N.2253, gift of Mrs Hall Warren, 1946
Probably London *c.* 1750

14.48 **Dish** A rim-to-rim scene of a house with trees of stippled foliage. Decorated in manganese, red, green and yellow on an off-white glaze.
Diameter 33.0cm, height 5.3cm, shape I
No. N.4892, purchased ex Hodgkin collection, 1951
Probably London *c.* 1760

14.49 **Plate** A rim-to-rim scene of a lady between trees with sponged manganese foliage and blue stems. Decorated in blue and manganese only on a pale bluish-greenish glaze.
Diameter 22.3cm, height 2.8cm, shape A
No. N.6463, J. Stone Hodges bequest, 1961
Probably London *c.* 1740

14.50 **Plate** A lady with a basket on her head walking between sponged-foliage trees. The decoration in blue and manganese on a pale bluish glaze.
Diameter 18.9cm, height 2.5cm, shape A
No. N.3193, Sir Gilbert Mellor bequest, 1947
Probably London *c.* 1740

14.51 **Plate** A central red rosette surrounded by a ring of interlocking blue arcs, and on the rim alternate dark green and manganese half flower heads. The colours blue, red, green and manganese.
Diameter 22.4cm, height 2.5cm, shape A
No. N.3201, Sir Gilbert Mellor bequest, 1947
Probably London *c.* 1730

14.52 **Plate** An eight-pointed star with alternate spikes in blue and white, and yellow and white, with a red sunburst behind. The inner rim with a circle on which are arrows and noughts, and the outer rim with green dashes on triple blue circles. Decorated in blue, red, green and yellow on an off-white glaze.
Diameter 22.6cm, height 2.7cm, shape B
No. N.6477, J. Stone Hodges bequest, 1961
Perhaps London *c.* 1720, or Continental(?)

The unusual style of decoration causes one to have doubts about the provenance of this plate, but there seems no reason why it should not be English.

14.53 **Plate** A cupid flying with an olive(?) branch in each
hand, the rim painted blue with Chinese scroll pattern
superimposed. Decorated in blue, red, green and yellow on a white
glaze.
Diameter 22.7cm, height 3.3cm, shape B
No. N.3188, Sir Gilbert Mellor bequest, 1947
Probably Bristol *c.* 1720

Compare Garner and Archer pl. 66B and Mundy pl. XXVIII(1).

15   Coloured grounds

The use of coloured grounds was a common style of decoration on delftware. These grounds were either painted on, or were what have come to be known as powdered grounds, though this may not be an accurate description of the method by which the effect was achieved.

The method may indeed have involved the use of powder, sprinkled onto the surface by means of a pounce pot, or a simple tube covered over at one end by a piece of gauze; and close examination of some pieces does suggest that this was the method used. However Pountney, on p. 84, says 'The painter then took his brush, containing a moderate supply of liquid colour, which he tapped on his mahlstick, thus causing a sprinkling to go over that part of the dish not covered with paper. This he repeated until he got an evenly sprinkled surface, which then formed the ground cover.' Yet others suggest that dry powdered pigment was loaded onto a stiff brush, and that the bristles were flicked to achieve the desired result.

There was evidently yet another method of achieving a 'powdered' ground. This was to dip the article, such as a bowl, into a container full of a slurry of powdered pigment in suspension in a glaze mixture. A clue to such a method having been used is when one finds the area within the footrim coloured in the same manner as the rest of the outside of the bowl; while the considerable amount of slurry picked up by dipping is often evident from the mixture having 'run'. This method of decoration precludes the use of paper cut-outs to form reserves, as the slurry would have got under the paper, but it does permit graffito decoration subsequently. It must have been a tricky operation to get the colour up to the rim of the bowl on the outside, and no further. One suspects that the barrels, nos. 15.61 to 15.63, were coloured by dipping, and they could of course have been completely submerged. Note that Charleston's article 'Bristol & Sweden: Some Delftware Connexions'[1] quotes a report on a visit to a Bristol factory as saying 'The vessels which are to be brown, are similarly dipped in a lime-substance composed of reddle, etc.', which is evidently a reference to this technique.

In any case, with methods other than painting or dipping, the ground was usually applied leaving reserves of uncoloured areas within which other decorative motifs could subsequently be painted. These reserves were made by cutting out pieces of paper and applying them to the surface. The reserve might in fact comprise the whole centre of a plate or dish, thus giving a powdered rim. Such styles are often found with a pinky red, or a blue rim, into which vine patterns have been traced with a graffito stylus, the vines being subsequently filled in in yellow in the pinky ground, or left the colour of the basic glaze with the blue ground.

In other cases there is a central reserve, most commonly of round, octagonal or woolsack shape, while four or eight small reserves round the rim may be shaped as fleurs-de-lis, Prince of Wales' feathers, shells, wheatsheafs, fans, flower faces, maple or sycamore leaves, or fish.

The pigment used was most commonly manganese, and the effect obtained with it varied all the way from pink, achieved by sparse use of very fine powder, to a rather unpleasant blotchy liver colour, probably obtained by the method described by Pountney. Other powder grounds were a solid blue, a fine powdery blue-grey, a pinky red, a dark brown – as at no. 15.34 – and a yellow ochre. The only example of the latter known to the author is a plate illustrating the capture of

15.18 **Plate**

Portobello, now in the National Maritime Museum, Greenwich.

The first eleven pieces in the catalogue entries represent a dark blue ground, of which the first seven were probably achieved by one of the 'powder' methods, and the next four appear to have been applied by brush. On nos. 15.5 to 15.7, we encounter rim graffito decoration consisting of stem and leaf outlines traced with a stylus, and flower faces which must have been left clear of powder by sticking paper in the appropriate places, the petal outlines then being added later. It is notable that these flower faces invariably appear to have twelve petals, suggesting that the piece of paper may have been folded in four, and the quadrupled edge then trimmed to a three petal outline.

The next group of six pieces, nos. 15.12 to 15.17, illustrates what is known as the 'woolsack', the central reserve being in the form of a woolsack with tufted corners, while the other reserves round the rim are in the shape of maple leaves. In some cases these reserves are decorated with floral subjects, and in others with a Chinaman fishing. All these reserves are clearly obtained by cut-out paper patterns; sometimes the edges are outlined by a fine brush, sometimes they are left alone.

No. 15.18 is a unique plate in the manner of its rim decoration, although there are four others known with a similar central political cartoon. The symmetry of the graffito decoration suggests that it could not possibly have been done freehand, without some marking out, which is not evident; on the other hand it is scarcely conceivable that such an intricate design was achieved by using a flimsy paper pattern.

There follows a group of seven plates, nos. 15.19 to 15.25, with pinky-red rims with graffito decoration of trailing stems done with a stylus, and in several cases filled in in yellow. The central decoration of all these is in the Chinese style with flowers from fences or hollow rocks, and birds or insects, and in one case a Chinaman. These seem to have been the speciality of one of the London potteries.

But manganese was used for by far the largest number of powdered ground articles, and the Bristol collection contains twenty-three such plates and dishes as well as seven other shapes. A lot of this was done in Bristol and Wincanton, but there are also plenty of examples from London, and some notably fine specimens from Liverpool. All these plates and dishes had the ground applied with paper cut-outs to provide the reserves. The central reserves vary in shape from octagonal to round, lobed, or more tortuous forms, and the reserves round the rims show examples of all the shapes mentioned above. Plates nos. 15.48 to 15.50 have geometrical patterns in their centres, which are more unusual though they are also found on tiles. The rim decoration on plate no. 15.51 is quite remarkable; it appears to have been an experimental attempt to apply a powdered ground by sponging, and was no doubt abandoned as disastrous.

Among the bowls with powdered ground, one should note particularly nos. 15.56 and 15.57, on which there has been graffito decoration of stems with a stylus, and also of leaves and flower petals with perhaps a cloth or special brush, the veins in the leaves and shading of the petals having been added subsequently.

But perhaps, to find the epitome of powdered ground decoration, we should go back to the matching basin and bottle at nos. 15.2 and 15.3. The reserves are of many and interesting shapes, the floral decoration in them, in the Chinese style, is delicately fine, and altogether the workmanship is outstanding and the result most decorative.

Note
1 In *English Ceramic Circle Transactions*, vol. 5, part 4, 1963, pp. 222–234.

15.1 **Mug** With blue powder ground and twelve-lobed reserve with delicate scene of a willow tree and flowers, the oval handle in a leaf-bordered reserve, and marked with diminishing Chinese scroll pattern. The base glazed. Painted in blue only on an off-white glaze.
Height 15.2cm, diameter 10.5cm
No. N.3236, Sir Gilbert Mellor bequest, 1947
Probably London *c.* 1790

Compare Victoria and Albert Museum no. C.25-1958, illustrated in the Rijksmuseum exhibition catalogue no. 167, and lot 53 in Sotheby's London sale of 15 May 1979, which is dated '1790'. There is yet another example of this type in a private collection, dated '1 May 1791'.

15.2 **Basin** With everted octagonal rim, decorated in powdered blue inside with six reserves – three of quatrefoil shape, two of pomegranate shape and one of cloud shape. The reserves all containing delicately drawn flowers and fine grasses. The decoration all in blue on an off-white glaze.
Diameter 26.1cm, height 8.0cm
No. N.3233, Sir Gilbert Mellor bequest, 1947
Probably Liverpool *c.* 1760   COLOUR PLATE, p. 35

Compare the almost identical basin and bottle in the Louis Lipski collection (lot 108 in Sotheby's London sale of 10 March 1981), illustrated in the Rijksmuseum exhibition catalogue no. 128; and also a differently shaped bottle in Mundy pl. XXIV(2).

15.3 **Bottle** Of double gourd shape decorated in powdered blue with three eight-lobed reserves below, and three elongated reserves up the neck, all containing delicately drawn flowering plants. The decoration in blue on a white glaze.
Height 19.7cm, maximum diameter 10.6cm
No. N.3234, Sir Gilbert Mellor bequest, 1947
Probably Liverpool *c.* 1760   COLOUR PLATE, p. 35

See the remarks on the previous entry; two other bottles of similar type are known, but both are of different shapes.

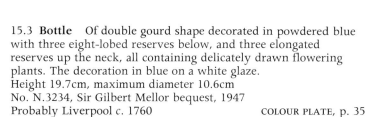

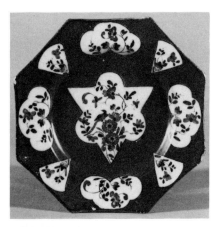

15.4 **Plate** With blue powder ground and a lobed triangular reserve in the centre with a delicately drawn flowering plant and a perched bird. Round the rim, four cloud-shaped and four fan-shaped reserves all containing sprigs of similar flowers. Decorated in shades of blue on a pale blue glaze.
Diameter 20.3cm, height 2.5cm, shape F octagonal
No. N.6488, J. Stone Hodges bequest 1961, ex Freeth collection
Probably Liverpool *c.* 1760

15.5 **Dish** A Chinaman in a fenced garden with flowers from a hummock, and a flying insect. The rim in powdered blue with five white daisies in reserve and graffito stems and leaves. The edge with twenty-seven fluted scallops. All decoration in blue on a pale bluish glaze.
Diameter 29.3cm, height 3.3cm, shape G
No. N.3235, Sir Gilbert Mellor bequest, 1947
Probably London *c.* 1750

Garner's 'Lambeth Earthenware' in the *English Ceramic Circle Transactions*, 1937, illustrates a sherd of this pattern. A very similar dish is illustrated in Mundy pl. XLVII(1), and there is a plate in the British Museum of this type dated '1748'.

15.6 **Plate** Of similar description to the previous dish, but the rim has twenty-eight fluted scallops and four flowers on it. The decoration in blue on a pale bluish glaze.
Diameter 22.3cm, height 2.4/3.3cm, shape F
No. N.6422, J. Stone Hodges bequest, 1961
Probably London *c.* 1750

15.7 **Plate** Of similar description to the previous two entries, but with a circular rim, and the edge red-brown.
Diameter 22.3cm, height 2.9cm, shape F
No. N.7118, Ernest Blatch bequest, 1964
Probably London *c.* 1750

15.8 **Plate** In the centre a flower spray with rhomboidal leaves, surrounded by a band of lozenges. The rest of the plate painted in manganese with four oval reserves containing similar sprays of flowers, and four lozenge-shaped reserves each with a single leaf. The decoration in manganese, blue, red, green and yellow on a white glaze.
Diameter 22.2cm, height 3.0cm, shape G
No. N.6512, J. Stone Hodges bequest, 1961
Probably Bristol *c.* 1740

15.9 **Plate** The whole surface with dark blue powder ground on which are strewn twenty playing cards in reserve. The rim with four flowers in reserve and graffito stems and leaves. The decoration in blue, black and red on a pale bluish glaze of pinky tinge on the back.
Diameter 22.2cm, height 2.9cm, shape F
No. G.2221, gift of T. Charbonnier, 1925
Probably London *c.* 1750

Compare Mundy pl. XXXVIII(2), and lot 50 in Sotheby's London sale of 15 May 1979.

15.10 **Plate** In the centre a rosette surrounded by twelve bud motifs with floral and scroll embellishments. Outside a band of petal-diaper, a blue painted ground containing panels of embellished floral motifs and cactus-like plants. On the back the letter 'S' within the footrim. Decorated in blue on a pale bluish glaze.
Diameter 22.4cm, height 2.7cm, shape C
No. N.6511, J. Stone Hodges bequest, 1961
Probably Bristol *c.* 1730

This piece may be related to those in catalogue chapter 13, but is included here as representative of a type of blue-painted ground.

15.11 **Dish** In the centre a chrysanthemum and leaves against a blue painted ground. On the curvature a border of double curl pattern, and on the rim floral motifs on a blue painted ground. On the back noughts and crosses under-rim markings. Decorated in blue on a white glaze; the back slightly pitted.
Diameter 36.7cm, height 6.3cm, shape I
No. N.7385, purchased 1965
Probably Bristol *c.* 1740

15.12 **Plate** With powdered manganese ground and central woolsack reserve with tufted corners, containing a sprig of flowers and leaves. On the rim four maple-leaf reserves with smaller sprigs of flowers. Green leaves contain manganese veins, and blue leaves graffito veins. The colours manganese, blue, green and yellow on a white glaze.
Diameter 22.7cm. height 3.0cm, shape F
No. G.1178, purchased from T. Charbonnier, 1918
Probably Bristol *c.* 1740

15.13 **Dish** With pale blue-grey powdered ground containing a tufted woolsack reserve and a spray of flowers and leaves within it. On the rim four maple-leaf reserves with smaller flowers. Decorated in blue-grey and blue on a pale bluish glaze.
Diameter 33.5cm, height 5.1cm, shape I
No. N.8465, found in store and accessioned 1974
Probably Bristol *c.* 1760

15.14 **Dish** With blue powder ground and a woolsack reserve containing three flowers and foliage. On the rim four maple-leaf reserves containing smaller sprigs of flowers. On the back ribbon under-rim markings. Decorated in blue, manganese and yellow on a pale bluish glaze.
Diameter 33.3cm, height 5.6cm, shape I
No. N.3360, purchased ex Maddicks collection, 1936
Probably Bristol *c.* 1760

15.15 **Plate** With blue-grey powder ground and a woolsack reserve of a Chinaman with a long pole in a garden with rock, shrubs and flowering trees. Round the rim, four maple-leaf reserves each with a man fishing. Decorated in blue on a pale bluish glaze.
Diameter 22.9cm, height 2.5cm, shape F
No. N.6447, J. Stone Hodges bequest, 1961
Probably Bristol *c.* 1750

15.16 Plate With pale blue-grey powder ground and woolsack reserve of a Chinaman in a garden. Round the rim four maple-leaf reserves of a man stooped over fishing. Decorated in pale blue-grey and blue on a pale bluish glaze.
Diameter 22.4cm, height 3.5cm, shape F
No. N.6497, J. Stone Hodges bequest, 1961
Probably Bristol *c.* 1760

15.17 Plate With similar decoration to the previous one, but the ground of grey powdered pigment. Decorated in grey and blue on a white glaze.
Diameter 22.5cm, height 3.2cm, shape G
No. N.3199, Sir Gilbert Mellor bequest, 1947
Probably Bristol *c.* 1760

15.18 Plate The centre inscribed above 'Libertas Populi' and showing the figure of Justice with sword and scales trampling on a chained man holding a label 'Place/men' in his hand. Enclosed by a pair of garlanded columns and an arch with two cupids blowing trumpets. The rim of powdered manganese with twining leaves and flowers outlined in it and veined in blue. The decoration in manganese and blue on a white glaze. On the back the letter 'B' within the footrim.
Diameter 23.1cm, height 2.4cm, shape F
No. N.4885, purchased 1950
Probably Bristol *c.* 1740

See Ray, *English Delftware Pottery*, pls. 8 and 9, and pp. 132 and 133. The central scene clearly derives from a political cartoon, but one which we have been unable to find. In the *Catalogue of Political and Personal Satires* published by the British Museum, Department of Prints and Drawings, garlanded pillars appear in nos. 1842 and 1869 of 1730 and 1731 respectively, while there are references to Placemen in nos. 1868, 2423 and 2448 of 1731 and 1740. The rhyme below no. 1868 reads:

> 'See Placemen where ends all your Fobbing
> Places, Votes & Boroughs jobbing
> 'Tis but to be the tools of Robin.'

This latter is a reference to Sir Robert Walpole. Placemen were members of Parliament who held offices of profit under the crown or received other financial benefit, and were therefore liable to be corruptly influenced in their voting.

Cartoon no. 2448 is of interest in that it may possibly explain the initials 'T.C.' which appear at the head of three of the plates illustrated by Ray. This cartoon is by Caleb D'Anvers, *nom de plume* of Nicholas Amhurst, who published the political journal *The Craftsman*, and who was prominent in carrying on the campaign against placemen. It is possible that 'T.C.' stands for *The Craftsman*, and that the cartoon we seek was issued with a copy of that journal, in the same way that no. 2448 was issued with the *Daily Gazeteer*, but we have been unable to find any evidence that this was so.

We have already commented on the nature of the border decoration in the introduction to this chapter. A comparison of this plate with the similar one illustrated by Ray shows remarkably few detailed differences; however this was achieved the decorator was undoubtedly a past master of his art.

15.19 Dish Lotus flower and cherry blossom from a Chinese fenced garden, the curvature and rim covered with a pink powder ground in which meandering flower stems are traced in graffito and filled in in yellow. The decoration in manganese-pink, blue, red, green and yellow on a pale bluish-lilac glaze.
Diameter 26.0cm, height 3.9cm, shape I
No. N.6504, J. Stone Hodges bequest, 1961
Probably London c. 1750

15.20 Plate A Chinaman on a fenced terrace, his back to a rock from which flowers sprout. A pagoda on an island beyond. The rest of the plate with a pink powder ground with three twining stems in yellow-filled graffito. The decoration in manganese-pink, blue, red, green and yellow on a white glaze.
Diameter 22.3cm, height 2.5cm, shape F
No. N.3206, Sir Gilbert Mellor bequest, 1947
Probably London c. 1750

15.21 Plate A Chinaman carries a box to the shore where a boat is moored, and on the rim a pink powder ground with vines traced in it in graffito. The colours manganese-pink, blue, red, green and yellow on a pale bluish glaze.
Diameter 22.7cm, height 2.5cm, shape F
No. N.3182, Sir Gilbert Mellor bequest, 1947
Probably London c. 1740

15.22 Saucer In the centre many floral stems sprouting from a rock, with a green perched bird pecking at an insect, and a rim covered in pink powder ground with sprigs of graffito flowers filled in in yellow. The edge yellow. Decorated in pink-manganese, blue, red, green and yellow on a pale blue glaze.
Diameter 22.4cm, height 4.4cm, shape J
No. G.142, purchased 1911
Probably London c. 1750

This and the next saucer are mentioned by Pountney on p. 73. These two pieces are of different shape to the rest of the group, but all are thought to be of London provenance.

15.23 **Saucer** Bamboo and peony flowers from a rock in the foreground, and a tiny willow from the top of a tall rock beyond. The rim with pink powder ground and graffito sprigs filled in yellow. The colours pink-manganese, blue, red, green and yellow on a pale bluish glaze.
Diameter 22.4cm, height 4.0cm, shape J
No. G.138, purchased 1913
Probably London *c.* 1750

15.24 **Plate** A green parrot perched among flowers; the rim with pink powder ground and yellow-filled floral and insect outlines in graffito. The edge light brown. The decoration in manganese-pink, blue, red, green and yellow on a pale bluish glaze.
Diameter 22.6cm, height 3.0cm, shape F
No. N.3205, Sir Gilbert Mellor bequest, 1947, ex Gautier collection
Probably London *c.* 1750

15.25 **Plate** A rock with plants growing from it, and a flying insect. The rim with a pink powder ground with two branching flower sprays and two insects in graffito filled in yellow. Decorated in pink-manganese, blue, red, green and yellow on a pale bluish glaze.
Diameter 22.6cm, height 2.6cm, shape F
No. N.3203, Sir Gilbert Mellor bequest, 1947
Probably London *c.* 1750

15.26 **Dish** An octagonal central reserve on a powdered manganese ground, with a tower and farm buildings, with ships at sea on the left. On the rim four lozenge reserves with floral sprigs, and four wheatsheaf reserves. On the back noughts and crosses under-rim markings and the figure '10' within the footrim. The decoration in manganese, blue and green on a white glaze; the edge beige.
Diameter 34.7cm, height 4.8cm, shape I
No. N.2208, gift of Mrs M. H. Williams, 1945
Probably Bristol *c.* 1750

15.27 Two Plates Both with purple powdered ground with hexagonal central reserves reading:

> *'(1)/When thou sit/down to meat/1739'*

and

> *'(2)/Give thanks/before thou eat/1739'*

Both also inscribed 'B L C/1739' in a lozenge at the top, and with floral sprigs in two other lozenge-shaped reserves, as well as three 'wheatsheafs' in reserves. The edges red-brown.
Diameter (1) 16.7cm, (2) 17.2cm, shapes F
No. G.170, purchased 1914
Bristol or Wincanton 1739

A set of plates in the Museum of London no. A.13490–4, dated 1748 read:

> *(1) When thou sit down to meat*
> *(2) Give thanks before thou eat*
>
> *(4) The mercies thou recieve*
> *(5) That such favours may be*
> *(6) Repeated unto thee*

Ray, *English Delftware Pottery*, p. 145 states that line (3) reads 'To him that always gives'. Reading Museum no. 246.72.52 is a similar plate to no. 6, dated 1746. These are known as 'Grace Plates'.

15.28 Three Plates All with manganese powder ground and a central octagonal reserve showing a fort with corner towers and two sailing ships at sea. In a hexagonal reserve at centre bottom is 'N R V/1739' on two plates and 'R N V/1739' on the third. Three other hexagonal reserves on the rims show sprigs of flowers, and four fan-shaped reserves show Prince of Wales' feathers. The edges of the plates are brown. The decoration otherwise in blue on a white glaze.
Diameters 21.8/22.6cm, height 2.6cm, shapes F
No. G.117, purchased from Alderman J. F. Eberle, 1906
Bristol or Wincanton 1739

The different initials may be a mistake on the part of the decorator, or may have some other significance which escapes us. The initial 'V' was rare either for a Christian or a surname, and we have endeavoured to find a solution to the initials in the Bristol and Wincanton neighbourhoods without success.

There is a resemblance between these and other plates and the arms of the City of Bristol. They are: *On the sinister side a castle with two towers domed, on each a pennon; the dexter base barry wavy, thereon a ship with three masts sailing from behind the castle.* This does suggest a Bristol origin for these plates, though the design might of course have been copied elsewhere.

15.29 **Plate**   An octagonal central reserve on powdered manganese ground, with a fort with towers and ships at sea. On the rim four fan-shaped reserves with Prince of Wales' feathers, and four hexagonal reserves with small floral sprigs. On the back the figure '4' within the footrim. Decorated in manganese and blue on an off-white glaze. The edge brown.
Diameter 22.4cm, height 2.6cm, shape F
No. N.6448, J. Stone Hodges bequest, 1961
Bristol or Wincanton *c.* 1740

Note the similarity of the decoration with no. 15.28.

15.30 **Plate**   Dark manganese powder ground with an octagonal central reserve of a tower and farm buildings, and three ships at sea. On the rim four round reserves of fir cones and four of palm leaf fans. The edge manganese painted. On the back noughts and crosses under-rim markings. The decoration in manganese and blue on an off-white glaze.
Diameter 22.0cm, height 2.7cm, shape G
No. N.6449, J. Stone Hodges bequest, 1961
Probably Bristol *c.* 1750

15.31 **Dish**   Purple manganese powder ground with an octagonal central reserve of a tower and farm buildings, and ships at sea. On the rim four lozenge reserves with floral sprigs and four wheatsheaf reserves. The edge painted yellow. On the back noughts and crosses under-rim markings, and the figures '10' within the footrim. The decoration in manganese and blue on a white glaze.
Diameter 29.3cm, height 4.1cm, shape I
No. N.6766, J. Stone Hodges bequest, 1961
Probably Bristol *c.* 1750

15.32 **Dish** On a powdered manganese ground a central reserve with a man in a cloak by a tree in a landscape. On the rim four round reserves with fleurs-de-lis, and four reserves of wheatsheafs. On the back noughts and crosses under-rim markings. The decoration in manganese and blue on a white glaze.
Diameter 26.1cm, height 3.5cm, shape I
No. N.6479, J. Stone Hodges bequest, 1961
Wincanton or Bristol *c.* 1740

15.33 **Plate** A manganese powder ground with an eight-lobed central reserve of bamboo and flowers. On the rim four hexagonal reserves of an aerobatic bird, and four fan-shaped reserves with leaf stems. Decorated in manganese and blue on a pale bluish glaze.
Diameter 22.8cm, height 2.9cm, shape F
No. G.118, purchased from Alderman J. F. Eberle, 1906
Perhaps London *c.* 1750

15.34 **Plate** A brown powder ground with an eight-lobed central reserve of bamboo and flowers. On the rim eight reserves as on the previous example. The decoration in brown and blue on an off-white glaze.
Diameter 22.9cm, height 2.5cm, shape F
No. N.6428, J. Stone Hodges bequest, 1961
Perhaps London *c.* 1750

15.35 **Plate** Manganese powder ground with an indented-edged lozenge reserve showing a Chinaman with a staff, and two others on their knees before him under a cherry tree. On the rim four fish in reserves. The edge brown. On the back concentric circles under-rim marking. Decorated in manganese and blue on a pale bluish glaze.
Diameter 21.6cm, height 2.9cm, shape F
No. N.6459, J. Stone Hodges bequest, 1961
Probably Liverpool *c.* 1760

15.36 **Plate** Manganese powder ground with an indented circular reserve of a Chinaman on a terrace waving a hand to a bird in flight. On the rim five irregular shield-shaped reserves with flowers from hollow rocks. On the back the letter 'S' within the footrim. Decorated in manganese and blue on an off-white glaze.
Diameter 22.5cm, height 2.9cm, shape F
No. N.6505, J. Stone Hodges bequest, 1961
Bristol or Wincanton *c.* 1760

15.37 **Dish** Pale manganese powder ground with decoration as on the previous example; the edge brown. Decorated in manganese and blue on a pale bluish-grey glaze.
Diameter 38.8cm, height 5.0cm, shape I
No. G.113, purchased 1904
Bristol or Wincanton *c.* 1760

This dish is mentioned by Pountney on p. 73, who attributed it to the Limekiln Lane pottery in Bristol, with no supporting evidence.

15.38 **Plate** Manganese powder ground with an indented circular reserve with a sprig of flowers, and on the rim three fan-shaped reserves with similar flowers. The decoration in manganese and blue on a pale bluish-greenish glaze; the edge yellow.
Diameter 23.0cm, height 2.7cm, shape G
No. N.6435, J. Stone Hodges bequest, 1961
Perhaps Wincanton *c.* 1740

15.39 **Plate** On an even blue ground an indented circular reserve with a house on a fenced terrace under an overhanging tree. On the rim three cloud-shaped reserves with the same house and foliage, and three round reserves with an insect in each. Decorated in blue and blue wash on a pale bluish glaze; the edge dark brown.
Diameter 22.5cm, height 2.3cm, shape F
No. N.6486, J. Stone Hodges bequest, 1961
Probably London *c.* 1760

15.40 Dish A powdered manganese ground with octagonal reserve of a lady with a basket by a rotunda, and round the rim four fan-shaped reserves with delicate floral sprays. The decoration in manganese and blue on a pale bluish glaze with a tinge of violet on the back.
Diameter 34.9cm, height 4.5cm, shape I
No. N.2243, gift of Mrs Hall Warren, 1946
Probably London *c.* 1760

15.41 Dish A powdered manganese ground with indented circular reserve of a Chinaman carrying a bowl of fruit on a fenced terrace, and round the rim four fish in reserves. Decorated in manganese and blue on a white glaze. On the back noughts and crosses under-rim markings.
Diameter 33.5cm, height 4.7cm, shape I
No. G.175, purchased 1913
Bristol or Wincanton *c.* 1750

15.42 Dish A purple manganese powder ground with an indented circular reserve of a Chinaman at a table on a terrace being served wine, and round the rim four fish in reserves. On the back the figure '1' inside the footrim. The decoration in manganese and blue on an off-white glaze; the edge chocolate.
Diameter 32.9cm, height 5.3cm, shape I
No. N.5559, gift of Miss E. Nesbitt, 1955
Bristol or Wincanton *c.* 1750

15.43 Dish Manganese powder ground with an indented roughly circular reserve of a Chinaman in a fenced garden, and round the rim four fish in reserves. Decorated in manganese and blue on a pale bluish glaze, tinged with violet on the back; the edge chocolate.
Diameter 30.5cm, height 3.8cm, shape G
No. N.6767, J. Stone Hodges bequest, 1961
Perhaps Liverpool *c.* 1760

15.44 **Dish** A purple powdered manganese ground with an
indented square reserve of a Chinaman in a fenced garden, similar
to the previous example; and round the rim four fan-shaped
reserves with floral vines. The decoration in manganese and blue
on a pale bluish glaze.
Diameter 34.8cm, height 4.6cm, shape G
No. N.6724, J. Stone Hodges bequest, 1961
Probably Liverpool *c.* 1760

15.45 **Plate** A circular reserve on a pink powder ground with a
vase in front of an urn, both containing flowers, and round the rim
four red wheatsheafs and four motifs of five fish eggs with blue
dots. Decorated in pink-manganese, red and blue on a white glaze.
Diameter 22.8cm, height 3.4cm, shape F
No. N.7112, Ernest Blatch bequest, 1964
Perhaps London *c.* 1760

15.46 **Dish** A circular reserve on a pink powder ground with
profuse flowers from a bowl, and round the rim four fleurs-de-lis
and four wheatsheafs. On the back noughts and crosses under-rim
markings. The decoration in pink-manganese and red on a white
glaze, with some pitting on the back.
Diameter 33.8cm, height 4.9cm, shape I
No. N.6775, J. Stone Hodges bequest, 1961, ex Maddicks collection
Probably Bristol *c.* 1750

15.47 **Dish** An octagonal reserve on a pale blue powder ground
with cherry blossom from a Chinese fence, and round the rim four
octagonal and four tulip-flower-shaped reserves all with delicate
plants. The decoration all in light blue on a pale bluish glaze. On
the back whiplash under-rim markings and the letter 'X' within
the footrim.
Diameter 35.5cm, height 4.4cm, shape I
No. G.112, purchased 1904
Probably Liverpool *c.* 1760

15.48 Plate A manganese powdered ground with central circular reserve containing eight segments alternately of trellis and of a scroll pattern, and on the rim four round reserves of cruciform floral decoration and four wheatsheafs. On the back noughts and crosses under-rim markings. The decoration in manganese and blue on an off-white glaze.
Diameter 22.5cm, height 2.6cm, shape F octagonal
No. N.6431, J. Stone Hodges bequest, 1961
Wincanton or Bristol c. 1740

Tiles occur with this type of decoration. Ray, in *English Delftware Tiles* illustrates one in the Bristol collection at no. 590, and the author has seen others in the possession of Jonathan Horne, the dealer.

15.49 Dish A purple powdered manganese ground with circular central reserve containing ten segments alternately of trellis and fir-cone scale pattern, and round the rim four round reserves of fir-cone and four of wheatsheafs. The edge brown. Decorated in manganese and blue on a pale bluish glaze. On the back noughts and crosses under-rim markings.
Diameter 32.4cm, height 4.1cm, shape I
No. N.5348, purchased 1952
Wincanton or Bristol c. 1740

15.50 Plate Manganese powder ground containing a circular reserve with eight segments alternately of trellis and scroll pattern; round the rim three fish in reserve, and six little rings in graffito, three between the fish and three in the well. Decorated in manganese and blue on a pale bluish glaze.
Diameter 22.2cm, height 2.7cm, shape F
No. G.135, purchased from T. Charbonnier, 1911
Wincanton or Bristol c. 1740

15.51 Plate In the centre a Chinaman dancing between plants, surrounded by a narrow band of Chinese motifs and a broad band of trellis diaper containing four round reserves with flowers among dots. On the rim manganese sponging(?). The decoration in manganese and blue on an off-white glaze.
Diameter 22.7cm, height 2.7cm, shape F
No. N.6460, J. Stone Hodges bequest, 1961
English, first half of eighteenth century

Being unique it is extremely difficult to give this plate either a provenance or a date. The manganese decoration on the rim may have been sponged or may have been applied by tapping a wet brush, but in any case the effect is not aesthetically pleasing.

15.52 Bowl Inside, a small spray of flowers and leaves. Outside pale purple manganese powder ground with three reserves of cloud shape containing two flowers and leaves. Manganese powder inside the footrim. Decorated in manganese and blue on a pale bluish glaze, violet-tinged.
Diameter 23.3cm, height 9.8cm
No. N.6797, J. Stone Hodges bequest, 1961
Probably Bristol *c.* 1750

15.53 Bowl Inside, a small spray of flowers within a double circle. Outside a blue powder ground with three reserves of a spray of flowers and leaves. There is powder colour within the footrim, but most of the outside of the footrim will be seen to be clear of it. The decoration in shades of blue on a white glaze.
Diameter 22.4cm, height 9.6cm
No. G.2034, purchased from T. Charbonnier, 1923
Probably Bristol *c.* 1750

15.54 Bowl Inside, a Chinese landscape of geometrical trees and a house. Outside, four reserves in grey powder ground, each with a similar Chinese scene. Powder within the footrim. Decorated in grey and blue on a pale blue-grey glaze.
Diameter 25.1cm, height 11.7cm
No. N.6784, J. Stone Hodges bequest, 1961
Probably Bristol *c.* 1750

Geometrical trees of this type occur on three sherds illustrated in R. H. Price's forthcoming 'Pottery Kiln-Waste from Temple Back, Bristol' in *City of Bristol Museum and Art Gallery Research Monograph* no. IV.

15.55 Bowl Inside, a spray of flowers and leaves outlined and hatched in blue, surrounded by a border within the rim of trellis containing four Chinese artemisia leaf motifs tied with ribbons. Outside, manganese powder ground with four fish in blue reserves. The decoration in manganese and blue on an off-white glaze, the edge light brown.
Diameter 25.9cm, height 12.4cm
No. N.5545, gift of Miss E. Nesbitt, 1955
Wincanton or Bristol *c.* 1750

15.56 Bowl The inside with two fine circles only. Outside, manganese powder ground with three sprays of flowers in reserve with graffito stems, and with graffito lines encircling the bowl above and below. Blue wash over the manganese on the footrim and some powder within the footrim. The decoration in manganese and blue on a white glaze.
Diameter 26.2cm, height 13.2cm
No. N.3057, purchased ex Hodgkin collection, 1947
Bristol or Wincanton *c.* 1740

15.57 Bowl Inside, three blue circles only. Outside, manganese powder ground with three sprays of flowers in graffito: the white petals with blue striations and yellow centres, the leaves with blue veins and the stems in yellow. Blue wash on top of manganese on the footrim; no colour within the footrim. The colours manganese, blue and yellow on a white glaze.
Diameter 26.3cm, height 13.6cm
No. G.1987, purchased from T. Charbonnier, 1923
Bristol or Wincanton *c.* 1740

15.58 Tea Bowl With powdered manganese ground and four hexagonal reserves of a flower stem. Decorated in manganese and blue on an off-white glaze.
Diameter 6.8cm, height 3.5cm
No. G.1179, gift of T. Charbonnier, 1918
Bristol or Wincanton *c.* 1750

15.59 Brick The top perforated with seven rows of three holes each, and the base flat. Decorated with manganese powder ground with on each side two circular reserves of delicately drawn flowers, and six wheatsheaf reserves. On either end a flying bird in dark brown. The edges marked in brown and the letter 'R' painted over the glaze on the base. Decorated in manganese, blue, red and green on a white glaze.
Length 15.5cm, height 9.0cm
No. G.1177, gift of T. Charbonnier, 1918
Probably Bristol *c.* 1750

Compare Glaisher collection no. 1594 which is similar. Compare also the decoration on the rims of nos. 15.26 and 15.31 above.

15.60 Mug With powdered manganese ground, decorated with the figure of a man riding a horse in graffito, outlined in manganese; the coat blue, and a blue shadow on the ground. A stem and leaves in graffito in front and behind. The narrow strap handle pierced through at the top, and chamfered into the body at top and bottom. The earthenware light in weight and dark in colour. The decoration in manganese and blue on an off-white glaze.
Diameter at top 11.0cm, height 15.3cm
No. G.165, purchased ex Hodgkin collection, 1914
Perhaps Bristol or Continental, first half of eighteenth century

The decoration appears amateurish, and together with the nature of the clay which was used, this piece poses some problems. It may have been an experimental piece to test a sample of clay, but the technique of graffito decoration is not far removed from that on bowls nos. 15.56 and 15.57. See Pountney p. 73.

15.61 **Barrel** Decorated all over in powdered manganese with a bung hole in a rectangular boss in the centre, and with seven diminishing raised rings at each end.
Length 12.5cm, maximum diameter 8.9cm
No. N.4855, purchased 1950
Probably Bristol mid-eighteenth century

Compare Victoria and Albert Museum no. C.15–1963, from Sir Gilbert Mellor's bequest. These are rare articles, and may have been used for a gift of spirit or liqueur. Other such barrels over twice the size of these are illustrated in the catalogue of the exhibition of *Irish Delftware* in Castletown House in 1971.

Three similar barrels are illustrated in pl. X on p. 201, of an article on Lambeth Delft by Celia Hemming in *The Connoisseur* (vol. LII, no. 208) December 1918. She states that she had bought them about twenty years before near Berkhampstead, and gives her opinion that they are of Lambeth origin. There can be no certainty as to where these articles were made until archaeological evidence comes to light.

15.62 **Barrel** The description as for the previous example, but the shape is less sharply tapered.
Length 14.2cm, maximum diameter 10.2cm
No. N.6602, J. Stone Hodges bequest, 1961
Probably Bristol mid-eighteenth century

15.63 **Barrel** Powdered manganese all over with a bung hole in a rectangular boss in the centre with two transverse holes passing through it. Eight raised rings of diminishing size to each end with a sharp taper.
Length 14.8cm, maximum diameter 10.0cm
No. N.6603, J. Stone Hodges bequest, 1961
Probably Bristol mid-eighteenth century

The holes through the boss were no doubt for a cord to secure the bung.

16 Bianco-sopra-bianco

The technique of decoration called *bianco-sopra-bianco* is not literally white on white, as the term would imply, for if that were so much of its effect would be lost. It is, in fact, a decoration in the purest white obtainable, on a glaze containing a tinge of colour – usually bluish or pale blue – which thus enables the decorative patterns to be clearly seen in all their delicate beauty.

The technique is probably in imitation of the somewhat fainter patterns achieved in Chinese porcelain by carving under the glaze. *Bianco-sopra-bianco* appears in several European countries in the early eighteenth century, and in his excellent paper 'Bristol & Sweden: Some Delftware Connexions', in the *English Ceramic Circle Transactions*, 1963, Robert Charleston shows that it was almost certainly brought to England from the Rörstrand factory by a Swede named Magnus Lundberg, whom he clearly identifies as working in Frank's Bristol factory in 1767. As a Bristol-made bowl in the Nationalmuseum, Stockholm, dated 1757, has Magnus Lundberg's name within the footrim, it seems fairly certain that he worked there at least during that ten year period.

Ray, on p. 94 of his *English Delftware Pottery* shows that the earliest *bianco-sopra-bianco* decoration in England is on a plate made in London in 1747; and an identical plate occurs as no. 16.1 in this collection. These early London plates all seem to have a geometric style of decoration. Examples may be found in Garner's article 'Lambeth Earthenware' in the *English Ceramic Circle Transactions*, 1937, pl. XV, and in his *English Delftware* (London 1948) pls. 68A and 69B. A similar pattern is seen on a London sherd in Ivor Noël Hume's *Early English Delftware from London and Virginia*, fig. XVII(8). Apart from these plates, there are a considerable number of London bowls with an almost identical outside decoration in blue and manganese of a *chinoiserie* landscape of pagoda, rocks, trees and fences. Nos. 16.2 to 16.7 are representative of this group, and they have a wide variety of *bianco-sopra-bianco* decorative patterns within the bowls, mostly of trellis or floral type, and faint in colour. These may all be dated between about 1750 and 1755; one such, dated 1755, was sold in London at a Sotheby sale on 14 March 1978, lot no. 50.

Ray showed that the earliest known dated piece of Bristol *bianco-sopra-bianco* decoration is bowl no. 16.8 in this collection, which bears the date 1755. A large number of plates and dishes, and examples of many other shapes, with *bianco-sopra-bianco* decoration then continued to be made in Bristol over the next fifteen years or so. These are nearly all characterized by a glaze of pronounced pale blue colour and a pigment of notably pure white.

Because no London *bianco-sopra-bianco* is known with a date later than 1755, and no Bristol *bianco-sopra-bianco* is known before this date, one would be tempted to suggest that Magnus Lundberg first came to London in about 1747, and moved on to Bristol in 1755. However, there is clear evidence that he was running a pottery warehouse in Bristol in 1750, from an advertisement in the *Bristol Weekly Intelligencer* of 21 April that year. We have already noted that he probably worked in Frank's factory between 1757 and 1767; in 1768 John Wedgwood's account book shows that he was in debt to them, and in 1782 he was declared bankrupt, being described as 'Rope-maker, Broker, Dealer and Chapman'. There may be some confusion in identity, because he had a son named Magnus; but it seems unlikely that either of them had any influence in delftware manufacture much

Fig 20 *Bianco-sopra-bianco*
decorations

after 1767. A booklet, *Magnus Lundberg and the Redcliff Back Pottery* by R. G. and P. Jackson (Bristol 1979) sheds some interesting new light on this elusive Swede.

It would appear that *bianco-sopra-bianco* decoration spread to Liverpool in the early 1760s, perhaps by migration of a Bristol workman. Garner recognized this in *English Delftware* p. 31 and pls. 68B and 69A, though we now think it more likely that plates such as nos. 16.26 to 16.28 were made in Bristol. However, if the evidence of the last chapter of this catalogue, on under-rim markings, is to be believed, then this assists us to identify several more pieces with *bianco-sopra-bianco* decoration, such as nos. 16.37 and 16.38, as Liverpool.

Bianco-sopra-bianco decoration in London and Liverpool was less effective than that produced from Bristol, first because the weaker pigmentation in the glaze provided a paler background for it, and second because the white pigment used was less intense. Charleston and Ray both quote a recipe for making *bianco-sopra-bianco* calx from calcining tin enclosed in clay at a high temperature. This calx would then probably have been mixed with silica sand or ground felspar and made into a slurry for painting on the delftware. We do not know where London or Liverpool obtained their tin calx, but there is good reason to suppose that Bristol obtained it, in common with practically all its mineral requirements, from Cornwall. Moreover a drawing of a calcining kiln appears in *Mineralogia Cornubiensis* of 1778, where it is made evident that its design and operation was an art requiring considerable expertise and experience. Perhaps therefore the Cornish mining industry should take a lot of the credit for the excellence of Bristol *bianco-sopra-bianco* decoration, and perhaps also this goes some way towards explaining the unique dish in the collection, inscribed to Richard Wood of Port Isaac in 1764, at no. 16.33.

The styles of decoration with *bianco-sopra-bianco* were many and varied, and we are indebted to Oliver Van Oss in 'Some Notes on English Delft', *English Ceramic Circle Transactions* vol. V, part 4, 1963, for illustrating and discussing them. For ease of identification we illustrate the patterns on the plates and dishes in this collection (fig. 20). Type B is the most common with thirteen examples, and type C next with eight. It should be noted that the subordinate motifs separating the main motifs of types C and D appear to be interchangeable, as is seen by comparison of nos. 16.27 and 16.28.

Bianco-sopra-bianco was usually used round the rims of plates and dishes, and around the insides and sometimes also the outsides of bowls. But it also occurs on tea caddies, as with no. 16.34, and in this collection there is, too, a puzzle jug with an overall decoration in leaf pattern – no. 16.31 – which is believed to be unique.

There is one rare plate in the collection, no. 16.16, in which the rim decoration may more properly be described as *rosa-sopra-bianco* and this is discussed fully in the catalogue entry.

16.1 **Plate** The rim decorated with *bianco-sopra-bianco* in a
Chinese scroll pattern. The centre with a *chinoiserie* scene of
flowers from a fenced garden, and a small boat at sea. On the back
'I ᴵ S/1747'. Decorated in blue on a pale blue glaze.
Diameter 22.8cm, height 3.0cm, shape F
No. G.1971, purchased from T. Charbonnier, 1923
London 1747

Compare Hall Warren collection no. 152, which is similar. Garner in
'Lambeth Earthenware', *English Ceramic Circle Transactions*, 1937,
illustrates in pl. XV(a) sherds of a plate with similar *bianco-sopra-
bianco* decoration, which were recovered in Lambeth. Moreover
Ivor Noël Hume in *Early English Delftware from London and
Virginia*, illustrates a related sherd in pl. XVII(8).

   It is possible that the initials relate to the marriage of John
Jackson of St Margaret's Westminster and Sarah Cronk of St
Saviour's (i.e. Southwark Cathedral) in St George's Chapel on 26
June 1747. The fact that the bride came from within a few hundred
yards of several delftware factories makes this sound likely. St
George's Chapel in Curzon Street was much used for clandestine
weddings, though after 1744 the ceremonies were held in an
adjoining house.

16.2 **Bowl** Inside, 'Success To The/British Arms' surrounded in
part by *bianco-sopra-bianco* leaf sprays, and in part by polychrome
flowers and leaves. Outside, Chinese houses in a rocky landscape
and a Chinaman walking by a fence. The footrim is splayed out.
The decoration in blue, green, yellow, manganese and white on a
pale blue-grey glaze.
Diameter 25.8cm, height 11.7cm
No. G.2059, purchased from T. Charbonnier, 1923
London *c.* 1750

16.3 **Bowl** Inside, 'One/Bowl more/And then' surrounded by a
faint deep band of a variation of trellis pattern in *bianco-sopra-
bianco*. Outside, a Chinese island with rocks, willows, houses and
trees. The colours blue, manganese and white on a pale blue glaze;
the edge yellow.
Diameter 22.1cm, height 9.0cm
No. G.101, gift of A. Trapnell, 1904
London *c.* 1750

16.4 **Bowl** Inside, 'Success/To the British/ARMS' surrounded in *bianco-sopra-bianco* by an inner ring of leaves, and round the rim by four repeats of flowers with twining stems. Outside, a Chinese island with rocks, willows, houses and trees. The decoration in blue and white inside, and blue and manganese outside on a clear pale blue glaze. The edge brown.
Diameter 26.6cm, height 10.6cm
No. G.157, purchased ex Hodgkin collection, 1914
London *c.* 1750

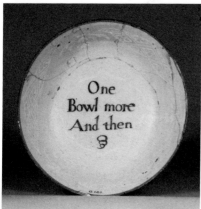

16.5 **Bowl** Inside 'One/Bowl more/And then' surrounded by faint *bianco-sopra-bianco* in three panels of trellis pattern and three of a floral motif. Outside, Chinese fences with a pagoda, rocks and trees. Decorated in blue and white inside and blue and manganese outside on a clear pale blue glaze; the edge yellow-brown.
Diameter 17.1cm, height 7.5cm
No. G.161, purchased ex Hodgkin collection, 1914
London *c.* 1750

16.6 **Bowl** Inside, a spray of flowers in blue with shaded leaves and petals, within an ogee-shaped panel and surrounded by sparse floral motifs round the rim, all in *bianco-sopra-bianco*. Outside, a Chinese landscape of pagoda, rocks, fences and trees. The decoration in blue, manganese and white on a pale blue glaze. The edge brown.
Diameter 22.2cm, height 10.4cm
No. N.3247, Sir Gilbert Mellor bequest, 1947
London *c.* 1750

16.7 **Bowl** Inside, a plant in manganese with shaded petals and leaves, surrounded by decoration in *bianco-sopra-bianco* of a shaped panel and two fan-shaped areas with spreading vines. Outside, a Chinese house, fence, rocks and trees. Decorated in manganese and blue outside on a clear pale blue glaze; the edge brown.
Diameter 23.0cm, height 9.9cm
No. N.6796, J. Stone Hodges bequest, 1961
London *c.* 1750

16.8 Bowl Inscribed inside 'ONE:BOWL:MORE,/AND:THEN./ 1755' surrounded by faint *bianco-sopra-bianco* in a floral pattern with trailing stems and florets interspersed in the inscription. Outside, a Chinese scene of four men in a boat, another boat by a rocky shore and Chinese buildings. The decoration in blue and white on a pale blue glaze.
Diameter 34.8cm, height 14.4/15.2cm
No. G.155, purchased ex Hodgkin collection, 1914
Bristol 1755

This and NO. 16.32 are the earliest known dated pieces of *bianco-sopra-bianco* attributed to Bristol; see Ray, *English Delftware Pottery*, pp. 92–95. This one is illustrated by Pountney in pl. XI among the pieces acquired by the City of Bristol Museum and Art Gallery from the Hodgkin collection in 1914. It is mentioned by Charleston in 'Bristol & Sweden: Some Delftware Connexions', *English Ceramic Circle Transactions*, 1963, footnote 48. The faintness of the *bianco-sopra-bianco* decoration suggests that the pigment used had not yet reached the state of perfection that we find exemplifying this work in Bristol.

16.9 Plate A Chinese island with conical tree, houses and rocks, a Chinaman fishing, and two men in a boat in the foreground. On the rim *bianco-sopra-bianco* decoration type B. The centre decoration in blue on a pale blue glaze.
Diameter 22.9cm, height 2.9cm, shape F
No. G.134, purchased from T. Charbonnier, 1911
Bristol *c.* 1760

16.10 Plate Similar in description to the previous. The decoration in white and blue on a blue glaze.
Diameter 23.0cm, height 2.3cm, shape F
No. G.134, purchased from T. Charbonnier, 1911
Bristol *c.* 1760

16.11 **Plate** Similar in description to the previous two.
Diameter 22.8cm, height 2.7cm, shape F
No. N.3225, Sir Gilbert Mellor bequest, 1947
Bristol *c.* 1760

16.12 **Dish** Similar description to the previous three, though on a larger scale. The border decoration is repeated six times instead of three times on the plates.
Diameter 42.5cm, height 5.2cm, shape I
No. N.6689, J. Stone Hodges bequest, 1961
Bristol *c.* 1760

16.13 **Dish** A pair to the previous one. The decoration in blue and white on a pronouncedly blue glaze.
Diameter 41.7cm, height 5.5cm, shape I
No. G.198, purchased from W. J. Pountney, 1917
Bristol *c.* 1760

16.14 **Plate** Of similar description to others of this group, though the leaves of the 'pineapple' in the rim decoration are much extended.
Diameter 22.8cm, height 2.8cm, shape F
No. N.6454, J. Stone Hodges bequest, 1961
Bristol *c.* 1760

16.15 **Meat Dish** The decoration similar to that of the plates and dishes, but adapted to the elongated shape. The shape oval with slightly indented edge.
Dimensions 31.2 × 25.0cm, height 2.3cm
No. N.5410, purchased 1953
Bristol *c.* 1760

16.16 **Plate** The central scene as on previous examples in this group, but the rim decoration in *rosa-sopra-bianco*. Decorated in blue and pink on a pale blue glaze.
Diameter 22.3cm, height 2.6cm, shape F
No. G.2016, purchased from T. Charbonnier, 1923
Bristol *c.* 1760

The author is aware of only six articles on which this *rosa-sopra-bianco* occurs. It was first presumed that some trace element had been added to the tin calx used for *bianco* decoration, either by accident or design, which had caused the discoloration. We are indebted firstly to Dr A. R. Lang of the H. H. Wills Physics Laboratories, Bristol University, for conducting tests to identify the cause. However, tests he undertook by energy dispersive X-ray microanalysis on a scratch sample from a similar plate belonging to the author did not disclose any reason for the abnormal colour.

Assistance was then sought from Mr Tom Smith of the Geochemical Laboratories, Institute of Geological Sciences, whose report is appended in Appendix III. This confirms that there is no chemical difference between *bianco* and *rosa* detectable by the most searching non-destructive testing available. It is a fact that there are eighteen petals in the multi-petal flower faces of *rosa* decoration, as against the more normal twelve with *bianco* decoration. This suggests that either the consistency of the slurry, or the surface to which it was applied, differed from the normal.

The conclusions of the I.G.S. report lead one to believe that the white tin calx must have been applied to the plate in its biscuit state, before being dipped in the glaze, thus permitting a reaction between the calx and some element (iron?) in the clay body of the plate during its firing, without any barrier of glaze between them.

The ready assistance of the Institute of Geological Sciences and of Ortec Ltd. in this research is greatly appreciated.

16.17 **Dish** With the same central scene as all the preceding in this group, but *bianco-sopra-bianco* pattern of type C, and a rim with twelve scallops, alternately double and single. On the back ribbon under-rim markings.
Diameter 25.4cm, height 4.0cm, shape F
No. G.1965, purchased from T. Charbonnier, 1923
Bristol *c.* 1760

16.18 **Plate** A Chinese island with tall fir trees, houses and a rock, surrounded by a narrow band of trellis. The rim decorated with *bianco-sopra-bianco* type C. Decorated in blue and white on a pale blue glaze.
Diameter 23.0cm, height 3.1cm, shape F
No. G.3600, Mrs A. Robinson bequest, 1942
Bristol *c.* 1760

16.19 **Plate**   The description similar in every respect to no. 16.18.
Diameter 22.5cm, height 2.6cm, shape F
No. N.3602, purchased 1948
Bristol *c*. 1760

16.20 **Plate**   With the same central decoration as the last, but the
bianco-sopra-bianco pattern of type B. Decorated in blue and white
on a pale blue glaze.
Diameter 22.8cm, height 2.7cm, shape G
No. N.3790, purchased 1949
Bristol *c*. 1760

16.21 **Plate**   The centre scene as in the previous three examples,
and the rim with *bianco-sopra-bianco* type C on a rim shaped with
twenty-four scalloped edge.
Diameter 22.8cm, height 3.1cm, shape F
No. N.2251, gift of Mrs Hall Warren, 1946
Bristol *c*. 1760

16.22 **Plate**   In the centre profuse peony and bamboo from a
four-panelled Chinese fence, the rim heavily painted with *bianco-
sopra-bianco* type B. The decoration in blue and white on a pale
blue glaze.
Diameter 22.6cm, height 2.6cm, shape F
No. N.6453, J. Stone Hodges bequest, 1961
Bristol *c*. 1760

16.23 **Plate** In the centre a delicately drawn Chinese island with a willow from the top of a tall rock, two Chinamen on a bridge, a house and a boat, all surrounded by a narrow band of trellis and floral motifs. The rim with twenty-four scalloped edge decorated with *bianco-sopra-bianco* type C. On the back almond branch under-rim markings.
Diameter 22.4cm, height 2.8cm, shape G
No. G.756, A. Robinson bequest, 1917
Bristol *c.* 1765

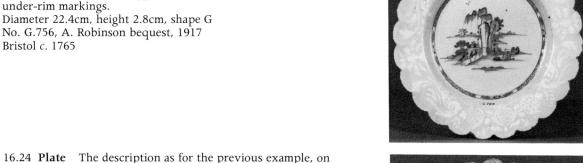

16.24 **Plate** The description as for the previous example, on front and back, except that this is a smaller plate with a deeper well.
Diameter 17.6cm, height 3.6cm, shape F
No. N.6956, purchased 1962
Bristol *c.* 1765

16.25 **Dish** The central scene as on the last two, though the narrow band around it is of petal diaper and floral motifs. The rim with twenty-nine fluted scallops decorated with *bianco-sopra-bianco* type G. The decoration in manganese, blue, yellow and white on a blue glaze.
Diameter 34.0cm, height 4.3cm, shape G
No. N.8462, found in store, and accessioned 1974
Perhaps Bristol *c.* 1760

There are several plates with this type of *bianco-sopra-bianco* decoration, and polychrome centres, inscribed to Charles Cordy of Norwich, 1760, in a private collection. The uncertainty as to provenance arises because it will be seen that nos. 16.35 and 16.36 have the same centre decoration, yet are attributed to different cities; moreover the *bianco-sopra-bianco* in several plates of this type has an iridescence not seen in any other Bristol pieces. Compare Rijksmuseum exhibition catalogue no. 145, (Victoria and Albert Museum no. 3704–1901).

16.26 **Plate** A bunch of flowers in typical Fazackerly style tied with manganese twine, the stems green and the petals and leaves shaded in manganese. On the rim *bianco-sopra-bianco* of type D. The decoration in blue, red, green, yellow, manganese and white on a pale blue glaze. A piece of the plate broken out.
Diameter 22.2cm, height 2.8cm, shape F
No. G.2043, purchased from T. Charbonnier, 1923
Bristol or Liverpool *c.* 1760

The provenance of this and the two succeeding pieces is debatable. The glaze and the quality of the *bianco-sopra-bianco* suggest Bristol; the Fazackerly flowers suggest Liverpool, while the pattern of the *bianco-sopra-bianco* decoration does not seem to occur outside this group of pieces. The evidence of under-rim markings suggests that Fazackerly decoration was not exclusive to Liverpool – see nos. 17.6, 17.13 and 17.14 – which thus leads us to favour a Bristol provenance for these pieces.

16.27 **Plate** A bunch of flowers in Fazackerly style, tied with twine, with the rim decorated in *bianco-sopra-bianco* type D. Decorated in blue, red, green, yellow, manganese and white on a blue glaze.
Diameter 22.9cm, height 3.0cm, shape F
No. N.3068, purchased ex Hodgkin collection, 1947
Bristol or Liverpool *c.* 1760

16.28 **Plate** The description as for the preceding two plates.
Diameter 23.0cm, height 2.2cm, shape F
No. N.3213, Sir Gilbert Mellor bequest, 1947
Bristol or Liverpool *c.* 1760

This plate is illustrated in Rackham and Read fig. 116.

16.29 **Plate** A Chinaman seated by a fence in a garden, in the middle of a three-tier decoration in similar style. The rim with *bianco-sopra-bianco* type B. Decorated in blue and white on a blue glaze.
Diameter 22.5cm, height 4.2cm, shape F deep
No. G.1980, purchased from T. Charbonnier, 1923
Bristol *c.* 1760

16.30 **Bowl** Decorated with *bianco-sopra-bianco* inside and out down to six centimetres from the rim, inside with alternate pine cones and flower faces, and trellis panels, and outside with pine cones and flower faces only. Inside are a lady and gentleman by a tall elm on the sea shore, with ships at sea, the foreground with rococo acanthus scrolls, and a 'tiara' of *bianco-sopra-bianco*. The outside with four country scenes divided up by tall elms with sponged foliage: (i) a house among trees, (ii) a gentleman between two ladies, (iii) a river with two ships, (iv) a country house with lady balancing a basket on her head. The decoration in shades of blue, and in white on a pale blue glaze.

Diameter 37.5/38.3cm, height 15.1/15.7cm
No. N.8837, purchased 1975
Bristol *c.* 1765   COLOUR PLATE, p. 36

Compare the John and Susanna Mays bowl in the Cecil Higgins Museum, Bedford, which is dated 1766, and the Wigelantia bowl in the Greg collection, Manchester, which can be dated to about 1765. Many details of the 'Bowen' style of decoration are closely similar.

16.31 Puzzle Jug With spherical bowl and wide straight-sided neck formed of ten interlocking circles. The bowl covered in petals outlined in *bianco-sopra-bianco*, with three rococo reserves showing scenes typical of *chinoiserie*. Floral motifs decorate the handle and rim, the handle having one hidden hole in it. The decoration in blue and white on a pale blue glaze.
Height 16.8cm, bowl diameter 12.4cm
No. N.3357, purchased ex Maddicks collection, 1936
Bristol *c.* 1765   COLOUR PLATE, p. 37

For other puzzle jugs see catalogue chapter 6. This is believed to be the only jug with this type of decoration on the bowl.

16.32 Dish Inscribed 'DE MOEDER ENDE HAAR DOGTER ANNO 1755 – F.L.G.' showing a three-masted ship in full sail all in blue with two red crosses on the flag at the stern. The rim with a twenty-four scalloped edge decorated in *bianco-sopra-bianco* type B. On the back under-rim markings, and an 'HB' monogram and the figure '2' within the footrim. The colours blue, red and white on a pale blue glaze.
Diameter 32.7cm, height 6.0cm, shape I deep
No. N.8563, purchased 1974
Bristol 1755   COLOUR PLATE, p.37

The inscription is Dutch for 'The Mother and her Daughter'. There is no trace of this ship having visited Bristol, either in the records of the Merchant Venturers, or the Port Books in the Public Record Office, or Lloyd's Lists of Shipping. Enquiries in Holland and Belgium have been equally unproductive. However, by chance, in going through some Liverpool Port Books in the Public Record Office we were struck by a ship named *The Father and his Two Sons* of Danzig, which is the only ship's name we have ever found resembling 'The Mother and her Daughter'. It is also notable that the flag on this ship bowl bears two red crosses – the only red in the decoration – and the only flag resembling this is that of Danzig, though the crosses are differently disposed. The National Maritime Museum have now very kindly acted as intermediary in making enquiries of a source in Gdansk with whom they have previously corresponded, and this may in due course bear fruit.

16.33 **Dish** Inscribed 'RICH^D WOOD/Port Isaac./1764' in the centre, the rest of the area of the dish being decorated in *bianco-sopra-bianco* with four panels of trellis diaper and floral designs. The decoration in blue and white on a pale blue glaze.
Diameter 34.1cm, height 4.5cm, shape I
No. G.2182, purchased 1924
Bristol 1764

We find Richard Wood described as a shopkeeper in Port Isaac, Cornwall, but he was probably the only one in a village then consisting of some seventy houses. It was to his house that John Wesley went after he first preached there on the quay in 1765, and also in several later visits. Richard Wood bought the Wesleyan Chapel there in 1804 jointly with William Billings, Mariner, who was also a witness to his will, made in 1794.

In the Bristol Outwards Port Books in the Public Record Office, for 3 September 1755 we find the 'Three Sisters of and for Padstow R^d Billing Mr' and for 20 September 1756 the 'Three Sisters of Port Isaac, Master Jno Billings' sailing for Padstow. These masters must surely have been members of William Billings' family? In the Padstow Outwards Port Books we find that cargoes included 'Coyned Tin, Lead Oar, Copper Oar and Pewter', while one inbound cargo included:

1 basket galleypots
6 crates Earthenware
6 bask^t Apoth^y ware

Thus it would seem that Messrs Wood and Billings were the merchants of Port Isaac, and that they were involved in coastal trade with Bristol, including delftware and the raw materials involved in its manufacture. Other minerals available from the vicinity of Port Isaac were iron, cobalt, manganese and antimony, and all these minerals were refined locally, while calcining kilns were also operated. It is therefore quite likely that Richard Wood supplied the Bristol delftware potters with many of their needs, and this could have included the particularly fine tin calx which characterized *bianco-sopra-bianco* decoration in Bristol at this time, and of which this dish is surely a uniquely fine example.

16.34 **Tea Caddy** Of upright rectangular shape with protruding chamfered corners. Decorated on the two sides with a Chinaman under a willow tree, and a Chinaman with a parasol in a garden. The two ends with delicate floral sprays, and the four chamfered surfaces with *bianco-sopra-bianco* type B. Round the neck 'ANN SCOTT 1763'. The decoration in blue and white on a pale bluish glaze.
Body height 8.6cm, base 7.9 × 5.5cm
No. G.1976, purchased from T. Charbonnier, 1923
Bristol 1763   COLOUR PLATE, p. 37

16.35 Plate A Chinese temple with fences and a man walking past with a staff, surrounded by a narrow band of lozenge and floral motifs. The rim decorated with *bianco-sopra-bianco* of type C. On the back edge grasses under-rim markings. Decorated in blue, manganese and yellow on a pale blue glaze.
Diameter 22.9cm, height 2.5cm, shape F
No. G.2222, gift of T. Charbonnier, 1925
Bristol *c.* 1760

16.36 Plate The same central decoration as the previous example, though by a different hand. On the rim faint *bianco-sopra-bianco* decoration of type C, the rim being fluted with twenty-four scallops. The decoration in blue, manganese, yellow and white on a pale bluish-greenish glaze. On the back herbal sprig under-rim markings.
Diameter 22.5cm, height 2.5cm, shape F
No. N.3227, Sir Gilbert Mellor bequest, 1947
Probably Liverpool *c.* 1760

16.37 Dish A Chinaman with a teapot meets a lady with a streamer on a stick on a fenced terrace with huge cherry blossom. On the rim faint *bianco-sopra-bianco* type E. On the back four herbal sprig under-rim markings. Decorated in blue, red, green, yellow, manganese and white on a pale bluish glaze.
Diameter 30.2cm, height 4.0cm, shape I
No. N.3166, Sir Gilbert Mellor bequest 1947, ex Gautier collection
Liverpool *c.* 1770

16.38 Plate A delicately drawn scene of a figure sitting under a tree, with buildings beyond, surrounded by a narrow band of lozenge and floral motifs. The rim with faint *bianco-sopra-bianco* of type F. The decoration in blue, grey-green, yellow, manganese and white on a pale blue glaze with slight violet tinge.
Diameter 22.4cm, height 3.0cm, shape F
No. N.5877, purchased 1958
Probably Liverpool *c.* 1770

The reasons for attributing these last three pieces to Liverpool really arise from consideration of the herbal sprig under-rim markings on the first two of them, which is discussed on p. 315. The faintness of the *bianco-sopra-bianco*, the uncommon patterns in which it is applied, the character of the glaze and the colours employed in decorating the central scenes, all come into consideration.

17   Fazackerly

The style of decoration which we call Fazackerly is probably the most beautiful in all English delftware, and is almost exclusive to Liverpool. The name arises from two pieces in the Liverpool Museum of which Joseph Mayer, in the *History of the Art of Pottery in Liverpool*, 1855, wrote:

> *Among the specimens now exhibited are two 'mugs', the body and glaze similar to the other specimens just named, but ornamented with flowers and leaves in blue, yellow and green colours. The larger one, a quart mug, having on the side near the handle the letters and date 'T.F., 1757,' was made at the pot works in Shaw's Brow, and presented to Thomas Fazackerly by a friend of his, a workman there. Mr Fazackerly having married during the following year, his friend made the smaller mug, which holds a pint, ornamented in the same style and colours, but the initials and date, are 'C.F., 1758,' being in an oval. This he gave to the newly-married lady, Catherine Fazackerly, from whose son, now living at Newton-le-Willows, I purchased them last year.*

Mrs C. Hemming, in an article 'Liverpool Delft' in *The Connoisseur*, April 1918, states that they were 'certainly made at Samuel Shaw's pottery', though she quotes no evidence to support this assertion.

It has not been previously remarked that there was a Fazackerly in what was presumably a managerial post in a delftware factory in Liverpool as early as 1718. Nicholas Blundell's Diary for that year, on 25 November, reads: 'I went to ye Mugg-hous and congratulated Capt: Fazak: for his Post there, young Mr Faz: gave me a bowl of Punsh.' It is clear from other entries that this refers to Captain Robert Fazackerly, who died only three years later, and that the 'Mugg-hous' was a delftware factory. Thus there was a direct family connection with the industry some thirty-nine years before the first of the famous Fazackerly mugs was made.

Unfortunately the two Fazackerly mugs were destroyed by enemy bombs during the last war, but there is a water colour painting of them in the Liverpool Museum by the artist who illustrated Joseph Mayer's book, and also a pair of water colour paintings by an anonymous artist showing the decoration of the mugs rolled out flat. We are most grateful to the Merseyside County Museums for permission to reproduce these latter in colour for the first time in colour plate p. 38. These show that, as well as the blue, yellow and green quoted by Mayer, the first mug was also decorated in manganese, while the second one omitted blue but added red, and that both had manganese stems and veining. Thus the full Fazackerly palette includes blue, yellow, green, amethyst purple (manganese), and red, while the stems and veins in the leaves are often drawn in manganese, as well as the shading of the petals. One also notices a series of manganese dots or strokes on the green stems of some pieces, for example no. 17.7.

We have said that the Fazackerly palette is almost exclusive to Liverpool. One exception seems to be some plates with an undoubted Bristol glaze and *bianco-sopra-bianco* rim decoration, with a bunch of Fazackerly flowers in their centres, such as we have catalogued at nos. 16.26 to 16.28. An unusual feature of this group of pieces is that in every case of which the author is aware the bunch of flowers is tied with a piece of twine drawn in manganese. But this string also appears in no. 17.10 which is thought to be a Liverpool piece. One can only account for an anomaly such as this by supposing that a Liverpool potter migrated to Bristol, and brought the style of decoration with him.

Another anomaly is that dishes nos. 17.6, 17.13 and 17.14 all have under-rim markings which we associate with Bristol on the basis that sixty-one other pieces in the collection, with such markings, tally with the Bristol attributions we had already given to them from other considerations, (see p. 315). It will also be noted that these same pieces have what we have called 'lobster claw' buds, which may thus be a characteristic of Bristol decoration rather than of Liverpool.

As we have seen from the two original mugs, a Fazackerly article did not always have every colour of the palette in it. Thus it will be noted among articles in this chapter that red has been omitted from no. 17.4, blue from nos. 17.6, 17.13 and 17.18, and manganese from no. 17.3. Moreover colours from the Fazackerly palette may be recognized in the decoration of other articles, and may thus assist one in assigning to them a Liverpool provenance.

The City of Bristol Art Gallery is extremely fortunate in having what must surely be the most beautiful piece of Fazackerly which does survive: the William Rowland jug, no. 17.1, here illustrated in colour in all its glory.

17.1 **Jug** With elongated spherical bowl curving in to the neck and out to the spouted rim, standing on a turned-out footrim. The neck inscribed 'William Rowland 17–63' and the bowl decorated with blue and yellow flower faces, and a profusion of red, manganese, yellow and blue buds, with green stems and leaves with manganese veining. A spray of similar flowers is on either side of the neck. The handle of double-ridged section painted solid blue, the tail curled up. The colours as recited on a pale bluish glaze.
Height 24.3cm, bowl diameter 16.2cm
No. G.173, purchased ex Trapnell collection, 1914
Liverpool 1763   COLOUR PLATE, p. 39

This jug is discussed by Pountney on pp. 148–149, who confused the inscription with Thomas Rowland, and suggested a Bristol provenance. It is also illustrated in colour in Garner and Archer pl. G, and mentioned on p. 33. The identity of William Rowland is elusive. There was a William Rowland who married a Mary Robinson at St George's, Liverpool, in 1753, and there were John, Charles and George Robinson, all of whom were potters. But we have not been able to trace their births or establish that they were related to Mary.

17.2 **Bowl** Inside, a spray of flowers with yellow flower face, two red buds and green leaves with manganese veins. Outside, blue and yellow five-petal flower faces, two blue and four red buds with similar foliage; and on the reverse side a spray as inside. The colours as recited on a pale blue glaze.
Diameter 26.4cm, height 11.0cm
No. N.3242, Sir Gilbert Mellor bequest, 1947
Liverpool *c.* 1750

17.3 **Bowl** Inside, a small sprig with red bud. Outside, a yellow flower face with four blue, three red and two yellow buds among leaves with no veining; and a small sprig on the reverse side as inside. The glaze bluish-greyish.
Diameter 22.7/23.1cm, height 9.5cm
No. N.6790, J. Stone Hodges bequest, 1961
Liverpool *c.* 1760

17.4 **Plate** A bunch of Fazackerly flowers in the centre and smaller sprays of flowers and leaves on the rim. On the back herbal sprig under-rim markings and a simple plant within the footrim. The decoration in blue, manganese, yellow and green on a pale blue glaze.
Diameter 22.7cm, height 2.6cm, shape F
No. N.3065, purchased ex Hodgkin collection, 1947
Liverpool *c.* 1760

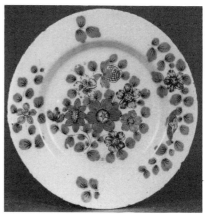

17.5 Dish A red flower face in a spray of three yellow, one blue and one manganese buds, and round the rim four sprigs of small red flowers and yellow buds. All foliage and stems green with manganese veins. The colours as recited on a pale blue glaze.
Diameter 34.1cm, height 4.2cm, shape I
No. N.3154, Sir Gilbert Mellor bequest, 1947
Liverpool *c.* 1760

17.6 Dish 'Fazackerly'-style flowers across the plate in manganese, yellow and red-brown, with green foliage veined in manganese. At top and bottom a small sprig with 'lobster claw' bud. On the back noughts and crosses under-rim markings. The glaze pale bluish.
Diameter 33.1cm, height 5.1cm, shape I
No. N.3155, Sir Gilbert Mellor bequest, 1947
Probably Bristol *c.* 1760

Note the different style of painting in the right hand flower face, and the lobster claw buds, together with the under-rim markings.

17.7 Plate A red flower face, three yellow and one blue buds in green leaves with manganese veining, and round the rim three sprigs with one red face and one yellow bud each. The colours on a pale bluish glaze.
Diameter 22.3cm, height 2.6cm, shape F
No. N.3211, Sir Gilbert Mellor bequest, 1947
Liverpool *c.* 1760

17.8 Dish A bunch of flowers in Fazackerly style, with four small sprigs round the rim. Decorated in blue, red, green, yellow and manganese on a pale blue glaze.
Diameter 25.4cm, height 2.9cm, shape I
No. N.3067, purchased ex Hodgkin collection, 1947
Liverpool *c.* 1760

17.9 Dish A bunch of flowers from rim to rim, with a blue and a yellow flower face, and blue and red buds in green foliage veined with manganese. At top of the rim a yellow bud, and at bottom four leaves. Decorated on a pale blue glaze.
Diameter 33.8cm, height 3.7cm, shape I
No. N.6744, J. Stone Hodges bequest, 1961
Liverpool *c.* 1760

17.10 Dish A manganese flower face with yellow, blue and red buds in green foliage with manganese veins; the bunch tied with a twine. On the rim four sprigs with buds and four patterns of petals. The decoration on a pale blue glaze.
Diameter 33.8cm, height 4.8cm, shape I
No. N.6747, J. Stone Hodges bequest, 1961
Probably Liverpool *c.* 1760

Note the piece of twine which also appears on those with *bianco-sopra-bianco* rims at nos. 16.26 to 16.28. Compare Hall Warren collection no. 111.

17.11 Dish A manganese flower and three yellow buds in green foliage with manganese stems, and round the rim four sprays of flowers in various colours, and four crosses with a floral motif in each quarter. The decoration in blue, red, green, yellow and manganese on a pale bluish glaze.
Diameter 35.0cm, height 4.0cm, shape I
No. G.1558, purchased 1920, ex Lloyd collection
Probably Liverpool *c.* 1750

17.12 Plate Rim-to-rim decoration in the Fazackerly palette of flowers growing from a fenced garden. Decorated in blue, red, green, yellow and manganese on a pale bluish glaze.
Diameter 23.1cm, height 2.7cm, shape F
No. N.6489, J. Stone Hodges bequest, 1961
Probably Liverpool *c.* 1760

17.13 Dish Rim-to-rim decoration of a manganese flower face and red and yellow buds, and green leaves with manganese veining, all from a rather frail garden fence. Two more buds on the rim. The decoration in red, green, yellow and manganese on a pale blue glaze. On the back ribbon under-rim markings.
Diameter 33.2cm, height 5.2cm, shape I
No. N.3153, Sir Gilbert Mellor bequest, 1947
Bristol *c.* 1760

Note the reappearance of lobster claw buds on this and the following piece, both attributed to Bristol.

17.14 Dish A rim-to-rim spray of a manganese flower face and blue, yellow and red buds from a frail fence on the right. On the rim two sprigs with red buds. Decorated in blue, red, green, yellow and manganese on a pale blue glaze. On the back noughts and crosses under-rim markings.
Diameter 33.4cm, height 5.3cm, shape I
No. N.6748, J. Stone Hodges bequest, 1961
Bristol *c.* 1760

17.15 Plate A yellow bowl full of flowers and foliage in the Fazackerly palette, and round the rim three long sprays of similar flowers. Decorated in blue, red, green, yellow and manganese on a pale bluish glaze.
Diameter 22.4cm, height 2.7cm, shape F
No. N.3066, purchased ex Hodgkin collection, 1947
Probably Liverpool *c.* 1750

17.16 Brick The top perforated with two rows of three holes at each end, and a centre square hole, and standing on a hollow flat base. On each side are flowers from a Chinese fence, and on each end a sprig of three 'lobster claw' buds. Decorated in red, blue-green, yellow and manganese on a pale blue glaze.
Length 14.8cm, width 6.9cm
No. N.5059, gift of Lady Wills, 1951
Bristol or Liverpool *c.* 1760

17.17 **Brick** The top perforated with three rows of three holes at each end and a large round hole in the centre, standing on a hollow base, the skirt cut away in indented curves. On each side red and yellow flowers among green and blue leaves with manganese veining, from a fenced garden. At each end a sprig of yellow flowers with leaves. The decoration in blue, red, green, yellow and manganese on a pale bluish glaze. The top blue painted.
Length 12.8cm, width 5.5cm
No. N.6588, J. Stone Hodges bequest, 1961
Liverpool *c.* 1750

17.18 **Cup** Of cylinder shape curving in to the footrim, and round-section handle. Decorated with a bunch of flowers in the Fazackerly palette. The colours red, green, yellow and manganese on an off-white glaze.
Height 6.3cm, diameter 5.9cm
No. N.3784, found in store and accessioned 1949
Liverpool *c.* 1760

18 Landscapes with figures

Hugh Owen, in his *Two Centuries of Ceramic Art in Bristol*, published in 1873, illustrated in Figs. 123 and 124 (which we reproduce as Fig. 21) a delftware dish fourteen inches in diameter, which he describes as 'a fine circular dish with wavy margin, dated and signed by the decorator. It is a good example of Bristol delft. The landscape is clear blue, with the figures in the peculiar manganese colour that is characteristic of Bristol pottery.'

His Fig. 123 shows the back of the dish, inscribed 'Ye 1st Septr 1761 Bowen fecit'. On the basis of this inscription all articles decorated with a landscape and figures approximating to those on this dish, tend to be known as Bowen style. Most such landscape scenes include tall elm trees with foliage applied by sponging, but it has been pointed out that in fact the foliage in Owen's Fig. 124 does not appear to be sponged. However, his illustrations are wood engravings, and a friend of the author's who is an artist experienced in this field, after examining Fig. 124 has said that it probably is as close to sponged foliage as an artist in this medium could achieve, particularly at that scale.

Hugh Owen's book was originally printed privately by John Bellows of Gloucester, and subsequently published by Bell and Daldy of London in the same year. Unfortunately the successors to both these publishers have none of the original art work, which might have shed further light on the nature of the decoration on this dish.

Now, when the Alexandra Palace was opened in June 1873, it contained an exhibition of English pottery and porcelain. Its catalogue, of which there is a copy in the Victoria and Albert Museum Library, includes 2353 items. No. 577 reads:

'Large DISH of delft ware, signed "T. Bowen, fecit 1761"
figured in H. Owen's "Ceramic Art", Bristol

Mr Henry Willett.'

It will be noted that the quoted inscription varies in several respects from that in Owen's Fig. 123, and as the latter appears to be a facsimile of the original, one is inclined to believe it.

Fig 21 Front and back of a Bristol delft dish illustrated in Hugh Owen's *Two Centuries of Ceramic Art in Bristol* (1873) at Figs. 123 and 124.

There is a note following the 'Preliminary Notice' to the catalogue, which reads (in part):

> ∴ *The collection here described perished when the Alexandra Palace was destroyed in the disastrous fire of Monday 9th June. A very few pieces were rescued, and some specimens not wholly destroyed by the fire were recovered from the ruins; it was then observed that the Bristol porcelain resisted the heat which fused the Chelsea, Worcester, etc. and had it not been for the destruction caused by the masses of falling masonry, many examples might thus have escaped . . .*

It will be realized that the fire took place within a week of the opening of Alexandra Palace, and it caused such destruction because the Palace was built on the crest of a hill, and the only source of supply of water for the fire engines was from ornamental pools at the foot of the hill. In these circumstances it was beyond the capabilities of the engines to pump water as high as the roof. As nothing further has ever been heard of the 'Bowen fecit' dish, it must be assumed that it undoubtedly perished in the fire.

Pountney on p. 175 says that 'Bowen' was John Bowen who was apprenticed at the Limekiln Lane pottery in 1734, and later worked at Temple and Redcliff. There is no record of his becoming a Burgess. On the other hand there was a Henry Bowen, of whom there is no apprenticeship record, who did become a Burgess in 1741 by vote of Common Council and on paying a fine of fifteen guineas. This is the year in which John Bowen should have completed his seven years' apprenticeship, and one cannot help wondering if these two were in fact the same person with some confusion over the Christian names. A fine might have been levied because a person had not been apprenticed at all; on the other hand it might have been imposed because he broke the terms of his apprenticeship in some way, and was thus not eligible to become Free in the normal manner. For instance, an apprentice may not marry during the term of his apprenticeship, unless his master releases him from that obligation, and we know that John Bowen married in 1738.

A dish with a 'wavy margin' as illustrated is most unusual from any English delftware factory, but it perhaps strengthens one's belief that this was a very special piece and merited the inscription on the back, which was equally uncommon. The inclusion of figures in manganese is another unusual feature of this dish. The 'Bowen style' pieces in this collection are all painted in monochrome blue or manganese. Many different types of article are so decorated, and there are many of them, so that one is bound to conclude that there was a team of artists all working to the designs of their master, whoever he was.

It is interesting to note that, on two baluster-shaped vases in a private collection, the decoration includes tall elm trees with sponged foliage; however, on one of this pair the artist has drawn in the tall stems of the tree, but no foliage has been added. This, also, suggests a team of artists each adding his own particular contribution to the decoration, and indeed this was the probable procedure with all types of decoration. One is reminded that in Père d'Entrecolles' letter from China in 1712, he states that 'I am told that a piece of fired porcelain has passed through the hands of seventy workmen'.

There are eleven pieces in the collection which one really associates with 'Bowen style', and they all show a pair of figures in a landscape of typical trees, and have the same feeling as the original 'Bowen fecit' dish, notwithstanding, as we have pointed out, that that dish had several unique features. There follow seven plates which all show a man poling a boat on a river, with barrack-like buildings on the far shore. These plates, which are attributed by Pountney on p. 151 and pl. XLI to Bowen, are no doubt all supposed to be of the same pattern, but the variations introduced by a different painter are in some cases quite obvious. All these first pieces have been attributed to Bristol *c.* 1750 or *c.* 1760. As we have seen, Bowen (John or Henry) finished his apprenticeship in 1741, so that, if we attribute this work to him there is no reason why his style should not have developed earlier; but we simply have no dated pieces to guide us.

The pieces which follow in the catalogue illustrate other types of landscape decoration, nearly all with figures, in most of which are trees with sponged foliage. Where the style of decoration does not give us the same feeling, where examination of its features show differences – such as trees with short branching trunks, rather than long slender ones – and where the tint of the glaze and colour of pigment used, all suggest a different provenance, we have made our judgement accordingly.

In the case of no. 18.39 there is the feeling of a Dutch influence, but as this might equally arise from a Dutch artist coming to this country, or from its manufacture in Holland, we cannot be at all certain of its provenance. Nos. 18.44 and 18.45 are polychrome plates of a quite distinct style, in which the trees are not sponged, but a colour wash has been applied over outlined foliage. The final two pieces show the favoured style of decoration to be found in the centre of many Bristol *bianco-sopra-bianco* plates and dishes in catalogue chapter 16. Two other notable examples of 'Bowen style' are posset pots nos. 4.18 and 4.19.

18.19 **Square Brick**

18.1 **Dish** A rim-to-rim scene of two figures in a landscape, a tall elm with sponged foliage in the foreground, a building on right, other trees and hills in the distance. Decorated in blue on a pale bluish glaze.
Diameter 34.0cm, height 4.3cm, shape I
No. N.3082, purchased ex Hodgkin collection, 1947
Bristol *c.* 1760

18.2 **Plate** A rim-to-rim scene of two figures in a landscape, a tall elm with sponged foliage in the foreground, a building on the right, and other trees and hills beyond. Decorated in blue on a pale bluish glaze. The edge with twenty-four scallops.
Diameter 22.5cm, height 2.6cm, shape F
No. N.3362, purchased ex Maddicks collection, 1936
Bristol *c.* 1760

18.3 **Dish** A rim-to-rim scene of two figures in a landscape, with a tall elm with sponged foliage in the foreground, and many shrubs; a building on the right, and other trees and substantial buildings in the distance. The decoration in blue on a bluish glaze.
Diameter 37.7cm, height 4.0cm, shape I
No. N.6746, J. Stone Hodges bequest 1961, ex Vassall collection
Bristol *c.* 1760

18.4 **Plate** A rim-to-rim scene of two ladies walking in a landscape, with a tall elm with sponged foliage in the foreground, a rocky outcrop in front, a house on the right and open country beyond. The decoration in blue on a pale bluish glaze. (Damaged.)
Diamcter 23.0cm, height 2.3cm, shape F
No. G.120, gift of F. Lyne, 1913
Bristol *c.* 1750

This plate is mentioned by Pountney on p. 73.

18.5 **Plate** A rim-to-rim scene of two ladies walking in a landscape, a sapling with sponged foliage in the foreground, and a house on the right. Decorated in blue on a pale bluish glaze.
Diameter 22.5cm, height 3.4cm, shape F
No. G.3598, Mrs A. Robinson bequest, 1940
Bristol *c.* 1750

18.6 **Brick** The top perforated with three rows of three holes with two large square holes interposed. The skirt cut away to leave L-shaped feet at the corners. On each side two ladies in a landscape with elms with sponged foliage, and a house. At each end a barrack-like building with central tower and two small elms. Decorated in blue on a pale bluish glaze.
Length 15.0cm, width 6.1cm
No. N.3071, purchased ex Hodgkin collection, 1947
Bristol 1750-60

18.7 **Brick** The description as for the previous example, except that the scene on the ends is of a small cottage with a single elm tree by it.
Length 15.0cm, width 6.3cm
No. N.3072, purchased ex Hodgkin collection, 1947
Bristol 1750-60

18.8 **Basin** A wash basin with everted rim decorated with a scene matching that on the following bottle. The scene surrounded with two bunches of grapes and acanthus leaves. On the outside of the bowl, four Chinese artemisia leaf symbols tied with ribbons. The decoration in blue on a clear pale blue glaze.
Diameter 26.8cm, height 8.9cm
No. N.3223, Sir Gilbert Mellor bequest, 1947
Bristol *c.* 1750   COLOUR PLATE, p. 40

The bottle and basin were clearly intended as a matching set, and their decoration is fairly closely related to that of the preceding pieces.

18.9 **Bottle** Of beetle shape with tapering neck and chamfered rim. On the body a gentleman and a lady stand, he waves a hand towards a house on the right; on the left is a tall elm and the sea with a sailing boat and rocky island. A bunch of grapes hangs down the neck. The decoration in blue on a white glaze.
Height 26.0cm, diameter 12.0cm
No. G.2024, purchased from T. Charbonnier, 1923
Bristol *c.* 1750   COLOUR PLATE, p. 40

18.10 **Tea Pot Stand** A circular disc standing on three knob feet, with a scene of a gentleman in a three-cornered hat and a lady in a country landscape of slender-stemmed trees with sponged foliage and bushes and part of a fence in the foreground. Decorated in blue on a pale blue glaze.
Diameter 21.9cm, height 2.6cm
No. N.3080, purchased ex Hodgkin collection, 1947
Bristol *c.* 1750

18.11 **Dish** A rim-to-rim scene similar to the last piece, but the two figures are on a smaller scale, and some mountain peaks have appeared on the horizon. The decoration in blue on a pale blue glaze.
Diameter 34.1cm, height 4.2cm, shape I
No. N.6764, J. Stone Hodges bequest, 1961
Bristol *c.* 1750

18.12 Dish A rim-to-rim scene of two men in a punt being poled, a very slender stemmed tree on the left with sponged foliage, and a long barrack-like building across the water with hills beyond. On the back noughts and crosses under-rim markings. Decorated in blue on a pale blue glaze.
Diameter 33.6cm, height 5.3cm, shape I
No. G.186, purchased 1915
Bristol *c.* 1760

Compare Ray, *English Delftware Tiles*, pl. 188.

18.13 Plate The description as for the previous one, except that there are no under-rim markings.
Diameter 22.7cm, height 3.1cm, shape F
No. N.3251, Sir Gilbert Mellor bequest, 1947
Bristol *c.* 1760

18.14 Plate The description as for the previous two, without under-rim markings, but the edge of the plate shaped with six single and six double lobes.
Diameter 18.0cm, height 2.2cm, shape F
No. N.3250, Sir Gilbert Mellor bequest, 1947, ex Gautier collection
Bristol *c.* 1760

18.15 Plate A pair to the previous plate in every respect. The decoration in blue on an off-white glaze.
Diameter 18.1cm, height 2.2cm, shape F
No. G.187, purchased from W. J. Pountney, 1915
Bristol *c.* 1760

18.16 **Dish** A rim-to-rim scene of a boat being poled, and a
sailing boat, with slender stemmed trees with sponged foliage in
the foreground, a barrack-like building and trees on the far shore.
On the back edge grasses under-rim markings. Decorated in blue
on a pale bluish glaze.
Diameter 33.4cm, height 4.2cm, shape I
No. N.6770, J. Stone Hodges bequest, 1961, ex Gautier collection
Bristol *c.* 1760

18.17 **Plate** A boat being poled off the shore and a sailing barge
in mid-stream, with a tall elm with sponged foliage in the left
foreground. Buildings and trees on the far shore. Decorated in blue
on a pale blue glaze.
Diameter 22.9cm, height 2.7cm, shape F
No. N.2249, gift of Mrs Hall Warren, 1946
Bristol *c.* 1760

18.18 **Brick** The top perforated with three rows of three holes
with two large square holes interposed, standing on a flat base.
On either side a central tall slender stemmed tree with sponged
foliage, a sailing barge beyond, and a spire and more trees on the
far shore. On the ends, a tree with a spire one end, and a tree with
a tower the other. Decorated in blue on a pale blue glaze.
Length 14.3cm, width 6.2cm
No. N.6590, J. Stone Hodges bequest, 1961
Bristol *c.* 1760

18.19 **Square Brick** The top perforated with five large and
sixteen small holes, the base flat. Decorated on each of four sides
with a lady and gentleman walking in a hilly landscape, an urn on
a pedestal to the left, and church with conical hills on the right.
The decoration in blue on a pale blue glaze.
The top 12.7cm square, height 10.3cm
No. G.1867, purchased 1922
London or Bristol *c.* 1760

For other bricks of this shape see chapter 7.

18.20 Puzzle Jug With spherical body and wide neck formed of interlocking circles; the hollow rim with three spouts and hollow handle, decorated with blue dashes and Chinese artemisia leaf motifs tied with ribbons. The body decorated with a lady and gentleman in a hilly landscape with elms with sponged foliage, a house, haystacks and a fence. The decoration in blue on a pale bluish glaze.
Height 21.8cm, bowl diameter 13.6cm
No. G.2040, purchased from T. Charbonnier, 1923
Bristol *c*. 1760

Illustrated in Garner and Archer pl. 101, Rijksmuseum exhibition catalogue no. 119, and Rackham and Read fig. 111. Many features of the decoration will be recognized from the preceding plates and dishes. For other puzzle jugs see catalogue chapter 6.

18.21 Vase Of urn shape with two flat strap handles curled top and bottom, painted with the scene of a countrywoman with a basket among sponged-foliage trees by a sphere on a pedestal. The base with a stiff leaf design. Decorated in blue on a pale bluish glaze.
Height 15.2cm, rim diameter 13.5cm
No. N.6598, J. Stone Hodges bequest, 1961
Perhaps Wincanton *c*. 1750

See Garner and Archer pl. 123A and p. 66; this seems to be a related piece.

18.22 Vase Of urn shape with two lion-mask moulded handles outlined in blue; decorated on one side with a woman carrying a basket, and on the other with a couple walking, all among trees with foliage of finely painted whorls, and buildings with hills beyond. The base decorated with scrolling floral stems. The decoration in blue on a pale bluish glaze.
Height 20.7cm, rim diameter 16.8cm
No. N.3253, Sir Gilbert Mellor bequest, 1947
Probably London *c*. 1750

18.23 Vase A pair to the preceding one, viewed from the reverse side.
Height 20.0cm, rim diameter 16.5cm
No. N.2247, gift of Mrs Hall Warren, 1946
Probably London *c*. 1750

18.24 **Vase** Of urn shape with two lion-mask moulded handles painted all in blue. On one side a lady and gentleman in a landscape, she pointing, he with tricorn hat and walking stick. Slender trees with feathery foliage, and buildings. On the other side a countrywoman with a sheaf of corn under her arm in similar landscape. Decorated in blue on a pale bluish glaze.
Height 23.5cm, rim diameter 18.9cm
No. G.2050, purchased from T. Charbonnier, 1923
Probably London *c.* 1750

Compare Garner and Archer pl. 97, which appears to be almost identical.

18.25 **Tea Pot Stand** A flat disc on three shaped feet, decorated with two men in a landscape with slender-stemmed trees with sponged foliage, and buildings and hills beyond. The decoration in blue on a pale bluish glaze.
Diameter 19.1cm, height 3.0cm
No. N.6586, J. Stone Hodges bequest, 1961
Bristol *c.* 1760

18.26 **Square Brick** The top perforated with five large and twelve small holes; a hollow flat base. Each side with a hut among rocks in fern-like vegetation; all somewhat blurred. Decorated in blue on a pale blue glaze.
The top 12.6cm square, height 10.8cm
No. N.3070, purchased ex Hodgkin collection, 1947
Probably London *c.* 1750

18.27 **Bottle** With globular body, the neck gently curved to an everted trumpet mouth. A man with a mule walks towards a house with lattice windows and a five-barred gate; on the other side a boy and girl sit by an ornamental pillar pierced with a circular hole and surmounted by an urn, while serpentine tree trunks intertwine and end with sponged foliage at the neck. Decorated in blue on an off-white glaze.
Height 26.2cm, maximum diameter 15.1cm
No. N.6625, J. Stone Hodges bequest, 1961
Probably London *c.* 1750

18.28 Dish A rim-to-rim scene of a large mill(?) building beside a river in a landscape including six figures, trees and bushes. Decorated in blue on a pale blue glaze. On the back ribbons under-rim markings.
Diameter 19.8cm, height 8.0cm
No. N.5560, gift of Miss E. Nesbitt, 1955
Probably Liverpool *c.* 1750

Compare Garner and Archer pl. 110A and p. 43.

18.29 Bowl With concave strainer top (centre broken) with rings of holes interspersed with trefoil tufts and grasses, and with a border of Chinese scroll pattern. Outside, a man with a stick takes his dog for a walk and on the reverse a lady and gentleman walk together in landscapes with sponged-foliage trees. The decoration in blue on a pale bluish glaze.
Diameter 22.9cm, height 9.8cm
No. N.3246, Sir Gilbert Mellor bequest, 1947
Probably London *c.* 1750

For comments on this type of bowl see chapter 8 of the catalogue.

18.30 Bowl Inside 'One Bowl more and Then' in concentric circles. Outside, a man with a staff walks with his dog in a rocky landscape towards a church. Trees with sponged foliage, and shrubs brush-painted. Decorated in blue on a pale blue glaze.
Diameter 19.8cm, height 8.0cm
No. G.2013, purchased from T. Charbonnier, 1923
Probably Bristol *c.* 1750

18.31 Bowl Inside a child with a violin. Outside, a continuous landscape among sponged foliage trees, of figures going about country pursuits. The decoration in blue on an off-white glaze.
Diameter 30.8cm, height 14.2cm
No. N.2254, gift of Mrs Hall Warren, 1946
Bristol or London *c.* 1750

Compare Mundy pl. VII, which appears to be of this actual bowl; he comments 'Thos. Frank's initials are at base of tree in foreground.', but this probably results from a rather vivid imagination. Compare also Victoria and Albert Museum no. C131-1916.

18.32 **Plate** A rim-to-rim scene of a man walking by a hut, with fences and slim-trunked sponged-foliage trees, and a stone monument on the extreme right. Decorated in manganese on a bluish-greenish glaze.
Diameter 22.7cm, height 2.5cm, shape F
No. N.6457, J. Stone Hodges bequest 1961, ex Revelstoke collection
Probably London *c*. 1750

18.33 **Dish** A rim-to-rim scene of a farmyard, with thatched farmhouse, rick, a lady with a bucket on her shoulder and a man with a wheelbarrow, and two geese. Inscribed 'K - H / 1771'. Decorated in blue on a pale blue glaze.
Diameter 33.8cm, height 5.8cm, shape I
No. G.182, gift of W. Strahan, 1914
Perhaps Bristol 1771

Illustrated in Pountney pl. VIII, who suggests it was made at Brislington, which other evidence suggests had then ceased work.

18.34 **Dish** A rim-to-rim scene of a man and woman meeting in an open landscape with slender stemmed trees and sponged foliage. Decorated in purple-brown manganese on a pale bluish glaze with a pinky tinge on the back.
Diameter 35.5cm, height 4.5cm, shape I
No. N.3875, purchased 1949
Probably Wincanton *c*. 1740

Compare Victoria and Albert Museum no. C65-1967, illustrated in Garner and Archer pl. 122B and discussed on p. 66.

18.35 **Dish** A rim-to-rim scene of a sponged-foliage tree and a hollow rock, with two sailing boats at sea beyond, and a hilly coast to right. Rather roughly decorated in blue on a pale bluish glaze.
Diameter 34.0cm, height 4.8cm, shape I
No. N.6769, J. Stone Hodges bequest, 1961
Perhaps Bristol *c*. 1750

18.36 Dish A rim-to-rim scene of a lady and gentleman walking in a landscape; slender stemmed trees with sponged foliage at their summits, and a hilly scene beyond with trees and some buildings. Decorated in shades of blue on a pale bluish glaze. On the back twiggy herbal sprig under-rim markings.
Diameter 28.9cm, height 3.8cm, shape I
No. N.6676, J. Stone Hodges bequest, 1961, ex Clarke collection
Perhaps Bristol *c.* 1760

18.37 Plate A rim-to-rim scene of a herdsman driving two long-haired cows in a landscape of trees and shrubs with sponged foliage. The decoration in blue on a pale blue glaze.
Diameter 22.3cm, height 2.5cm, shape G
No. N.6474, J. Stone Hodges bequest, 1961
Probably London *c.* 1740

18.38 Tea Pot With somewhat short conical spout, and generous looped handle, decorated on one side with a man and woman in a landscape, standing, while a youth kneels, and on the reverse a countryman and woman stand with a church spire beyond; the trees all with sponged foliage. The lid probably does not match. Decorated in blue on a pale bluish glaze.
Height without lid 10.0cm, maximum diameter 11.6cm
No. N.6654B, J. Stone Hodges bequest, 1961
Perhaps Bristol *c.* 1760

18.39 Dish A rim-to-rim scene of a lady and gentleman walking along a path in the woods, and a pedlar with sack walking towards them. Trees with sponged foliage, and a rocky background with a castle. Decorated in heavy blue on a pale bluish-greenish glaze. On the back the figures '16' within the footrim.
Diameter 34.4cm, height 6.0cm, shape I
No. N.6672, J. Stone Hodges bequest, 1961
Possibly London *c.* 1730, or Dutch

18.40 **Bird Feeder**   Of cylinder shape with five arched openings round it, decorated with country scenes of a yokel with his dog, trees with sponged foliage, a swan, and a little round summerhouse – the door of the house forming one opening. Decorated in blue on a pale blue glaze.
Height 11.1cm, diameter 12.3cm
No. N.6650, J. Stone Hodges bequest, 1961
Probably Bristol *c.* 1750

For other examples see no. 9.3 in this catalogue, Hall Warren Collection no. 182, Glaisher Collection no. 1540, and Victoria and Albert Museum no. C111–1935.

18.41 **Bowl** Inside a tree with sponged foliage and birds in the sky, surrounded on the rim by patches of sponged foliage. Outside, a continuous landscape with four sponged-foliage trees, a house on one side, and a man in a long jacket on the other. Decorated in blue on a pale bluish glaze.
Diameter 26.2cm, height 10.4/11.2cm
No. N.6914, purchased 1962
Perhaps London *c.* 1750

18.42 **Plate** A rim-to-rim scene of a lady perched on a bank stretching her arm towards a ruined arch, while a shepherd with stave leans against the bank from behind. Decorated in blue on a pale blue glaze.
Diameter 23.6cm, height 2.9cm, shape G
No. N.7111, Ernest Blatch bequest, 1964
London *c.* 1760

A pair of similar dishes in Temple Newsam House, no. 4.219/46, have a milkmaid and cow added on the right hand side. See also Garner and Archer pl. 98A, Victoria and Albert Museum no. C192–1923, Mundy pl. XIX, and Morgan collection no. 72.

The instrument carried by the shepherd is a *houlette*, a cross between a spoon and a shoe horn, attached to the end of a staff, with which one scooped up stones or earth and cast them at sheep straying from the flock, or at marauding wolves. Many young ladies, painted by Lely, are shown carrying one; and Pepys, in July 1667, records meeting a shepherd on Epsom Downs 'and I tried to cast stones with his horne crook'. Although the word *houlette* is French and there appears to be no English equivalent, it is clear that they were in use in this country; but we have been unable to trace an English or Continental engraving from which this scene derives.

18.43 **Plate** The description as for the previous example, but the foreground is treated differently, and the sponging of the foliage on the tree is so heavy that it has cracked.
Diameter 23.0cm, height 2.6cm, shape F
No. G.3599, Mrs A. Robinson bequest, 1940
London *c.* 1760

18.44 **Plate** A man doffs his tricorn hat to a seated lady, who waves back. The tall trees are outlined in manganese, and washed over partly in manganese, and partly in yellow and green. Decorated in blue, green, yellow and manganese on a bluish-grey glaze.
Diameter 22.8cm, height 2.8cm, shape F
No. N.6444, J. Stone Hodges bequest, 1961
Probably Liverpool *c.* 1760

This and the following plate are the only examples we include in 'Landscapes with figures' which are in polychrome. They are also among the very few in this chapter attributed to Liverpool.
Compare Garner and Archer pl. 106A.

18.45 **Plate** The description as for the previous plate, but the drawing is more delicate.
Diameter 22.9cm, height 2.8cm, shape F
No. G.191, purchased 1916
Probably Liverpool *c.* 1760

18.46 **Plate** A rim-to-rim scene of a rocky island with houses, a fisherman on the breakwater, and two small boats. The edge with sixteen scallops. On the back the letter 'E' within the footrim. The decoration in blue on a pale blue glaze.
Diameter 21.8cm, height 2.6cm, shape F
No. N.5489, purchased 1955
Bristol *c.* 1750

This is a scene with which we are familiar in the centre of so many plates and dishes with *bianco-sopra-bianco* rims. The central tree, which is usually of a rigid conical shape, is here more natural.

18.47 **Bowl** With hemispherical bowl and flat octagonal rim. Decorated inside only with a scene of the conical tree above a rocky island, with a man fishing. A small boat on the rim on either side, and four formations of birds in the sky. Decorated in blue on a pale bluish glaze.
Diameter 19.8cm, height 8.0cm
No. G.2032, purchased from T. Charbonnier, 1923
Bristol *c.* 1760

19 Miscellanea

This last chapter of the catalogue proper contains a variety of pieces which do not seem to fit in logically elsewhere, though it includes pieces of considerable importance. There are a number of plates with floral decoration, some distantly related to *chinoiserie*, and some to Fazackerly, though in monochrome. Three dishes with blue multi-petal daisies are particularly interesting because, although so similar, they have different under-rim markings; in the very next chapter we consider the anomaly which this presents us with. Then there is a plate with a bunch of grapes on it, of which one comparable example in the Victoria and Albert Museum is shown as from Bristol, while another in the Glaisher collection is shown as Dutch.

There are eight dishes with birds on them, ranging from a parrot which could well have come from an ornithological illustration, to the exotic and fanciful, and to the aerobatic birds of *chinoiserie*. A few pieces of portraiture extend from the divine to the ridiculous; while a group of geometrical designs based mostly on floral motifs face us with problems of provenance and date, as they are not of any known and recognizable style, and could in one or two cases be Dutch.

In contrast, the group of eleven pieces with mimosa pattern decoration are all probably English, but pose a different problem, as they are known to have been made in more than one centre. Pountney, on p. 71, says 'This pattern I have found upon fragments from the tip on Brandon Hill, and also at Wincanton, Somerset, where they were dug up in enormous quantities', and he illustrates two different varieties of this decoration in pl. XII, which he attributes to Limekiln Lane, Bristol, and Wincanton, respectively. We also illustrate in fig. 22 a waster from the Wincanton pottery, consisting of a pile of plates collapsed on one another due to breakage of a saggar pin. The decoration on the wasters is not very clearly visible, but is undoubtedly of mimosa pattern.

Further evidence comes from D. Cockell's article 'Some Finds of Pottery at Vauxhall Cross' in the *English Ceramic Circle Transactions*, vol. 9, part 2, 1974, where sherds of this same pattern are illustrated in pl. 123(e). This article draws attention to feathered lines opposing single leaves on some of the mimosa stems, but this characteristic does not seem to be confined to London wares. The examples of mimosa pattern we are able to illustrate are notable for their wide variety, both in the details of their design and in the colours employed; the latter ranging from monochrome blue to polychrome involving two, three and four colours. This variety is so great that we are unable to point to any particular characteristic of the decoration which is of any real help in determining provenance; we have rather had to rely on other aspects, including under-rim markings in three cases and a greyish tinge in the glaze which appears to be found more frequently on Wincanton pieces than others. Moreover there is one plate, no. 19.51, which has glaze, pigment and workmanship which even lead us to suspect that it might have been made in Liverpool, though we have no evidence that this pattern was ever made there.

Among the last plates illustrated in this catalogue we have a 'Merryman' plate; one from a set of six which between them would give us a contemporary rhyme. Perhaps this chapter serves to emphasize the remarkable variety to be found in the decoration of English delftware.

19.1 **Dish** A conical vase of single chrysanthemums with red striped petals, and foliage freely drawn. On the rim six double sprigs of similar buds. Decorated in blue, red, dark green and yellow on a pale blue glaze, pitted on the back.
Diameter 34.0cm, height 4.5cm, shape I
No. N.6686, J. Stone Hodges bequest, 1961
Probably Bristol *c.* 1740

19.2 **Plate** In the centre a large bunch of flowers and foliage including berries, encircled by a band of floral motifs. On the rim stylized flower buds and berries. The decoration in blue, red, green, yellow and manganese on a muddy blue glaze.
Diameter 22.9cm, height 3.1cm, shape F
No. N.6527, J. Stone Hodges bequest, 1961
Perhaps Liverpool *c.* 1770

19.3 **Plate** A small tree with one large flower artificially striped, and foliage. Round the rim three sprays of similar leaves from half flower faces on the edge of the rim. Decorated in blue and manganese on a pale bluish-greenish glaze.
Diameter 22.8cm, height 2.5cm, shape F
No. N.7122, Ernest Blatch bequest, 1964
Probably London *c.* 1780

19.4 **Plate** Flowers and willow sprouting from a fence, and on the edge of the rim four open red flowers and four blue buds. The drawing sketchy. The colours blue, red, green and yellow on a pale bluish glaze.
Diameter 22.5cm, height 2.3cm, shape A
No. N.6430, J. Stone Hodges bequest, 1961
Probably Bristol *c.* 1730

19.5 Plate   Two sprays of flowers from a hillock, and round the rim three smaller sprays from little mounds. Decorated in blue, red, dark brown, green and yellow on a pale bluish glaze.
Diameter 22.7cm, height 3.0cm, shape F
No. N.3204, Sir Gilbert Mellor bequest, 1947, ex Gautier collection
Perhaps Bristol *c.* 1740

19.6 Dish   In the centre a sprig of blue multi-petal daisies, and round the rim three more similar sprigs. The buds all in manganese and yellow, and leaves green. Pale bluish glaze. On the back noughts and crosses under-rim markings.
Diameter 26.5cm, height 3.0cm, shape I
No. N.5048, found in store and accessioned 1951
Probably Bristol *c.* 1760

19.7 Dish   In the centre a sprig of blue multi-petal daisies, with yellow buds and green leaves. On the rim five similar sprigs. The glaze pale bluish. On the back edge grasses under-rim markings.
Diameter 37.2cm, height 4.2cm, shape I
No. N.3729, gift of Mrs Goldingham, 1948
Probably Bristol *c.* 1760

19.8 Dish   In the centre a sprig of blue multi-petal daisies with manganese florets, a yellow bud, and green leaves, and round the rim four similar sprigs. The glaze pale bluish. On the back twiggy herbal sprig under-rim markings.
Diameter 34.8cm, height 4.0cm, shape I
No. N.8464, found in store and accessioned 1974
Probably Bristol *c.* 1760

The implications of three such similar dishes as these having different under-rim markings are discussed on p. 315.

19.9 Dish A boldly drawn sprig of flowers and leaves, surrounded by four small sprigs on the rim, and four crosses with dots in the angles. Decorated in blue outlines and wash on a pale bluish glaze.
Diameter 33.1cm, height 5.4cm, shape I
No. N.8463, found in store and accessioned 1974
Probably Liverpool *c.* 1770

This appears to be distantly related to Fazackerly decoration, though it is of course in blue only.

19.10 Dish In the centre a bunch of grapes with feathery leaves, and round the rim a meandering vine with a grape in each bend. Decorated in manganese and dark green on a white glaze with greenish tinge.
Diameter 34.7cm, height 5.9cm, shape I
No. N.3152, Sir Gilbert Mellor bequest, 1947
Perhaps Bristol *c.* 1740, or Continental

Compare Victoria and Albert Museum no. C18–1928 attributed to Bristol *c.* 1750, and Glaisher collection no. 20 attributed to Holland.

19.11 Plate A heavy drawing of a brick tower beyond a fence, with a rock to the right and two flowers to the left, all surrounded by a border of Chinese double curl pattern, and on the rim floral motifs embellished with scrolls. The decoration in dark blue on an off-white glaze. On the back the letter 'B' within the footrim.
Diameter 22.5cm, height 3.3cm, shape B
No. N.6692, J. Stone Hodges bequest, 1961
Probably London *c.* 1710

19.12 Dish In the centre a floral spray with rhomboidal leaves, and two flying birds and five insects, surrounded by a band of lozenges. The rim with six reserves in blue painted ground, each containing a floral motif. On the back noughts and crosses under-rim markings and the letter 'X' within the footrim. Decorated in blue on a pale bluish glaze; the edge red-brown.
Diameter 34.0cm, height 5.5cm, shape I
No. N.6713, J. Stone Hodges bequest, 1961
Bristol *c.* 1730

Illustrated in Garner and Archer pl. 62B with comment on p. 39.

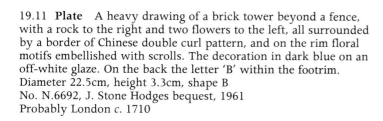

19.13 Dish A green parrot on a tree branch with a tuft of sponged foliage and wild flowers. The rim decorated in trellis diaper with five reserves of floral motifs. The decoration in blue, red and green on a pale bluish glaze.
Diameter 33.8cm, height 4.8cm, shape I
No. N.3144, Sir Gilbert Mellor bequest, 1947
Probably Bristol *c.* 1740

Eleazar Albin published his *Natural History of Birds* in 1738–40, and George Edwards another in 1743–51. Both these books, which extend to several volumes, are well illustrated with colour plates, and the parrot on this dish is very reminiscent of them, though not an actual copy.

19.14 Plate A parrot on a branch from a tree stump with flowers sprouting on the other side. Round the rim three pine cones with foliage. Decorated in blue, red, green and yellow on a pale blue glaze.
Diameter 22.4cm, height 3.0cm, shape F
No. N.6470, J. Stone Hodges bequest, 1961
London *c.* 1750

Compare Garner and Archer pl. 108B, Mundy pl. VIII(2) and (3) and Burnap collection no. 150. This pattern of plate was evidently popular, as many other examples exist. See also the sherd in pl. XIV of Garner's article on 'Lambeth Earthenware'.

19.15 Dish A branch of a tree with stippled foliage with an exotic coloured bird perched on it, and round the rim four similar branches. Decorated in blue, red, green, yellow and manganese on a white glaze.
Diameter 35.7cm, height 5.9cm, shape I
No. N.3160, Sir Gilbert Mellor bequest, 1947
Liverpool *c.* 1760

See Mrs C. Hemming's article 'Liverpool Delft' in *The Connoisseur* April 1918, illustration VII, which is a similar dish and which she says is 'attributed to Seth Pennington's Pot-works'. Compare Ray, *English Delftware Tiles* pls. 407 and 408 on which the same bird and foliage appear. Related exotic birds appear on bottle no. 6.27, and also on Liverpool Museum bowl no. 50.60.72, inscribed 'Success to the Plow 1762'.

19.16 Dish A rim-to-rim scene of a bird of paradise perched on a Chinese fence among cherry blossoms, and a house with trellis balcony on the right. On the back noughts and crosses under-rim markings. Decorated in blue, red, green and yellow on an off-white glaze; the back greyish.
Diameter 33.5cm, height 6.1cm, shape I
No. N.3218, Sir Gilbert Mellor bequest, 1947
Bristol *c.* 1750

19.17 Dish Rim-to-rim decoration of a long-tailed flycatcher(?) contemplating an insect clearly too large for him; flowers and twining stems spring from a Chinese fence. The decoration in blue, red, green, yellow and manganese on a pale blue glaze.
Diameter 34.1cm, height 4.4cm, shape I
No. N.3143, Sir Gilbert Mellor bequest, 1947
Probably Liverpool *c.* 1760

Compare one almost identical from the Royal Scottish Museum, Edinburgh, illustrated at pl. 155 of the Rijksmuseum exhibition catalogue, and a closely related one in Garner and Archer pl. 105.

19.18 Dish A rim-to-rim scene of a Chinese house with a twisted tree trunk in the foreground, and an exotic bird in flight. On the back noughts and crosses under-rim markings and 'X' within the footrim. The decoration in blue, red, green and yellow on an off-white glaze with greyish back.
Diameter 32.4cm, height 4.9cm, shape I
No. G.1196, purchased from W. J. Pountney, 1918
Bristol *c.* 1750

19.19 Dish A rim-to-rim scene of a church with a tree growing from rocks in the foreground, with leaves alternately brown and yellow; a large bird in flight chasing insects. On the back noughts and crosses under-rim markings. Decorated in blue, red-brown, green and yellow on a white glaze, greyish on the back.
Diameter 33.7cm, height 5.2cm, shape I
No. N.6720, J. Stone Hodges bequest, 1961
Bristol (Limekiln Lane) *c.* 1740

A sherd in the Bristol Museum, from a dig at Limekiln Lane Pottery, and due to be published next year, has this very bird on it.

19.20 Dish A rim-to-rim scene of a peacock on a Chinese fence among luxuriant twining stems. Decorated in blue, red and yellow on a pale bluish glaze.
Diameter 33.7cm, height 5.2cm, shape I
No. N.3159, Sir Gilbert Mellor bequest, 1947
Bristol *c.* 1750

The peacock is clearly related to the earlier ones at nos. 14.8 to 14.10.

19.21 Dish A stag and doe running through a bare landscape with a dog in pursuit, while a hare sits on a rock. The one tree has sponged foliage. The edge brown. The decoration in blue on a pale bluish glaze. On the back noughts and crosses under-rim markings and the figures '10' within the footrim.
Diameter 34.1cm, height 4.9cm, shape I
No. G.2240, obtained by exchange from R. Hall Warren, 1926
Bristol *c.* 1750

Note two other variants of this, belonging to R. Hall Warren, in Mundy pl. XLI(3) and (4), which was published 1928.

19.22 Plate A lady seated holding a cornucopia, with a vase of flowers on one side and a bird perched on a plant the other. Round the rim eight winged cupid's heads and eight lotus flowers. The decoration in blue on a pale bluish glaze. On the back noughts and crosses under-rim markings and the figures '10' in the footrim.
Diameter 19.9cm, height 2.8cm, shape F
No. G.2523, purchased 1930
Bristol *c.* 1720

19.23 Dish An actor and actress on a terrace with balustrade behind, perhaps singing and dancing, she with a hoop skirt, surrounded by a band of trellis diaper and floral motifs. The rim with four fences each with three posts and a flowering vine. On the back herbal sprig under-rim markings. Decorated in blue on a pale bluish glaze: the edge red-brown.
Diameter 36.5cm, height 3.0cm, shape I
No. N.6740, J. Stone Hodges bequest, 1961
Liverpool *c.* 1760

An almost identical scene is on a bowl in the Glaisher collection, no. 1676. A very similar rim border may be seen on nos. 12.47 and 12.48, also attributed to Liverpool.

19.24 Plate A gardener digging with a spade while a rake rests against a tree with fruit; two fruit bushes in pots. Surrounded by a border extending out from the curvature of four shaped panels of trellis with floral motifs between. Inscribed on the back 'T E C 1774'. Decorated in heavy dark blue on a pale blue-green glaze; the edge light brown.
Diameter 23.1cm, height 2.6cm, shape F
No. G.1993, purchased from T. Charbonnier, 1923
Probably London 1774

This is said to refer to Thomas Cantle, a potter of Temple Back, Bristol; but his wife's name was Bathsheba and he died in 1766 leaving two daughters. In any case the plate has all the appearance of a London product. A search in the records of the Worshipful Company of Gardeners does not disclose a solution to the initials.

19.25 **Plate** A man with a palm leaf over his shoulder leads an ass carrying a lady and infant past a leafy tree. The rim with two vines bearing grapes, leaves and tendrils, tied together with a bow, and an inscription at bottom on a scroll reading 'ANNO I – A 1680' (the last figure blotched). Decorated in blue on a white glaze.
Diameter 22.4cm, height 2.7cm, shape E
No. N.2255, gift of Mrs Hall Warren, 1946
Probably London 1680

This is evidently a portrayal of Joseph and Mary with the infant Jesus.

19.26 **Plate** The crucifixion, with Christ flanked by the two thieves, the centre cross marked 'INRI'. On the rim four flower buds with curling leaves. Decorated in blue on a pale blue glaze.
Diameter 22.5cm, height 3.6cm, shape I
No. N.3069, purchased ex Hodgkin collection, 1947, ex Gautier collection
Perhaps London c. 1720

19.27 **Plate** A lady with a fan and a gentleman walking with a stick doffing his hat, inscribed '16 I ^{M} E 96'. The rim filled with a band of flower and leaf design. Decorated in blue and blue wash on an off-white glaze.
Diameter 22.4cm, height 3.1cm, shape E
No. N.3364, purchased ex Maddicks collection, 1936
London 1696

19.28 **Plate** A red-cloaked and hatted man, face on, among trees and bushes with sponged foliage. Decorated in blue, red, green and manganese on an off-white glaze.
Diameter 22.2cm, height 2.6cm, shape B
No. N.6529, J. Stone Hodges bequest, 1961
Probably Bristol c. 1730

Compare Reading Museum no. 241.61.17. It is far from clear what these plates are supposed to represent.

19.29 Plate A rim-to-rim scene of a man on a prancing horse among sponged manganese foliage, painted extremely crudely. Decorated in blue, red, yellow and manganese on an off-white glaze.
Diameter 22.4cm, height 4.1cm, shape C
No. N.6482, J. Stone Hodges bequest, 1961
London or Bristol *c.* 1700

This is an extraordinary piece, which is probably English, though the circumstances in which it was made, and what precisely it is supposed to represent are a bit of a mystery.

19.30 Plate A central rosette with eight segments, alternately of trellis pattern and of graffito curls, surrounded by five quatrefoils, and five half flower faces on the rim, with other leaf motifs interspersed. On the back 'S P 1722'. Decorated in heavy blue on an off-white glaze, with some pink tinges.
Diameter 22.0cm, height 2.4cm, shape C
No. G.160, purchased ex Hodgkin collection, 1914
Perhaps London 1722

The central rosette appears much more elegantly in nos. 15.48 to 15.50.

19.31 Plate A central rosette surrounded by five bouquets springing from elaborate floral motifs round the rim. The decoration in dark blue on an off-white glaze.
Diameter 22.0cm, height 2.4cm, shape C
No. G.166, gift of W. J. Pountney, 1914
Perhaps London *c.* 1720

19.32 Dish A central disc with segments decorated alternately, surrounded by six segments containing floral motifs bounded by sponged manganese borders, encircled by a narrow green band containing red ovals and dashes. The rim decorated with twelve panels containing alternately green trefoils and yellow grubs. The colours blue, red, green, yellow and manganese on a pale bluish glaze.
Diameter 33.8cm, height 3.9cm, shape I
No. N.6741, J. Stone Hodges bequest, 1961
Probably Bristol *c.* 1740

It is possible that this manganese decoration was applied with a cork.

19.33 **Dish** A central multi-petal flower face, surrounded by
seven interlinked floral motifs, and round the rim twenty-one half
flower heads in an arcaded pattern. Decorated in two shades of
blue on a pale bluish glaze.
Diameter 33.5cm, height 5.0cm, shape I
No. G.1992, purchased from T. Charbonnier, 1923
Perhaps Liverpool *c.* 1740

19.34 **Dish** In the centre a red daisy with buds and rhomboidal
leaves, surrounded by a band of lozenges. On the outer rim
thirteen half flower faces and tufts of grass between. The
decoration in blue, red and green on a pale bluish-grey glaze.
Diameter 33.7cm, height 4.4cm, shape I
No. N.3171, Sir Gilbert Mellor bequest, 1947
Probably Bristol *c.* 1740

19.35 **Dish** In the centre two tall rectangular monoliths among
four flowers and rhomboidal foliage, surrounded by a band of
lozenges. On the rim five single monoliths with flowers and tufts of
grass. Decorated in blue, red, green and yellow on a pale bluish
glaze, the back greyish.
Diameter 33.8cm, height 4.3cm, shape I
No. N.6731, J. Stone Hodges bequest, 1961
Probably Bristol *c.* 1730

19.36 **Dish** A pair to the previous one. The glaze off-white with
a tinge of green.
Diameter 33.1cm, height 4.9cm, shape I
No. N.8114, gift of Mrs J. McG. Kennedy, 1971
Probably Bristol *c.* 1730

19.37 Dish In the centre, flowers with three petals and rhomboidal leaves interspersed with six-point stars; and round the rim similar decoration. Decorated in blue on an off-white glaze. On the back the figure '4' within the footrim.
Diameter 34.1cm, height 5.3cm, shape I
No. N.5558, gift of Miss E. Nesbitt, 1955
Probably Bristol *c.* 1730

Somewhat similar decoration is found on bowl no. 10.36.

19.38 Dish A *mille-fleurs* decoration of floral motifs, quadruple dots and 'spiders', and on the rim similar decoration divided into ten panels. On the back the figures '10' within the footrim. Decorated in blue on an off-white glaze, the back greyish.
Diameter 34.4cm, height 6.2cm, shape I
No. N.6716, J. Stone Hodges bequest, 1961
Perhaps Bristol *c.* 1720, or Continental?

19.39 Dish An all-over pattern, geometrically arranged, of floral and insect motifs and Chinese scroll pattern, both within a central circle and outside it. On the back noughts and crosses under-rim markings and the figure '1' within the footrim. Decorated in two shades of blue on an off-white glaze.
Diameter 33.5cm, height 4.2cm, shape I
No. G.1954, purchased from T. Charbonnier, 1923
Probably Bristol *c.* 1740

19.40 Dish In the centre an elaborate Chinese floral motif within a zig-zag banded circle, surrounded by five less elaborate motifs with vines and rhomboidal leaves. On the outer rim a border of trellis and floral motifs. The decoration in blue on a pale blue glaze; a tinge of violet on the back.
Diameter 30.6cm, height 4.8cm, shape I
No. G.1953, purchased from T. Charbonnier, 1923
Probably Bristol *c.* 1730

19.41 **Dish** In the centre a simple floral spray and two flying insects, surrounded by a border of anthemion frieze. On the rim twelve panels of floral tufts and arabesques. The decoration in blue, red and green on a white glaze; grey and pitted on the back.
Diameter 33.0cm, height 5.0cm, shape I
No. N.6711, J. Stone Hodges bequest, 1961
Probably Bristol c. 1740

19.42 **Dish** Flowers, including cherry blossom in a central circle, and more of the same within a band on the rim, with insects interspersed. The decoration in blue and red on a pale bluish glaze.
Diameter 34.4cm, height 5.2cm, shape I
No. N.6694, J. Stone Hodges bequest, 1961
Perhaps Liverpool c. 1730

19.43 **Dish** A central yellow multi-petal daisy with red markings, surrounded by blue and green lines enclosing red fir trees. On the curvature a band of the 'three-brick' pattern and round the rim trellis diaper with six reserves containing floral motifs. On the back noughts and crosses under-rim markings, and the figure '6' within the footrim. The colours blue, red, green and yellow on a white glaze; blue-grey on the back.
Diameter 32.7cm, height 4.8cm, shape I
No. N.6735, J. Stone Hodges bequest, 1961
Probably Bristol c. 1740

19.44 **Plate** Inscribed 'S T S/1737' in the centre surrounded by stylized Chinese motifs. On the rim eight hearts in leaf tufts embellished with cloud scroll tendrils. Decorated in dark blue on an off-white glaze, the edge brown.
Diameter 22.4cm, height 2.9cm, shape F
No. G.2001, purchased from T. Charbonnier, 1923
Probably London 1737

19.45 **Saucer** Marked within a circle 'E.B' and surrounded by three sprays of red flowers. A narrow border within the rim of diagonal hatching interspersed with six triple Chinese scroll motifs. The colours blue and red on a pale bluish glaze.
Diameter 8.0cm, height 1.5cm
No. N.6659, J. Stone Hodges bequest, 1961
Probably Bristol *c.* 1740

19.46 **Plate** Inscribed simply 'EW/1741' within a blue band and circles. The blue decoration on a pale blue glaze.
Diameter 20.0cm, height 2.2cm, shape E
No. G.1997, purchased from T. Charbonnier, 1923
Probably Bristol 1741

Theodore Charbonnier entered this in his list (see p. 21) with the annotation 'Edward Ward 3rd & last of the Wards'. One presumes that this was the 'Edward, son of James Ward, Bristol potter' who was apprenticed to 'Sam[l] Peach, Haberdasher of small wares' in 1738. This was probably wishful thinking on the part of Charbonnier, as there could be no proof for such an attribution.

19.47 **Plate** Inscribed in the centre 'A S/1713' within a band of trellis with Chinese motifs in reserve. Another similar trellis border round the outer rim, and the rest of the plate occupied by four flowers with fern-like shoots. Decorated in blue on an off-white glaze.
Diameter 22.1cm, height 2.7cm, shape B
No. N.2246, gift of Mrs Hall Warren, 1946
Probably Bristol 1713

19.48 **Dish** A cluster of mimosa flowers and three leaf stems with rhomboidal leaves within a central circle, and six more clusters outside the circle. On the rim six panels of trellis diaper with leaves and insects between them. On the back noughts and crosses under-rim markings. The decoration in blue on a pale bluish glaze.
Diameter 33.5cm, height 4.2cm, shape I
No. N.6709, J. Stone Hodges bequest, 1961
Probably Bristol *c.* 1740

Fig 22 Waster from Wincanton pottery: plates with mimosa pattern.

19.49 **Dish** Mimosa pattern, with six vertical fronds in the centre, surrounded by six flower clusters, and six more round the rim all with slender leaves. The decoration in blue on a greyish glaze, the edge brown.
Diameter 34.7cm, height 5.2/5.7cm, shape I
No. N.9243, gift of Mrs B. Brooke, 1978
Probably Wincanton *c.* 1740

19.50 **Plate** Mimosa pattern, with five vertical fronds in the centre surrounded by five flower clusters, and five more round the rim. On the back noughts and crosses under-rim markings and figure '2' within the footrim. Decorated in blue on an off-white glaze. The edge red-brown.
Diameter 22.2cm, height 2.9cm, shape G
No. N.8455, found in store and accessioned 1974
Bristol or Wincanton *c.* 1740

19.51 Plate Mimosa pattern, with three tall and two short fronds all with flowers; the stems blue, the leaves green and the flowers red. Surrounded by three similar sprays, and three more with different foliage inward from the edge of the rim. The decoration in blue, red and green on a pale bluish glaze.
Diameter 22.0cm, height 2.6cm, shape F
No. N.5876, purchased 1958
Bristol (or Liverpool?) *c.* 1750

19.52 Plate Mimosa pattern, with three skimpy fronds in the centre, surrounded by five clusters of flowers, with five more round the rim. Decorated in blue and red on a pale blue-grey glaze; the edge yellow-red.
Diameter 22.3cm, height 2.9cm, shape G
No. N.7110, Ernest Blatch bequest, 1964
Probably London *c.* 1750

19.53 Plate With pale powder-blue ground and central octagonal reserve and four cloud-shaped reserves round the rim, each containing five fronds of mimosa, the centre frond with a cluster of flowers. All the decoration in shades of blue on a pale bluish glaze.
Diameter 17.7cm, height 2.7cm, shape F
No. G.2225, gift of T. Charbonnier, 1925
Wincanton or Bristol *c.* 1740

19.54 Dish Mimosa pattern, with two slender curving stems in a central circle, surrounded by seven clusters of four flowers and foliage, and with seven more round the rim. The decoration in blue on a pale bluish glaze.
Diameter 34.5cm, height 4.6/5.5cm, shape I
No. G.2014, purchased from T. Charbonnier, 1923
Bristol or Wincanton *c.* 1740

19.55 **Deep Dish** Mimosa pattern, with a spray of foliage and cluster of flowers in the centre, surmounted by a yellow bird, and four more similar sprays round the bowl. On the back noughts and crosses under-rim markings and the figure '2' within the footrim. The decoration in blue, red, green and yellow on a pale bluish glaze.
Diameter 22.3cm, height 7.9cm, shape I deep
No. G.1975, purchased from T. Charbonnier, 1923
Probably Bristol *c.* 1750

This piece is mentioned by Pountney on p. 74.

19.56 **Dish** Mimosa pattern, with one central red flower in an orange ring, surrounded by two concentric rings with three and six sprays of three red flowers and blue rhomboidal foliage. The decoration in blue, red and orange on an off-white glaze; the back greyish.
Diameter 35.4cm, height 5.8cm, shape I
No. N.4893, purchased ex Hodgkin collection, 1950
Probably Wincanton *c.* 1750

19.57 **Vase** Of ovoid shape, decorated with five bands all with sprays of mimosa, and a border of Chinese scrolls round the neck. The decoration in blue on a white glaze. The figure '4' on the base.
Height 25.6cm, maximum diameter 17.6cm
No. N.3755, purchased 1949
Bristol or Wincanton *c.* 1750

19.58 **Brick** The top perforated with two rows of three holes on either side of the square centre hole. Decorated with two mimosa sprays on each side and one at each end, the foliage pale green and the flowers red, with blue stems. The glaze white.
Length 11.6cm, width 4.8cm
No. G.2035, purchased from T. Charbonnier, 1923
Probably Bristol *c.* 1750

19.59 Plate A 'Merryman' plate inscribed '5/But if his/Wife do frow/1717' in red letters, surrounded by a wreath of blue leaves on a green stem. The glaze off-white.
Diameter 21.7cm, height 1.8cm, shape B
No. N.5339, purchased 1952
Probably London 1717

For a complete set of Merryman plates see Ray, *English Delftware Pottery*, pl. 17 and the discussion on pp. 145 and 149–150. The plates were sold in sets of six, and dates from 1682 to 1752 are known. The rhyme runs:

> What is A Merry Man
> Let him do what he can
> To Entertain his Guests
> With wine & Merry Jests
> But if his Wife do frown
> All merriment Goes Down.

19.60 Saucer Dish The rim with fifty flutes, and in the centre a cartouche supported by winged horses, with a crown above and cupid's face below with pendent tassels, marked '$_I I_E$/1707'. The decoration in blue on a white glaze.
Diameter 22.5cm, height 4.7cm, shape J
No. N.3791, found in store and accessioned 1949
Probably London 1707

19.61 Plate A vase and urn on a plinth with peonies and twining vines, the rim with four sprigs of similar flowers. All flowers with shaded petals. Decorated in blue, green, yellow and manganese on a pale grey-blue glaze.
Diameter 22.5cm, height 2.6cm, shape F
No. N.6492, J. Stone Hodges bequest, 1961
Probably Liverpool *c.* 1760

19.62 Dish The scene a fenced garden with a bird on the left and profuse flowers on the right, with two insects. The rim with a trellis pattern containing six reserves of flower and leaf motifs. On the back noughts and crosses under-rim markings. The decoration in blue on a white glaze; the back off-white.
Diameter 34.0cm, height 7.1cm, shape I
No. N.6712, J. Stone Hodges bequest, 1961
Probably Bristol *c.* 1740

20 Under-rim markings

In cataloguing the Bristol collection it became evident that a considerable number of plates and dishes have markings under the rim. Some reference to the occurrence of such markings has been been made in Garner and Archer on p. 33, but the body of evidence available for the first time in the Bristol collection was of such size that it was decided to tabulate all these markings and to see if they were amenable to any sort of classification.

By the term 'under-rim marking' we mean any marks, other than letters or figures, appearing on the underside of the rim.

Marks within the footrim

A letter, a figure or a rebus within the footrim does occur nearly three times more frequently in association with under-rim markings than without them, and it may not be out of place to deal briefly with them in passing. The only rebus of which we are aware is a flower bud with two leaves, which is said to be that of Joseph Flower. One also meets the monogram of the letters W and P, which is said to refer to William Pottery of Limekiln Lane, Bristol. Both the rebus and the monogram are of course speculation.

Other than this one finds plenty of cases of a single letter or figure within the footrim. At the Antiques Fair in London a few years ago, one dealer displayed a dresser on which he had placed a set of two dishes and fifteen plates, all of the same pattern, similar to nos. 12.3 and 12.4 in this collection, and with similar under-rim markings to these two plates. The set of plates in the exhibition had the following marks within the footrims:

One dish marked	'11'
One dish marked	'12'
Five plates marked	'1'
Three plates marked	'6'
Three plates marked	'13'
Three plates marked	'17'
One plate marked	'9'

The general opinion is that these figures were the numbers allocated to the various members of the team of decorators employed in the factory. This does not necessarily imply that, in the factory which made these plates, there were seventeen decorators at work; some of those with lower numbers may have left and the newcomers may have been allocated the next higher numbers.

Classification

It was found that eighty-three dishes, twenty-six plates, two meat dishes and one saucer have under-rim markings. After tabulating them all, and copying off a fully representative selection of them, they appeared to fall into seven classes, as follows:

1 NOUGHTS AND CROSSES This is by far the largest category, including sixty-five out of the total of 112 pieces. Fig. 23 (i) and (ii) show a selection of these markings, and they are tabulated in the table on pp. 316–7. There are nearly always eight symbols, comprising four of one sort and four of another, alternately and symmetrically disposed round the rim. The symbols include noughts, crosses,

double brush strokes, triple or quadruple brush strokes – sometimes these brush strokes are crossed through by another stroke more or less at right angles – six-point stars, eight-point stars, and noughts with a bar across them; sometimes this bar appears to make a letter G, sometimes a letter Q, but we have not tried to differentiate between these as we are getting down to ones and twos, and it does not appear to affect provenance.

In thirty-four out of the sixty-five pieces in this category the under-rim markings are associated with potter's marks within the footrim, and in two such cases we find the WP monogram ascribed to William Pottery. However, on a dish in the author's collection this category of marking is associated with the so-called Joseph Flower trefoil rebus.

Markings of this nature do occur on other ceramics, notably on Dutch delftware, although in the course of a study trip to Holland, the author found few, if any, markings sufficiently similar to those in the Bristol collection as to be confused with them. There was, however, one notable exception to this in the Prinsenhof Museum, Delft, namely a plate marked with six-point stars and noughts with a bar across them. This plate bears a mark in the centre back which is attributed to the factory 'De Dissel' in Delft (1640–1701). One wonders whether the similarity of this under-rim marking to those employed in Bristol a few years later is pure coincidence, or whether there was some connection, such as the migration of a workman?

But before investigating under-rim markings we had made attributions of provenance to all these pieces on their face value alone, taking into account glaze, pigments, decorative style, etc. and in sixty-three cases out of sixty-five with noughts and crosses markings they had been attributed to Bristol or Wincanton.

2 EDGE GRASSES AND 3 RIBBONS   Fig. 23 (iii) shows examples of both these categories of marking. There are only five of each. The edge grasses always start with a tuft of short grasses at the edge of the rim, from which a long stem emerges. They are quite distinctive and can readily be identified.

The ribbon marking is an erratic wiggly line, often starting from a rough circle, and continuing at a constant radius from the centre of the plate. It varies considerably in the thickness of the brush used by the decorator. One marking included in this category is in the form of a bow knot.

In only two cases are any of these two markings associated with a mark within the footrim; both cases concern edge grasses, and in both cases that mark is the Joseph Flower trefoil rebus. Nine out of the ten pieces in these two categories had already been attributed to Bristol on their face evidence alone.

4 WHIPLASH AND 5 CONCENTRIC CIRCLES   Fig. 23 (iv) shows two more markings. The whiplash is always a continuous rhythmical wavy line, like a sinusoidal curve. It starts with a straight line, which suggests the handle of the whip, and ends in a curl, which suggests the crack of the lash. There are seven such markings in the collection, and in six of these there is a mark within the footrim.

The concentric circles are a group of five pieces, but they are quite unmistakable as a group, all using a soft blue in their decoration, and four of them having a very flat, wide rim, as in shape H (appendix I). The outermost circle is either under the rim or under the curvature, and the inner circle either just outside the footrim, or within it. In the case illustrated it comprises a double ring within the footrim. None of these pieces has any other mark within the footrim.

There is a very similar dish in the Victoria and Albert Museum, no. C155-1929, with an Irish armorial decoration and the inscription 'Dublin 1735' on the back, and it also has the concentric circles markings. This, and another like it in the Metropolitan Museum, New York, are said to be the only known products of

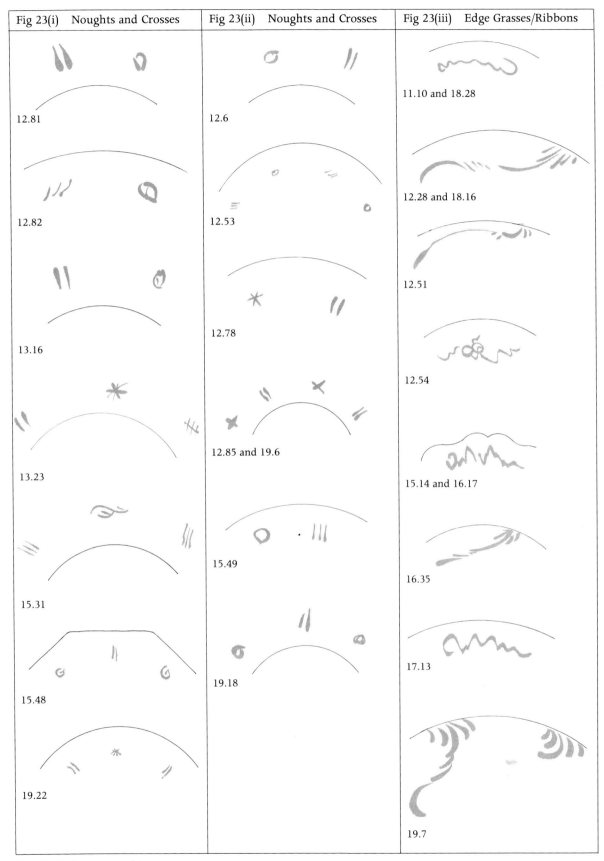

Fig 23(i) Noughts and Crosses	Fig 23(ii) Noughts and Crosses	Fig 23(iii) Edge Grasses/Ribbons
12.81	12.6	11.10 and 18.28
12.82	12.53	12.28 and 18.16
13.16	12.78	12.51
13.23	12.85 and 19.6	12.54
15.31	15.49	15.14 and 16.17
15.48	19.18	16.35
19.22		17.13
		19.7

Fig 23 Under-rim markings

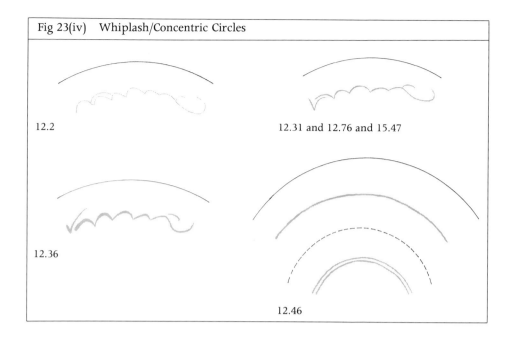

Fig 23(iv)   Whiplash/Concentric Circles

12.2

12.31 and 12.76 and 15.47

12.36

12.46

Chambers' Dublin factory. However, we have studied several pieces outside the Bristol collection with concentric circle markings, and found none that can be attributed to Dublin on other evidence. This suggests that the dish in the Victoria and Albert Museum may in fact have been made in Liverpool for Chambers to take to Dublin in support of his application to the Dublin Society to get a factory started there, or made in Dublin by a Liverpool potter.

All twelve pieces in categories 4 and 5 had previously been allocated to Liverpool, without regard to their under-rim markings.

6 HERBAL SPRIGS   There is a lot of variety in the markings shown in fig. 23 (v) and (vi). They are often quite accurate botanical drawings of herbs from the kitchen garden; hence the name by which we have christened them. There may be two, three or four of them around the plate or dish. There is a total of nineteen pieces in this category, of which only three also have marks within the footrim. In all but two cases these pieces had been attributed to Liverpool. The two exceptions had been attributed to London, but, as explained later, have since been reallocated to Liverpool.

7 ALMOND BRANCH   There are only two pieces in the Bristol collection with this marking, but it was identified and given its name over sixty years ago by W. J. Pountney when he compiled the catalogue of Theodore Charbonnier's collection. Item seventeen of that catalogue is a plate with scalloped and fluted rim, decorated with *bianco-sopra-bianco*, and its description concludes with the words 'The back has the usual almond branch on flange'. The next two pieces are also decorated with *bianco-sopra-bianco*, and their descriptions conclude 'Almond branch on back'. Unfortunately all three of these pieces appear to have been lost due to the bombing of the Bristol Art Gallery during the war.

The identifying features of the almond branch marking, shown in fig. 23 (vii), are a pair of complete leaves or buds near the start of the stem, and the arching of shoots at the tip across the main stem. We have observed this marking on a number of pieces outside the Bristol collection, but it only seems to occur on articles with *bianco-sopra-bianco* decoration on the face of the rim. There is little doubt that this marking is specific to Bristol.

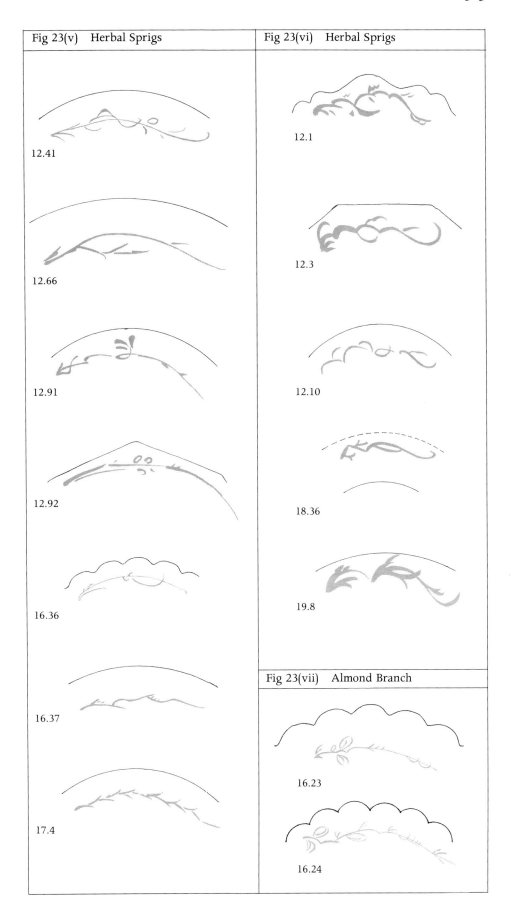

Fig 23(v) Herbal Sprigs	Fig 23(vi) Herbal Sprigs
12.41	12.1
12.66	12.3
12.91	12.10
12.92	18.36
16.36	19.8
16.37	Fig 23(vii) Almond Branch
17.4	16.23
	16.24

London factories

Mention has now been made of seven categories of under-rim markings, and it has been shown that they do appear to tally with remarkable accuracy with the attributions to cities of manufacture already made of the articles in question. This has however been confined to Bristol, Wincanton and Liverpool, and no mention has been made of London. In fact there are 106 plates and dishes in the Bristol collection which were attributed to London on their face value only, and of these only three were found to have under-rim markings. However, these markings are ones which we have now associated with Bristol or Liverpool and, in the light of this, those three pieces have since been reviewed, with the conclusion that none of the three has characteristics which give it a strong claim to a London attribution.

We have also consulted Mr Graham Dawson of the Cuming Museum, Southwark, a noted archaeologist with considerable experience of the exploration of London pottery sites. He states that he has never noticed an under-rim marking on any piece of delftware from a London kiln site. He adds that this probably means that there were not any, since it is the sort of thing which would be noticed in processing. It is also true that the amount of glazed material from kiln sites was small, and the amounts of decorated sherds even smaller, so that the certainty of their absence is not as great as it would be were the sample larger. To counterbalance this, the vast majority of work so far done on London pottery sites has been done on groups of material deriving from the first half of the eighteenth century, which is just the period when under-rim markings occur elsewhere.

Special cases

Mention must now be made of two pieces in the Bristol collection whose markings do not fall within the classifications we have identified. The 'De Moeder ende haar Dogter' dish, no. 16.32, is without doubt a Bristol product, but its markings do not tally with anything attributed to Bristol. It is illustrated in fig. 23 (viii), and it must be admitted that it is not very far from some of the more 'twiggy' herbal sprigs which we have attributed to Liverpool, though perhaps more stylized and geometrical. The other piece is the Joshua dish, no. 10.45. This must also be a Bristol piece, which Pountney claimed as the work of Joseph Flower. It has a unique marking, also shown in fig. 23 (viii), which certainly does not fall within any category. In this case it has a clear affinity with the decoration on the front of the rim.

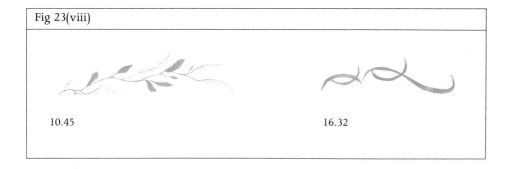

Fig 23(viii)

10.45   16.32

What do all these markings signify? The solution that most readily springs to mind is that they are factory marks, and that each factory adopted a particular type of marking. But on the other hand we have already mentioned one noughts and crosses marking and two edge grasses occurring with the Joseph Flower rebus.

While the evidence of Pountney, and the catalogue of the Victoria Art Gallery, Bath, suggest that noughts and crosses were associated with the Brislington and Temple factories, we have noted two WP monograms on these, and William Pottery worked at Limekiln Lane. So did decorators work for more than one factory, or did one factory use more than one marking? The answer is more probably that these markings under the rims are not factory marks, though they do appear to tell us the city of origin.

Anomalies

We must next consider some anomalies which these markings raise. First let us consider three dishes, nos. 19.6 to 19.8, all with multi-petal daisy decoration, which are so alike that one would surely say that they came from the same factory, and were even painted by the same hand. But if we examine their under-rim markings we find that one has noughts and crosses, one edge grasses, and the third a 'twiggy' herbal sprig. As this last may be compared with that on the 'De Moeder ende haar Dogter' dish mentioned above, perhaps it is after all a Bristol marking, albeit closely related to Liverpool. But the fact that three practically identical dishes bear dissimilar markings probably simply serves to reinforce the view that such markings are not factory marks.

The second anomaly arises with dishes nos. 17.6, 17.13 and 17.14, two of which have noughts and crosses markings, and the third ribbons, both of which are Bristol markings. But these dishes are in other respects representative of the Fazackerly decoration and of the coloration of glaze typical of Liverpool. They are the only articles, among sixty-five pieces with noughts and crosses and five pieces with ribbons, which are not clearly attributable to a Bristol provenance. It suggests the possibility that some Fazackerly decoration was practised in Bristol.

The third anomaly concerns three plates decorated with *bianco-sopra-bianco*, nos. 16.35, 16.36 and 16.37. The first two have the same design on the front, of a Chinaman walking past a temple, which is surrounded by a delicate band of decoration. However the quality of the *bianco-sopra-bianco* varies between these two, as well as its pattern. Considering their under-rim markings, we find the plate with the more distinct *bianco-sopra-bianco* has the edge grasses marking of Bristol, whereas the other has a herbal sprig. Moreover the third piece, decorated with a fine polychrome *chinoiserie* scene and feathery *bianco-sopra-bianco*, also has a herbal sprig marking. We believe that these last two pieces with herbal sprig markings are examples of Liverpool *bianco-sopra-bianco*, in spite of the fact that this then leaves us with a Bristol and a Liverpool plate with almost identical decoration on the front.

A plate similar to the second of these three is no. 51 in the Castle Museum, York, and a dish similar to the last is to be found in the Ashmolean Museum, Oxford, as part of the Oppenheimer gift collection. Both these pieces have herbal sprig markings.

The author disclosed his research into under-rim markings in a paper read to the English Ceramic Circle, published in their *Transactions*, vol. 10, part 4, pp. 213–222. There has not yet been time for its implications to be considered, or for its anomalies to be explained, but it is hoped that publication of the facts disclosed in the Bristol collection will lead to more evidence on this subject being brought to light, so that we may learn how reliable an adjunct under-rim markings are in the determination of provenance of delftware.

Table of noughts and crosses under-rim markings

CATALOGUE NUMBER	O	||	|||	||||	×	✳	θ	G	Q	~	⟆
8.29		4							4		
8.30	4	4									
10.12	4					4					
10.33	4	4									
10.46		4					4				
11.1					8		16				8
11.34		4			4						
11.35		4			4						
12.6	4	4									
12.7	4	4									
12.8	4	4									
12.9		4						4			
12.15		4									
12.16		4							4		
12.21	4	4									
12.22	4	4									
12.24	4				4						
12.49		4			4						
12.53	4		4								
12.63			4		4						
12.78		4				4					
12.81	4	4									
12.82			4				4				
12.83		4			4						
12.85		4			4						
12.88		4				4					
12.90		4			4						
12.94		4			4						
13.8	4	4									
13.10	4	4									
13.11	4	4									
13.12	4	4									

CATALOGUE NUMBER	O	||	|||	||||	×	✕	θ	G	Q	≺	⅀
13.14						4	4				
13.15	4		4								
13.16		4					4				
13.19	4	4									
13.20	4	4									
13.23		3	1			3					
13.24		4					4				
14.23		4			4						
15.11		4					4				
15.28		2	2							4	
15.30	4	4									
15.31			4							4	
15.32		4			4						
15.41	4	4									
15.46		4				4					
15.48		4					4				
15.49	5		5								
17.6		4			4						
17.14			4		4						
18.12		4			4						
19.7		4			4						
19.12		4			4						
19.16			4				4				
19.18	4	4									
19.19		4			4						
19.21		4					4				
19.22		4				4					
19.39		4					4				
19.43	4	4									
19.48		4			4						
19.50		4				4					
19.55	4	4									
19.63		4			4						

APPENDICES

Appendix I

SHAPES OF PLATES AND DISHES
and nomenclature used in catalogue entries

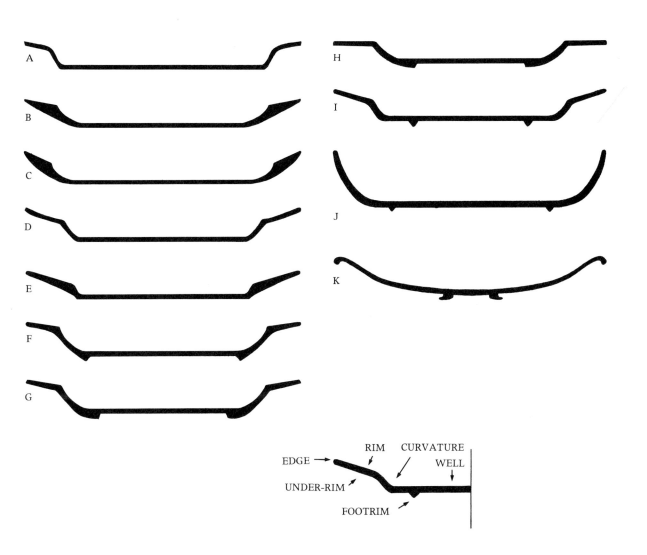

Appendix II

CORRELATION BETWEEN MUSEUM NUMBERS
AND CATALOGUE NUMBERS

G.101	16.3	G.190	3.37	G.1868	7.25	G.2021	3.14
G.103	5.12	G.191	18.45	G.1952	13.5	G.2024	18.9
G.110	13.18	G.192	12.57	G.1953	19.40	G.2026	4.9
G.112	15.47	G.195	3.6	G.1954	19.39	G.2027	6.7
G.113	15.37	G.198	16.13	G.1955	11.35	G.2028	6.11
G.114	11.37	G.753	12.86	G.1956	12.2	G.2029	10.8
G.117	15.28	G.756	16.23	G.1957	12.58	G.2030	4.16
G.118	15.33	G.1147	10.19	G.1959	10.33	G.2031	12.18
G.120	18.4	G.1149	6.8	G.1965	16.17	G.2032	18.47
G.121	6.14	G.1164	3.2	G.1970	8.22	G.2034	15.53
G.122	12.5	G.1165	12.3	G.1971	16.1	G.2035	19.58
G.123	11.14	G.1177	15.59	G.1974	8.43	G.2040	18.20
G.125	6.13	G.1178	15.12	G.1975	19.55	G.2043	16.26
G.127	8.49	G.1179	15.58	G.1976	16.34	G.2044	3.45
G.128	10.52	G.1181	3.7	G.1980	16.29	G.2046	14.22
G.131	13.3	G.1182	3.15	G.1982	9.32	G.2050	18.24
G.134	16.10	G.1184	3.30	G.1983	9.40	G.2052	10.3
G.135	15.50	G.1185	3.29	G.1984	12.7	G.2053	3.35
G.138	15.23	G.1186	3.27	G.1985	7.38	G.2054	3.34
G.139	10.36	G.1191	13.20	G.1986	7.33	G.2055	4.6
G.140	12.14	G.1192	3.57	G.1987	15.57	G.2056	7.1
G.142	15.22	G.1194	14.34	G.1988	8.31	G.2058	4.12
G.143	12.53	G.1195	7.2	G.1991	12.85	G.2059	16.2
G.149	9.7	G.1196	19.18	G.1992	19.33	G.2060	10.24
G.150	9.8	G.1197	3.23	G.1993	19.24	G.2061	9.23
G.155	16.8	G.1425	14.40	G.1996	12.50	G.2112	6.9
G.156	8.23	G.1427	12.31	G.1997	19.46	G.2114	10.34
G.157	16.4	G.1429	8.41	G.1998	10.31	G.2115	10.54
G.158	6.15	G.1440	3.55	G.1999	10.37	G.2138	4.19
G.160	19.30	G.1441	6.10	G.2000	10.39	G.2141	5.19
G.161	16.5	G.1443	3.13	G.2001	19.44	G.2142	5.20
G.162	8.37	G.1554	4.17	G.2003	9.15	G.2143	10.14
G.165	15.60	G.1555	5.14	G.2004	9.5	G.2145	11.17
G.166	19.31	G.1558	17.11	G.2006	9.36	G.2155	10.30
G.170	15.27	G.1643	3.18	G.2007	11.19	G.2182	16.33
G.172	10.35	G.1647	4.7	G.2009	7.7	G.2190	3.1
G.173	17.1	G.1690	8.1	G.2010	7.8	G.2213	3.43
G.174	4.11	G.1692	4.22	G.2011	12.54	G.2214	5.5
G.175	15.41	G.1693	7.40	G.2013	18.30	G.2217	4.15
G.182	18.33	G.1699	10.25	G.2014	19.54	G.2218	10.53
G.183	5.21	G.1730	12.23	G.2016	16.16	G.2221	15.9
G.184	12.91	G.1820	10.6	G.2017	4.23	G.2222	16.35
G.186	18.12	G.1866	11.2	G.2018	6.34	G.2223	9.31
G.187	18.15	G.1867	18.19	G.2019	9.10	G.2225	19.53

G.2227 10.55	G.2319 13.22	G.2915 5.1	G.3497 12.39
G.2228 3.62	G.2324 12.25	G.2916 11.48	G.3498 12.40
G.2229 9.24	G.2482 8.44	G.2917 10.18	G.3501 13.4
G.2230 4.14	G.2483 14.26	G.2918 12.1	G.3509 7.27
G.2231 8.48	G.2490 10.11	G.2919 3.50	G.3519 6.33
G.2232 10.22	G.2513 9.26	G.2920 3.51	G.3522 6.32
G.2233 4.10	G.2514 11.34	G.2924 10.49	G.3598 18.5
G.2237 3.40	G.2515 6.21	G.3106 12.92	G.3599 18.43
G.2240 19.21	G.2520 3.22	G.3162 5.7	G.3600 16.18
G.2309 5.18	G.2523 19.22	G.3170 10.27	G.3602 16.9
G.2310 9.19	G.2914 10.50	G.3241 10.45	

N.1601 8.50	N.3066 17.15	N.3157 12.81	N.3198 12.75
N.2208 15.26	N.3067 17.8	N.3158 12.8	N.3199 15.17
N.2241 3.58	N.3068 16.27	N.3159 19.20	N.3200 10.32
N.2242 11.6	N.3069 19.26	N.3160 19.15	N.3201 14.51
N.2243 15.40	N.3070 18.26	N.3161 11.45	N.3203 15.25
N.2244 11.26	N.3071 18.6	N.3162 11.44	N.3204 19.5
N.2245 6.12	N.3072 18.7	N.3163 11.43	N.3205 15.24
N.2246 19.47	N.3074 7.31	N.3164 11.36	N.3206 15.20
N.2247 18.23	N.3075 7.39	N.3165 11.30	N.3208 8.9
N.2248 4.3	N.3076 7.32	N.3166 16.37	N.3209 8.21
N.2249 18.17	N.3077 9.2	N.3167 14.30	N.3210 13.7
N.2250 11.41	N.3078 11.18	N.3168 12.88	N.3211 17.7
N.2251 16.21	N.3079 7.21	N.3169 11.11	N.3213 16.28
N.2252 12.42	N.3080 18.10	N.3171 19.34	N.3215 7.41
N.2253 14.47	N.3081 13.24	N.3172 11.8	N.3216 12.17
N.2254 18.31	N.3082 18.1	N.3173 14.45	N.3217 5.17
N.2255 19.25	N.3083 12.93	N.3174 10.10	N.3218 19.16
N.3045 6.35	N.3084 12.79	N.3175 10.2	N.3219 8.20
N.3046 8.46	N.3132 3.16	N.3177 10.1	N.3220 12.19
N.3047 11.28	N.3135 13.8	N.3178 14.10	N.3221 8.30
N.3048 6.29	N.3136 13.13	N.3179 14.4	N.3222 7.24
N.3049 6.31	N.3138 12.16	N.3181 14.3	N.3223 18.8
N.3050 6.28	N.3139 13.16	N.3182 15.21	N.3224 8.18
N.3051 7.19	N.3140 12.22	N.3183 12.20	N.3225 16.11
N.3052 7.17	N.3141 10.42	N.3184 14.16	N.3226 7.22
N.3053 7.18	N.3142 14.38	N.3185 14.31	N.3227 16.36
N.3054 7.13	N.3143 19.17	N.3186 11.7	N.3228 9.29
N.3055 7.12	N.3144 19.13	N.3187 11.3	N.3229 12.15
N.3057 15.56	N.3145 3.8	N.3188 14.53	N.3230 6.23
N.3058 13.21	N.3146 12.38	N.3189 14.19	N.3231 9.34
N.3059 8.3	N.3148 14.32	N.3190 14.20	N.3232 9.35
N.3060 8.36	N.3149 13.9	N.3191 14.41	N.3233 15.2
N.3061 8.51	N.3152 19.10	N.3193 14.50	N.3234 15.3
N.3062 5.22	N.3153 17.13	N.3194 14.8	N.3235 15.5
N.3063 11.13	N.3154 17.5	N.3195 14.39	N.3236 15.1
N.3064 12.10	N.3155 17.6	N.3196 14.7	N.3237 11.10
N.3065 17.4	N.3156 13.17	N.3197 14.5	N.3238 12.61

N.3239	6.4	N.4884	6.27	N.5950	11.21	N.6475	10.20
N.3240	6.2	N.4885	15.18	N.5951	8.16	N.6477	14.52
N.3241	8.34	N.4892	14.48	N.5952	4.5	N.6478	10.41
N.3242	17.2	N.4893	19.56	N.5963	9.28	N.6479	15.32
N.3243	11.46	N.4930	12.89	N.5996	5.11	N.6480	12.4
N.3244	8.17	N.5048	19.6	N.6392	9.12	N.6481	10.4
N.3245	8.24	N.5059	17.16	N.6420	12.43	N.6482	19.29
N.3246	18.29	N.5101	2.2	N.6421	11.29	N.6484	10.15
N.3247	16.6	N.5102	12.95	N.6422	15.6	N.6486	15.39
N.3248	10.12	N.5324	8.10	N.6423	12.30	N.6488	15.4
N.3250	18.14	N.5325	4.4	N.6425	14.35	N.6489	17.12
N.3251	18.13	N.5328	5.8	N.6428	15.34	N.6490	10.21
N.3252	12.29	N.5330	3.52	N.6429	14.33	N.6492	19.61
N.3253	18.22	N.5339	19.59	N.6430	19.4	N.6494	11.5
N.3354	11.1	N.5347	9.3	N.6431	15.48	N.6495	8.27
N.3356	6.20	N.5348	15.49	N.6432	14.2	N.6496	11.9
N.3357	16.31	N.5349	9.27	N.6433	14.11	N.6497	15.16
N.3358	9.4	N.5366	8.35	N.6434	11.12	N.6501	14.24
N.3359	7.30	N.5395	5.3	N.6435	15.38	N.6503	10.16
N.3360	15.14	N.5396	7.9	N.6436	10.38	N.6504	15.19
N.3362	18.2	N.5410	16.15	N.6437	12.60	N.6505	15.36
N.3363	12.32	N.5420	5.10	N.6438	12.70	N.6506	12.44
N.3364	19.27	N.5486	6.1	N.6439	14.43	N.6508	10.13
N.3365	3.60	N.5489	18.46	N.6440	14.9	N.6510	12.90
N.3366	3.41	N.5542	6.6	N.6442	11.4	N.6511	15.10
N.3367	12.72	N.5543	9.22	N.6443	14.14	N.6512	15.8
N.3368	9.25	N.5544	6.26	N.6444	18.44	N.6516	12.64
N.3376	7.10	N.5545	15.55	N.6446	11.47	N.6520	10.5
N.3602	16.19	N.5546	9.17	N.6447	15.15	N.6526	8.29
N.3729	19.7	N.5547	12.84	N.6448	15.29	N.6527	19.2
N.3753	10.28	N.5548	11.22	N.6449	15.30	N.6528	12.71
N.3755	19.57	N.5558	19.37	N.6452	12.13	N.6529	19.28
N.3765	2.1	N.5559	15.42	N.6453	16.22	N.6579	9.39
N.3766	5.2	N.5560	18.28	N.6454	16.14	N.6580	9.37
N.3772	9.6	N.5561	12.48	N.6455	12.56	N.6581	9.43
N.3777	4.8	N.5562	14.28	N.6457	18.32	N.6582	9.38
N.3778	8.2	N.5563	14.6	N.6458	14.46	N.6583	9.41
N.3780	12.59	N.5565	14.1	N.6459	15.35	N.6584	9.42
N.3781	10.47	N.5567	4.20	N.6460	15.51	N.6585	12.52
N.3782	3.5	N.5586	3.9	N.6461	14.44	N.6586	18.25
N.3783	7.28	N.5598	11.39	N.6463	14.49	N.6587	7.23
N.3784	17.18	N.5651	14.25	N.6464	10.9	N.6588	17.17
N.3785	8.7	N.5702	12.35	N.6465	14.21	N.6589	7.29
N.3790	16.20	N.5703	12.80	N.6466	10.51	N.6590	18.18
N.3791	19.60	N.5715	8.26	N.6468	14.13	N.6591	7.36
N.3874	9.16	N.5727	5.6	N.6470	19.14	N.6592	7.35
N.3875	18.34	N.5876	19.51	N.6471	14.42	N.6593	7.34
N.4074	12.67	N.5877	16.38	N.6472	12.12	N.6594	7.26
N.4075	12.34	N.5931	5.4	N.6473	10.7	N.6596	7.4
N.4855	15.61	N.5949	13.1	N.6474	18.37	N.6597	7.3

N.6598 18.21	N.6678 3.53	N.6745 10.48	N.6801 12.73
N.6599 7.6	N.6680 3.49	N.6746 18.3	N.6802 8.14
N.6600 9.20	N.6682 3.48	N.6747 17.10	N.6803 8.19
N.6601 9.21	N.6685 3.4	N.6748 17.14	N.6804 8.39
N.6602 15.62	N.6686 19.1	N.6749 12.51	N.6805 8.25
N.6603 15.63	N.6687 3.25	N.6750 12.83	N.6806 12.27
N.6605 7.14	N.6688 12.6	N.6751 12.77	N.6807 12.37
N.6606 7.15	N.6689 16.12	N.6752 14.17	N.6808 8.8
N.6608 9.9	N.6691 3.38	N.6753 12.62	N.6809 13.2
N.6612 6.16	N.6692 19.11	N.6754 12.87	N.6814 14.27
N.6613 6.17	N.6694 19.42	N.6756 12.36	N.6815 13.6
N.6615 6.18	N.6696 12.76	N.6758 12.9	N.6824 6.19
N.6618 11.15	N.6699 3.19	N.6759 13.12	N.6914 18.41
N.6622 11.16	N.6700 3.17	N.6760 12.24	N.6946 6.24
N.6624 6.5	N.6701 3.36	N.6761 14.23	N.6956 16.24
N.6625 18.27	N.6702 3.24	N.6762 12.78	N.7108 12.55
N.6626 11.27	N.6703 3.12	N.6764 18.11	N.7109 12.69
N.6627 11.20	N.6706 14.15	N.6766 15.31	N.7110 19.52
N.6628 4.13	N.6707 12.47	N.6767 15.43	N.7111 18.42
N.6629 4.2	N.6709 19.48	N.6768 10.43	N.7112 15.45
N.6631 4.1	N.6710 14.37	N.6769 18.35	N.7113 12.65
N.6632 4.18	N.6711 19.41	N.6770 18.16	N.7115 12.68
N.6641 6.25	N.6712 19.62	N.6771 12.45	N.7116 11.33
N.6642 6.30	N.6713 19.12	N.6772 3.46	N.7117 14.12
N.6644 5.8	N.6716 19.38	N.6773 11.40	N.7118 15.7
N.6645 9.18	N.6717 13.23	N.6775 15.46	N.7119 11.31
N.6646 5.15	N.6718 3.61	N.6776 3.11	N.7120 12.74
N.6647 9.30	N.6719 3.56	N.6777 3.3	N.7121 12.33
N.6650 18.40	N.6720 19.19	N.6778 12.46	N.7122 19.3
N.6651 11.24	N.6721 12.82	N.6779 14.18	N.7123 11.32
N.6652 8.45	N.6722 8.28	N.6780 12.63	N.7124 12.28
N.6653 5.16	N.6724 15.44	N.6782 11.38	N.7125 14.29
N.6654A 8.47	N.6725 3.26	N.6728A 10.17	N.7153 11.25
N.6654B 18.38	N.6726 12.11	N.6783 13.19	N.7154 7.16
N.6655 9.14	N.6727 3.47	N.6784 15.54	N.7155 9.33
N.6656 7.5	N.6728 3.31	N.6785 8.12	N.7157 7.20
N.6658 9.11	N.6729 3.32	N.6786 8.38	N.7158 5.9
N.6659 19.45	N.6731 19.35	N.6787 8.5	N.7159 5.9
N.6660 3.33	N.6732 12.21	N.6788 8.6	N.7385 15.11
N.6662 3.28	N.6733 3.59	N.6789 8.42	N.7391 1.1
N.6664 3.54	N.6734 3.21	N.6790 17.3	N.7455 11.23
N.6665 3.44	N.6735 19.43	N.6791 8.15	N.7461 10.46
N.6668 12.49	N.6737 13.11	N.6792 8.4	N.7892 6.3
N.6669 3.39	N.6738 11.42	N.6793 8.13	N.7956 9.1
N.6672 18.39	N.6739 13.15	N.6794 8.33	N.7977 10.26
N.6673 3.20	N.6740 19.23	N.6795 8.11	N.7988 9.13
N.6674 12.66	N.6741 19.32	N.6796 16.7	N.8114 19.36
N.6675 12.41	N.6742 12.26	N.6797 15.52	N.8194 10.23
N.6676 18.36	N.6743 12.94	N.6798 10.44	N.8452 4.21
N.6677 13.14	N.6744 17.9	N.6799 8.32	N.8455 19.50

N.8456 10.40	N.8464 19.8	N.8471 7.37	N.8806 10.29
N.8458 14.36	N.8465 15.13	N.8472 7.11	N.8837 16.30
N.8461 3.42	N.8466 13.10	N.8563 16.32	N.9243 19.49
N.8462 16.25	N.8467 8.40	N.8769 6.36	NX.949 5.13
N.8463 19.9	N.8468 6.22	N.8774 3.10	

Appendix III

REPORT OF THE INSTITUTE OF GEOLOGICAL SCIENCES ON THE CAUSE OF PINK COLOURATION

Introduction

Some pieces of English delftware have in the borders of plates and bowls a white tin decoration over a pale blue glaze. This technique, known as 'bianco-sopra-bianco', was probably brought here by Magnus Lundberg from the Rörstrand factory in Sweden. However a few examples have pink decoration, which could be called 'rosa-sopra-bianco'. Pink colouration in glazes has been reported to be accounted for by addition of gold, iron, copper, cobalt, or a mixture of chromium and tin.

Colour is a parameter which is very difficult to define. It depends on factors such as the illuminating source, which is normally polychromatic and may have a continuous spectrum (such as a tungsten filament) or not (such as a fluorescent tube). Fluorescence in the subject may be caused by an ultraviolet component. The angle of incidence of the radiation and the condition of the surface of the subject are also important. The human eye shows considerable variation between individuals and is also subject to colour fatigue. Within the item itself very low concentrations of chemical elements may cause colour changes and oxidation state may also be important. Interaction between components may also be a complicating factor. The levels of concentration may be well below the lower limits of detection of many analytical methods. A non-destructive method must be used for this type of investigation, which therefore necessitates a scratch sample or an instrument capable of accepting a plate-sized item.

Investigation

Energy-dispersive X-ray microanalysis of scratch samples at Bristol University had failed to identify the pink colouration. Arrangements were made for analysis of both types by Ortec Tefa energy-dispersive XRF systems, which can accept large samples, but no significant difference was found between their spectra.

Polarography was considered but the elements to be determined must be identified and interferences may occur. The EDAX MAX X-ray microanalysis system was unsuitable as it could not accept such large specimens. Enquiries at UKAEA Aldermaston indicated that neutron activation analysis would be insufficiently sensitive for a scratch sample and could not accept a large sample because of geometrical constraints.

The most useful information came from examination of the plates under a binocular microscope. It was known that the r-s-b type had narrower and more numerous petals than the b-s-b in its flower decoration. The former under microscope showed a discontinuity between the decoration and the glaze which did not occur with the latter. This took the form of a meniscus, suggesting a chemical or physical disparity The glaze had the appearance of overstepping the margins of the decoration as if more than one phase was present, in contrast with the b-s-b where glaze and decoration merged smoothly into one another both in colour and texture. There was therefore a difference in relief between the two types.

Conclusion

The analytical methods attempted or considered were limited by sensitivity, interference or geometry. Electron microprobe analysis might reveal the nature of the pink colouration but the taking of sections would be almost essential. It appears likely that the r-s-b was an underglaze decoration, and possible that iron was partitioned from the body. (Alternatively, the colour may have been partitioned from the glaze, or the decoration itself may have been impure.) The narrowness (and hence the greater number) of the petals could be explained by the absorption of water by the porous clay during decoration. Subsequent application of glaze might be followed by run-off through gravity and surface tension effects, either almost immediately or during firing. The apparent overlap of the glaze on the margins of the decoration is strong evidence for this theory.

T. K. Smith
28 July 1980

A selected bibliography

MICHAEL ARCHER 'Delftware from Brislington', *The Connoisseur*, vol. 171, no. 689, London July 1969, pp. 152–161

MICHAEL ARCHER *English Delftware/Engels Delfts Aardwerk*. Catalogue of an exhibition in the Rijksmuseum, Amsterdam 1974

MICHAEL ARCHER AND PATRICK HICKEY *Irish Delftware*. Catalogue of an exhibition in Castletown House, Dublin 1971

MICHAEL ARCHER AND BRIAN MORGAN *Fair as China Dishes. English Delftware from the Collection of Mrs Marion Morgan and Brian Morgan*, Washington D. C. 1977

BURNAP COLLECTION see under Ross E. Taggart.

ALAN CAIGER-SMITH *Tin-Glazed Pottery in Europe and the Islamic World*, London 1973

R. J. CHARLESTON 'Bristol and Sweden: Some Delftware Connexions', *English Ceramic Circle Transactions*, vol. 5, part 4, 1963, pp. 222–234

D. COCKELL 'Some Finds of Pottery at Vauxhall Cross', *English Ceramic Circle Transactions*, vol. 9, part 2, 1974, pp. 221–249

J. K. CRELLIN *Medical Ceramics. A Catalogue of the English and Dutch Collections in the Museum of the Wellcome Institute of the History of Medicine*, London 1969

E. A. DOWNMAN *Blue Dash Chargers*, London 1919

RHODA EDWARDS 'London Potters circa 1570–1710', *Journal of Ceramic History*, no. 6, Stafford 1974

F. H. GARNER 'Lambeth Earthenware', *English Ceramic Circle Transactions*, vol. 1, no. 4, 1937, pp. 43–66

*F. H. GARNER AND MICHAEL ARCHER *English Delftware*, London 1972

C. T. GATTY *The Liverpool Potteries*, Historic Society of Lancashire and Cheshire, vol. 33, Liverpool 1882

GLAISHER COLLECTION see under Bernard Rackham

GREG COLLECTION see under M. R. Parkinson

CELIA HEMMING 'Liverpool Delft', *The Connoisseur*, vol. I, no. 200, London April 1918

R. L. HOBSON, *Illustrated Catalogue of Early English Earthenware*. Catalogue of an exhibition at Burlington Fine Arts Club, London 1914

IVOR NOËL HUME *Early English Delftware from London and Virginia*, Colonial Williamsburg 1977

H. BOSWELL LANCASTER *Liverpool and Her Potters*, Liverpool 1936

R. LIGHTBOWN AND A. CAIGER-SMITH *The Three Books of the Potter's Art by Cipriano Piccolpasso*, London 1980

AGNES LOTHIAN 'Vessels for Apothecaries', *The Connoisseur Year Book*, London 1953, no. XXIX, pp. 113–121

AGNES LOTHIAN 'English delftware in the Pharmaceutical Society's Collection', *English Ceramic Circle Transactions*, vol. 5, part 1, 1960, pp. 1–4

JOSEPH MAYER *History of the Art of Pottery in Liverpool*, Liverpool 1855

MORGAN COLLECTION see under Michael Archer and Brian Morgan

R. G. MUNDY *English Delft Pottery*, London 1928

OLIVER VAN OSS 'Some notes on English delft', *English Ceramic Circle Transactions*, vol. 5, part 4, 1963, pp. 217–221

HUGH OWEN, *Two Centuries of Ceramic Art in Bristol*, Gloucester and London 1873

M. R. PARKINSON *The Incomparable Art, English Pottery from the Thomas Greg Collection*, Manchester 1969

W. J. POUNTNEY *Old Bristol Potteries*, Bristol and London 1920

R. H. PRICE 'Pottery Kiln-Waste from Temple Back, Bristol', City of Bristol Museum and Art Gallery Research Monograph no. IV (forthcoming publication)

BERNARD RACKHAM *Catalogue of the Glaisher Collection of Pottery and Porcelain at the Fitzwilliam Museum, Cambridge*, Cambridge 1934

BERNARD RACKHAM AND HERBERT READ *English Pottery*, London 1924

*ANTHONY RAY, *English Delftware Pottery in the Robert Hall Warren Collection, Ashmolean Museum, Oxford*, London 1968

ANTHONY RAY *English Delftware Tiles*, London 1973

ALAN SMITH 'An Enamelled, Tin-glazed Mug at Temple Newsam House', *Leeds Art Calendar*, no. 82, Leeds 1978

ROSS E. TAGGART *The Frank P. and Harriet C. Burnap Collection of English Pottery in the William Rockhill Nelson Gallery*, revised edition, Kansas City, Missouri, 1967

M. S. D. WESTROPP *Irish Pottery and Porcelain*, Dublin Science and Art Museums Catalogues, part 12, Dublin 1935

R. W. M. WRIGHT *Victoria Art Gallery Catalogue of Bristol & West of England Delft Collection*, Bath 1929

Note

Those publications marked with an asterisk are the two most valuable general books on the subject of English delftware.

Index